Science and Society

by

Hilary Rose and Steven Rose

Allen Lane The Penguin Press

First published in 1969

Allen Lane The Penguin Press
Vigo Street, London W.1

SBN 7139 0124 1

First printed in Great Britain by
Cox & Wyman Ltd,
London, Reading and Fakenham

Set in 10 on 12 pt. Monotype Times

To the memory of both our fathers

Contents

Acknowledgements

It is always hard to list comprehensively all those whose influence has been felt in the gestation of a book. Still more is this the case when, as now, an attempt has been made to synthesize material from many sources and different disciplines and, as with this book, its writing has occupied us, on and off, for several years. Our interest in this area, our belief that it was important to analyse the inter-relations of science, technology and society, perhaps began as a response to the writings of those physicists who confronted the moral and political dilemmas posed by the Bomb. But while the intellectual evolution of the book from that point is our own, our thinking on many points has been crystallized by informal discussions, seminars and meetings. Amongst these, in particular we would like to mention talks with Anthony Wedgwood Benn, Jeremy Bray, Eric Burhop, Ritchie Calder, Tam Dalyell, Alexander King and Tony Swain. Francis Aprahamian and Gary Wersky made unpublished material available to us. We have pursued hares started at seminars arranged by the Higher Education Group at L.S.E., by the Science of Science Foundation in London, the Science Studies Unit in Edinburgh, the Science Policy Research Unit in Sussex and the American Association for the Advancement of Science in New York. It is particularly appropriate that the book was completed in the light of the steady stream of discussion meetings and teach-ins that have followed the Bernal Library Conference on Chemical and Biological Warfare in 1968 and the subsequent establishment of the British Society for Social Responsibility in Science. In addition, and especially, we would like to thank those friends and colleagues who have read and commented on various drafts and sections of the book, Desmond Bernal, Christopher Freeman, Dennis Simms, Leslie Sklair and Tony Swain. We thank, too, *Minerva* for permission to use material ('Operation Megamouse') of which an earlier version appeared there, and Derek de Solla Price for the use of Figure 2. Dick Pountain and Elizabeth Singh have at various times helped with the collection of data. Finally, Simon and Ben Rose have patiently borne the brunt of parental distraction at those times when dialectical discourse has not run truly smooth.

None of these, of course, is in any way responsible for errors and misinterpretations that may remain; they are ours alone – even if we ourselves will no doubt continue to discuss *which* of our faults it was.

H. R.
S. R.
August 1969

Introduction

. . . I hereby swear and affirm. Affirm. On my . . . Honour? By my belief. My belief in . . . in . . . the technological revolution, the pressing, growing, pressing, urgent need for more and more scientists, and more scientists, for more and more schools and universities and universities and schools, the theme of change, realistic decisions based on a highly developed and professional study of society by people who really know their subject, the overdue need for us to adapt ourselves to different conditions, the theme and challenge of such rapid change, change, rapid change. In the ninety-seven per cent, ninety-seven, of all the scientists who have ever lived in the history of the world since the days of Euclid, Pythagoras and Archimedes. Who, who are alive and at work today, today, now, at this time, in the inevitability of automation . . .

Bill Maitland in John Osborne's *Inadmissible Evidence*

A hundred years ago a speech by any public figure was incomplete without careful reference to at least one member of the trinity of Church, Queen and Nation. Today a similar speech demands at the least its ritual bow in the direction of that indivisible pair: Science and Technology. No political manifesto, company chairman's annual report or novelist's reflections on the state of the times can afford to omit from its repertoire some passage aimed at science or the scientist. It can be argued that the rise in importance of the scientists and their activities has made them into a new Estate of the Realm. Certainly the extent to which scientific and technological developments dominate public consciousness is something new and characteristic of our contemporary society. Without doubt, individual scientists can be found in history who wielded considerable power and influence in their day; Archimedes, mathematician and inventor, is supposed to have occupied for King Hieron of Syracuse a position more or less comparable to what would now be called director of defence research, and in many ways as powerful as that of Lord Cherwell, adviser to Churchill during the 1939–45 war, or of Sir Solly Zuckerman to successive governments throughout the last decade. But although this intrusion of science and technology into affairs of state is not new, its extent certainly is. Prior to 1964, when a crusading political party promised that the new socialism would be 'forged in the white heat of the scientific revolution', an election in which a principal political issue was how to harness science and technology to the nation's needs was almost unthinkable. Now it is hard to imagine an election in which it would not be.

Awareness of the tremendous growth of science, and concern over its possible implications, has penetrated deeply into an uneasy public consciousness. A whole generation has come to adulthood with the terrible knowledge that the destructive powers revealed at Hiroshima and Nagasaki could be released at any moment. And this generation knows, too, that this new power represents the technological realization of the sensational advances in theoretical physics of the preceding thirty years. For the children conceived this year, the problems raised by nuclear power, though they are still unsolved, may be overshadowed by the equally dramatic technological changes of 1948–68, the decades of biological revolution which have brought control of human genetics, and hence of the evolution of mankind itself, within our grasp.

Familiarity with the *facts* of scientific advance is a prerequisite of existence in our contemporary world. The apparent inevitable reach forward of technology ensures a continuous high rate of innovation, of new machines, products, methods, at work, in the home, in transport and at play. New scientific triumphs are part of the regular diet of any newspaper reader. We take a very great deal for granted – we have to, in order to get on with the everyday business of living. And our children take even more: they discuss with complacent expertise the latest phase of a 'moon race' the very mention of which evokes in their elders irresistible echoes of

Jules Verne and H. G. Wells, however sophisticated and *blasé* they try to be about it.

Yet although the facts of scientific advance and technological innovation are widely recognized, there has been relatively little systematic attempt to understand *why* and *how* such advances occur. They have come to be regarded at the same time as inevitable but chancy affairs, unpredictable and essentially uncontrollable. The question whether such advances *should* occur is rarely asked. It is assumed that society will learn to live with the biological revolution, just as it is learning to live with computers and has learned to live with nuclear weapons.

But 'learning to live' implies a sort of acclimatization; a change comes over the environment, and society must adapt to it. Learning to live also implies a certain sense of regret. The change brought about by science and technology is, indeed, both welcomed and resented. Though it may be a change for the better – and it is always hoped that it will be, that we will learn how to harness atomic power to useful purposes before we blow ourselves up with it – nonetheless, the change in itself is upsetting. It alters our sense of an ordered universe, and most of us have at least a certain measure of regret, of nostalgia, at the passing of old ways. Even old technologies, which were hated in their youth, become venerable and loved as they assume the respectability of age. How else can we explain the passions that are aroused by old weapons, old steam trains, old cars, or even in the contemporary antique markets, old typewriters?

It may be this ambivalence towards change that characterizes some of our attitudes towards scientists and their activities. Before the Second World War, scientists generally appeared in novels, children's stories and so forth as rather endearing, absent-minded figures, possibly mad, preferably possessed of pretty daughters, but on the whole fairly innocuous, inventors of machines that did easy things in a complex way but which often failed to work. This is far from true today. The scientist, in novel, play, film and comic, is a figure of power, sometimes sinister, sometimes naïve and virtuous but if so a helpless tool in the hands of those who wish to misuse him. The machines he invents, rockets, atomizers, death rays, are dangerous and of immense military potential. Heroes tend to be occupied in either defeating his evil ways, or rescuing him from cold-war traps into which his folly or impracticalities have led him. But above all, he is no longer a figure of innocent fun. No one remains innocent about the potential application of seemingly highly theoretical research.

And so science, and scientists, have become matters of public concern. As the costs of research rise, seemingly indefinitely, the demands of the scientists – for funds, for space, for technicians – have begun to compete more and more sharply with other claims on national spending. Particularly in defence, research and development costs absorb substantial proportions of the overall budget and mistakes or changes of mind, like the ill-fated Blue Streak rocket and TSR-2 plane, become more and more embarrassing. As the political implications of scientific developments become increasingly clearly spelt out, politicians are bound to try to exert control over the type and direction of research.

It is the purpose of this book to explore these inter-relationships between science, technology and society. We set out to describe the manner in which science is organized in contemporary Britain, that is, how it is financed and controlled, how and why scientists embark upon particular pieces of research, how particular scientific decisions are made. We must be clear that we are not here primarily concerned with the intrinsic scientific or technological *content* of particular decisions – for example, whether the C.E.R.N. 300 GEV accelerator is better or worse than that of the Russians or the Americans, but how a nation like Britain arrives at a decision concerning a major issue in high-energy physics.

It is clear that decisions of this sort about priorities are becoming increasingly necessary. Simple calculations show that scientific activity in terms of manpower, finance and 'research output' has been expanding at a rate too rapid to continue for long. As long ago as 1956, the historian de Solla Price pointed out that in the 300 previous years, the numbers of active scientists, and their productivity, in terms of published papers, had increased exponentially – that is, doubling every ten to twenty years.[1] But for most of that 300-year period the actual rate of scientific spending had been small. As the amount of scientific growth has been greater than either that of the overall population of the country or its gross national product (G.N.P.), sooner or later expenditure must catch up. And within the last twenty-five years or so, that is, two scientific-doubling periods, the catching-up is nearly upon us. It has been calculated that if the increase in scientific manpower goes on at the present rate, by the middle of the next century, every man, woman and child on earth will have to be a scientist. Similarly, if the rate of production of new scientific papers – the form in which scientific discoveries are published – continues to increase as it is at present, within a hundred years the weight of the combined mass of scientific journals will exceed the weight of the earth. And long before that happy time arrives we will be spending the total gross national product on science and technology, with nothing left over for anything else.

Although, as will be argued later in the work, this thesis is simplistic, it serves to highlight the problem of choice between available scientific options. This is the dilemma for all nations, even the biggest, but it becomes particularly acute for a small country with perilously overstretched commitments, like Britain.

One can assemble the type of choice problems that exist in a hierarchical order beginning with those at the level of the individual researcher and ending with those of society as a whole. Only some of these levels of choice can be dealt with here. At the lowest level, the individual researcher, faced with a particular research problem, has to deal with a group of related choices. They are those of a research strategy, the long-term plan for investigating the chosen problem and the short-term tactics and the concomitant problems of investment of limited funds in, for instance, an additional technician or an automatic machine. It is the wisdom of these choices that distinguish good from bad scientists, the productive from the non-productive, and they are essentially those of scientific method *per se*. They are generally examined only in terms of the *post hoc* theorizing of the philosophers of science, who often seem remote from the realities of the laboratory bench, at which a working scientist finds himself for some part of his day at least, though interesting recent exceptions are the book by the Bristol physicist Professor John Ziman,[2] *Science and Public Knowledge*, and the elegant essays by the Director of the National Institute of Medical Research, Sir Peter Medawar,[3] *The Art of the Soluble*. But this class of problem is outside the scope of this book.

At the next hierarchical level the leader of a team of scientists, or head of a researching department, has to allocate resources between individuals, select or propose projects to be pursued and discourage those deemed unproductive. This is the level customarily considered by the devotees of the techniques of operational research, organization and methods and the burgeoning managerial sciences. There now exists a substantial literature[4] of 'Research Management', ranging from the detailed studies of actual practice such as those by C. D. Orth, J. C. Bailey and F. W. Wolek, *Administering Research and Development*, to the somewhat euphoric accounts by scientists turned administrators of how they themselves operate – or believe they do. A good example of this last is a group of essays on *The Organisation of Research Establishments*, edited by the late Sir John Cockcroft. It is not our purpose here to argue the merits or demerits of this managerial approach, essentially concerned to provide rules-of-thumb for the development of relatively painless techniques for the manipulation of individual researchers in the interests of the assumed long-term needs of the 'Unit' or 'Department' or 'Firm'. Once again, this order of problem in the hierarchy is at a level below those which are our concern here.

The next three hierarchical orders, which are those with which we shall attempt to come to terms, can be easily stated. The first is that of the allocation of resources within a particular research field, for instance within the field of physics. Thus, how should resources for research be allocated between the conflicting claims of different laboratories or research groups within any of these specialities? The second is how should one choose to allocate resources between fields; how, for instance, to resolve the contending claims of high-energy physics and molecular biology, Concorde and space research, desalination and computers, for substantial shares of the same limited funds? The third problem, the highest of all, is to decide how much money should be spent on science overall as against, say, the building of new roads, hospitals or primary schools or defence? J. D. Bernal is, more than any other man, the founder of such analysis. His book, *The Social Function of Science*,[5] first published in 1939, has remained the single comprehensive attempt to perform this analysis for Britain, though other books, comparable to Bernal's, have subsequently appeared, particularly in the U.S.A., analysing American science policy and institutions. Despite the dangers which must beset any such comprehensive attempt – and we are conscious of the increasing, and increasingly professional, number of researchers working in the area – there remains a need for a generalizing account of the form that these problems take in Britain today.

In broad terms, the plan of the book is as follows. The first five chapters set out to trace in historical perspective the changes that have taken place in the nature of the scientific endeavour and its relationship to society over the past century. They describe the transition of science from a quiet 'backroom' activity of a cultured few, to its present status like that of a major industry, massively financed and closely controlled. This analysis leads, in the sixth chapter, to a discussion of the structure of science in Britain as it stands today – by which is meant both the formal organization and financing of scientific and technological research in government, the universities and industry, and also the informal pattern of societies and pressure groups developed by scientists themselves.

Whilst the early chapters deal primarily with the British situation, the patterns evolved in this country are neither inevitable, nor necessarily the best, though Britain spends proportionately more on research than any other country in the world except the U.S.A. and the U.S.S.R. In terms of planning for science, Britain has a longer tradition than most European countries, but less than that which has characterized the U.S.S.R. It is important to try to see how other countries have faced these problems. Whilst in the past there may have been a contrast between centralized planning, epitomized by the U.S.S.R., and the more *laissez-faire* approach of the Americans, who have spent their way out of their difficulties, neither of these statements is any longer true. The science policies of many countries show broad areas of similarity, for the problems they set themselves are seen as parallel. Essentially, in most of the industrialized and industrializing nations science and technology are seen as one of the keys to economic growth. But there are alternatives to this economism, the sharpest being seen in Mao's China, and the validity of such alternatives is considered in Chapter 8 and again in Chapter 13.

Meanwhile, a new trend towards the internationalization of research, by the setting up of international planning and co-ordinating bodies, and the supranational running of actual projects or research centres, has begun to play an increasingly important role in both the development of scientific patterns of activity and in representing a new channel of diplomatic activity between nations. This theme is covered by Chapter 9. The relationships that exist between nations in terms of the flow of manpower and ideas, the brain drain and the technology gap, are discussed in Chapter 10.

In the real world there is a gulf between how people say priorities are decided and what actually happens. And while the debate continues about what should be the criteria for scientific choice, every day such choices are, implicitly or explicitly, being made. In Chapter 11, we examine the theoretical debate that is taking place about how priorities should be fixed, and contrast this debate in Chapter 12 with case studies of two major scientifico-political decisions of the last few years which have repercussions on the British economy and scale of scientific effort.

The lessons of such case studies form the background for the discussion in Chapter 13. In the short term, we argue the need to 'open' the decision-making process in science far more to the scrutiny of Parliament, the press, and the scientific community itself, and suggest how decisions on the direction of scientific research could be spread more widely and more democratically. Adopting a longer perspective we attempt to project the current problems and likely trends of science and technology into the future, for it is clear from what has gone before that just as science itself is rapidly evolving, so must the role of science within society. This projection is not in terms of new inventions but far more in the broader aspects of the relationship of the activity of research and the nature of the scientific expert to society at large.

We can, as we have said, propose no blueprints for these questions. What we can, and have tried to do in the pages that follow, is at least to start asking them.

CHAPTER ONE

The Rise of the Scientific Society

The Relationship of Science and Technology

Science traditionally may be taken to mean the advancement of our understanding of the way in which the observable world works, the development of logical, integrated and self-consistent descriptions of why and how such and such individual happenings occur, why apples fall from trees, why they are coloured red and green, why they are good to eat, irrespective of the immediate utility of these statements. That is to say, a derivation of the laws of gravity or of optics, chemical analysis of the constituents of the apple, or a knowledge of the physiology of digestion, is not supposed to make us immediately richer, stronger, or with greater power over nature. On the other hand, the invention of the telescope, of techniques for the cooking, canning, bottling or preserving of apples, or of medicaments to alleviate the stomach pains we will get if we eat too many of them, are seen as technologies – they do not add to our understanding of the working of the laws of nature, but they add to our control over the world around us.

In fact, of course, such a distinction cannot be long maintained. The telescope is the product of a study of the behaviour of lenses by a Dutch spectacle-maker; but in its turn it was developed by the Italian Galileo for sale as a new technology to the merchant traders of Venice and as a means to study the planets; this study, in its turn, led to the discovery of the moons of Jupiter, and ultimately to the proof that the earth revolved around the sun and to some of the experimental evidence for gravitation. Even the medical invention of the use of the alkali magnesium hydroxide to avoid stomach gripes also leads on to evidence that the stomach juices are acidic, and that their acidity is regulated by the body in the interests of efficient digestion.

So science and technology must be seen as interacting terms; discovery precedes invention, and invention in turn presages discovery – at least in our contemporary society. And because of the elision between science and technology, between scientific methodology and scientific culture, which together form the totality of science, it often becomes difficult to talk about any specific meaning for the word 'science'. Instead, it comes to stand for everything and nothing, a magical word expected to embrace all sorts of conceptual odds and ends. In this book we have not been able to succeed in making these distinctions where others have failed; to a considerable extent the word derives meaning from its use, and while the followers of the philosopher Wittgenstein or Lewis Carroll's Humpty Dumpty, who believed in words meaning what he wanted them to mean, might approve, the multipurpose character of the one word science does not help us sort out the complexities. Legitimately there are at least five current uses of the word:

(i) as the pursuit of natural laws;
(ii) as the application of certain rules of procedure and enquiry;
(iii) as the social institutions within which the activity is carried out;
(iv) as including the whole field of research and development, that is, both science and technology;
(v) as excluding the technological development of science, embracing instead only pure science, typically conducted in certain institutional forms, such as the university or basic research institute.

Often, attempts are made to clarify the ambiguities by refining the concepts further; thus distinctions are made between 'pure' and 'applied' research, nowadays sometimes fashionably jargonized into 'basic' or 'fundamental' and 'mission-oriented' research, and other further sub-divisions which need not concern us unduly here. The distinction being made is between research pursued in the search for 'knowledge for its own sake' (as if, to paraphrase Samuel Butler talking once about the nineteenth-century ideal of 'art for art's sake', knowledge had a sake at all) and research being narrowly directed towards one particular problem. An example of the former might be nuclear physics, and of the latter the development of a new alloy with particular properties of strength, stiffness, creep resistance, etc. for use in aircraft manufacture. But pursuit of the basic science of the former by Rutherford and his colleagues led, as we now know, to the atomic bomb, despite Rutherford's own belief, in 1933, that 'anyone who looks for a source of power in the transformation of atoms is talking moonshine'. Similarly, the narrow search for new alloys of specified properties has produced whole new areas of understanding of the nature of the crystalline interactions of molecules in the solid state. Thus the distinction between these different types of science, whilst sometimes useful from the managerial point of view, is difficult to maintain at the conceptual level. Even the broad distinction between 'research' and 'development', that is, between experiments made in the laboratory and the derivation of a pilot-scale industrial process, or between, say, the drawing-board designs and the wind-tunnel models of an aeroplane and the building of the first prototype, is in some degree unreal.

Thus these often contradictory uses of the word science, such as (iv) and (v) above, reflect both the richness and the complexity of the problem. What is more dangerous has been the failure, at least on a political level, to distinguish very clearly between the different aspects of science and the relationships between them. To no little extent this vulgarization has been aided by two processes. The first has been the growth of the political interest in science policy, and the second, which has become entangled with the first, has been the growth of the influence of what has become known as the 'exponential theory of scientific growth'. While innocent in itself, the theory of growth has enhanced the politicians' tendency to regard all science as both inevitable and internally interchangeable. Science, in this view, because of certain immutable laws, must continue to grow at a prescribed rate. Currently, therefore, it scarcely matters what science is done save that it is carried out at the mythically ideal cost of absorbing some three per cent of a nation's gross national product.

This obsession springs in part from attempts to measure what in a certain sense could be defined as the 'growth of science', initiated about fifteen years ago by the Yale historian of science Derek de Solla Price.[1] Such an examination showed that if one chose such indices as the numbers of practising scientists, or numbers of scientific research papers published, a steady 'exponential' growth of scientific activity could be detected. Exponential growth essentially means growth at compound interest, so that something is growing by a fixed percentage of itself each year. Exponential growth of this sort is fairly characteristic of many biological and social phenomena; both the human population and the income of a nation such as Britain, for example, grow exponentially. A graph showing exponential growth is drawn in Figure 1. A characteristic of this type of growth is that whatever is happening does so in such a way as to double the amount of itself after regular time intervals. Thus, if the politician's dream is realized, and Britain's gross national product manages to grow at the desirable rate of three or four per cent per annum it will double itself every thirty to forty years or so. Anyone with a political memory stretching back to the 'never had it so good' period of the late 1950s will recall the discovery of this elementary fact of life by Conservative Ministers, and the proud announcement by Mr R.A.Butler (now Lord Butler, Master of Trinity College, Cambridge) that the British population could expect to double its standard of living in twenty-five years. The amount of science also doubles itself in regular time intervals in the same way, but with the difference that because the rate of growth of science has been much faster than that of population or national income over the past two or three hundred years, the 'doubling period' for science is shorter; about ten to fifteen years.[2] It is this fact that makes true (or nearly true) the rather startling observations that John Osborne put into the mouth of Bill Maitland, the anti-hero of *Inadmissible Evidence*, which we quoted at the beginning of this book, that three-quarters of all the scientists who ever lived are alive and practising today. Such is the logic of an exponential growth curve of this sort that this statement has *always* been true for whatever point in the history of the past two or three hundred years we might care to examine. At any time – 1669, 1769, 1869, 1969 – three-quarters of the scientists who have ever existed up to that date were alive and practising.

Because the rate of growth for science, of ten-per-cent compound interest, is greater than the rate of growth of population or national income, it is clear that for a long time science and scientists have been steadily increasing as a proportion both of our national in-

Figure 1

EXPONENTIAL GROWTH, PLOTTED LINEARLY AND SEMI-LOGARITHMICALLY

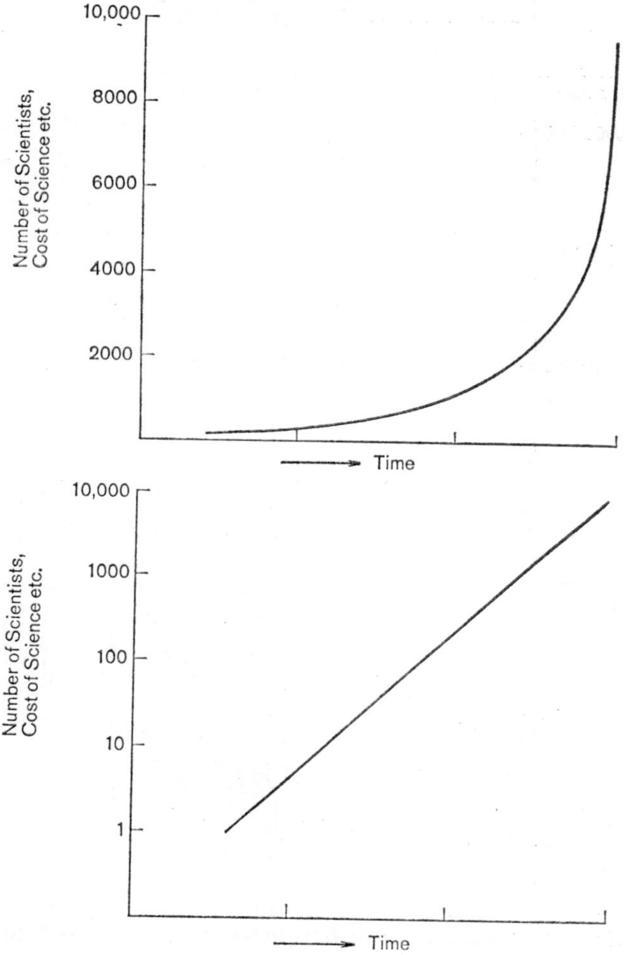

income and of our population. It is this fact, apparent to many in a qualitative sort of way, that de Solla Price has so clearly quantified. Thus the enormous jump in scientific spending that has taken place in Britain over the last thirty years, to over £800 million annually today, must be seen as part of this continuing process. We must take care, however, that we do not fall into the trap of regarding this growth as some kind of organic 'law' which is inevitable, or that can necessarily be used to predict

Figure 2

TOTAL NUMBER OF SCIENTIFIC JOURNALS AND ABSTRACT JOURNALS FOUNDED, AS A FUNCTION OF DATE

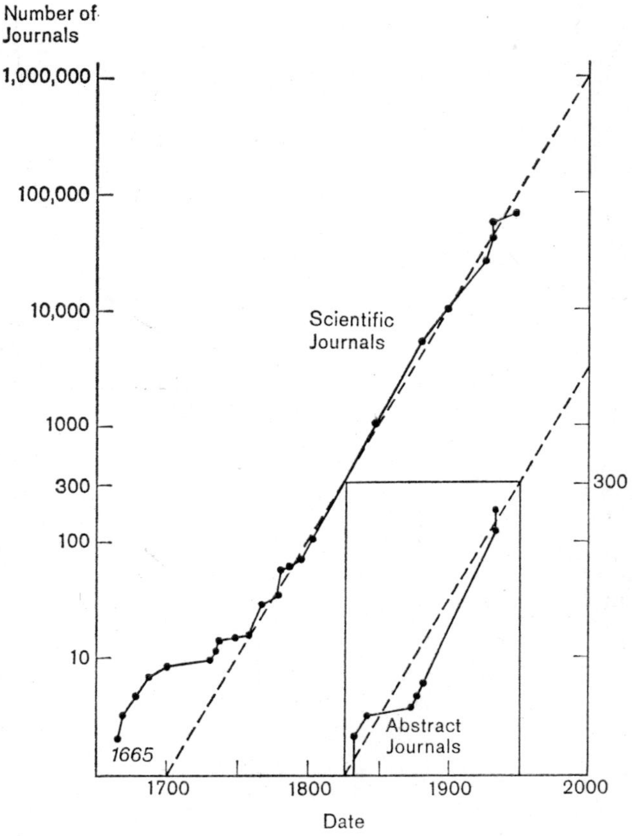

anything about scientific growth from today onwards. We must see it simply as a corollary of certain facts about the development of our society from early capitalist times to the mid twentieth century. We shall discuss the forward implications of scientific growth only much later in this book, in Chapter 10. For now, it is important to note that the derivation of these mathematical observations has led to certain prevalent, but not necessarily valid, beliefs about the inevitability of science and its relationship to technology and economic growth. In many respects, as we shall see, these beliefs are the results more of two decades of unremitting scientific expansion since the end of the Second World War, than of any more timeless reality.

What is more, the political concern that has been generated over the fate of science has been somewhat undiscriminating, failing to recognize that science is not *inevitable* as a cultural activity, but rather, as Max Weber wrote, 'the belief in the value of scientific truth is not derived from nature but is the product of definite cultures'. There has been an equal failure to recognize that, even for nations at the same level of economic development, different cultural values may well produce different sorts of science. This is not to say that any modern state can hope to survive with a denial of scientific procedure. It cannot, but it can produce remarkable deformations in the character of the science which is conducted within the society as a result of not always obvious political and economic constraints, and yet survive. The hatred of the Jews by Nazi Germany was a classical example of such constraints, leading to the complete suppression of what was described as 'Jewish' (that is, Einsteinian) physics, even though the great – and Aryan – physicist Wilhelm Heisenberg argued that it was not possible to proceed in the formulation of physical theory and research without taking Einstein's work into account. Yet the hatred of the Nazi state for this specific branch of science, and the general difficulties which resulted from the fact that the established rules of scientific procedure in the pursuit of knowledge were in direct conflict with the Nazi belief in the Leader's superior insight, did not entirely destroy science in Germany but instead turned it away from such politically hot areas of basic research as nuclear physics into the relatively quieter regions of rocketry.

Similar events took place in Soviet science in the period 1935–53, as the studies of the American historian of Soviet science, David Joravsky,[3] have documented. The distorted genetic theories of Trofim Lysenko retained an intellectual stranglehold on Soviet biology because that area was so politically sensitive. The chronic debility of agriculture, which has continuously obsessed the post-revolutionary leadership in Russia, had created an environment in which it became impossible for the normal rules of scientific conflict to be applied in order to prove or disprove, modify or reject, the theory of the inheritance of acquired characteristics put forward by the geneticist Michurin. The political need for the Lysenko/Michurin theory, even at its crudest, to be true and to work was sharp enough to preclude criticism and hence modification of the theory. As in Nazi Germany, the Russian scientist was almost certainly deflected into alternative research paths, probably of applied research.

At the core, then, of our interest in the relationship of science to society and its deliberate modification through the policies of governments is a need to define the business of the scientist. It is not so much that the activities of the pure scientist are uniquely responsible for the technology of a society, but that innovation depends on a process whereby science continuously transforms and informs technology (which in its turn plays no small role in the creation of new techniques which make it possible to test more and more elegant scientific hypotheses). This view of the marriage of science and technology is widely accepted, yet the acceptance itself is modern in character, for in some societies science has been a purely cultural activity, like painting or music, which, while culturally and intellectually enriching, bore little or no direct relationship to the technologies of the society. Mathematics and astronomy may have been highly developed in India, at their zenith in the eighth and ninth centuries A.D., but produced little or no technological spin-off in terms of inventions which physically altered the face of the land or the lot of the people other than the prediction of solar events such as eclipses for ritual purposes.

Thus it is possible to have both technological societies devoid of science, such as the so-called 'hydraulic societies' of Peru or Ceylon, and others, such as those of ancient Greece and India, that have science but no engineering. It is the marriage of the two which is specific to modern industrial society, with the dynamic from science forcing technological innovation.

Those seeking to explain the presence of modern science within society at all have typically taken as their archetype experimental science. John Ziman's recent book, *Public Knowledge*,[4] provides an illuminating exposition of this archetype. He identifies the character of scientific knowledge as 'consensual', that is, designed to command universal assent. Science is thus maintained by a value system which emphasizes universality and disciplinary communism and a reward system whereby the scientist, in return for the gift of knowledge to his readers, is accorded status and recognition. And while recognizing the importance of technology, it is with the social organization of science, the institutions and *mores* which mould and contain it, that this book is predominantly concerned. If, without assuming a crude mechanistic theory of human behaviour, whereby man is entirely straitjacketed by his own technologies, we accept that the technological character of a society substantially shapes the possible forms of conduct of its members, then this concern with the core of science is a concern with the mainspring of society. Whether a village is watered from a central well or from a drain which runs down the sides of its roads substantially determines whether the village is built in a compact central cluster or whether it is spread out in long ribbons. Whether a city is served by an effective public transport system or whether the preferred technology is the motor-car will determine whether the modern city is close-packed or diffuse and linked by freeways. Each technology will generate quite different forms of social interaction, and choosing the technology to be applied solely on grounds of efficiency may well bring unintended consequences. For those who dislike the urban sprawl of a city like Los Angeles, even the mixed success of a compact new town like that at Cumbernauld in Scotland represents an attempt to make technology serve man's preferences. The point about science and technology, to return to Humpty Dumpty again, is 'Who is to be master?'

The Birth of a Scientific Society

Whilst the number of scientists in relation to population was still very tiny – indeed the very term 'scientist' did not exist, for it was only invented by the Cambridge cleric and philosopher Whewell in the nineteenth century – science was a relatively unorganized activity. Cultivators of science, as they were called, were employed by the universities (Isaac Newton), in the churches (Copernicus or Roger Bacon), as doctors (William Harvey), or, if they were lucky, obtained a grant from some enlightened prince (Galileo, Tycho Brahe and Kepler, the astronomers). Still more, of course, they were men of means who were essentially amateurs, like Robert Boyle, nephew of an Irish peer who was also one of the founders of modern chemistry, or like Francis Bacon, otherwise Lord Verulam, not only one of the most powerful early exponents of the theory of scientific method, but also Lord High Chancellor. Indeed, Bacon obviously regarded his own combination of political and scientific eminence as the ideal, for in one of his books, *New Atlantis*, he describes a Utopian society in which the state would be run by scientists, and its chief activity would be the furtherance of natural knowledge and technology.

It was only following the creeping changes of many preceding millennia that a much more rapid series of advances in science and technology began in the fifteenth century in Western Europe, and has proceeded ever more rapidly in the five hundred subsequent years. These changes were related, as we shall see, to the growth of cities, increasing trade and the development of protestantism, all of which can be broadly grouped together as representing the decline of feudalism and the birth of a capitalist type of society. Scientific and technological advances were an integral part of this development from the invention of the compass and telescope through steam power and onwards. Because of this reciprocal relationship between science and technology, once some sort of scientific 'take-off' point had been reached in Western Europe in the fifteenth and sixteenth centuries science developed at considerable speed. Each scientific advance brought new technology, and new technology made new science, completing what in electronic or computer language would be termed a self-excitatory positive feedback link.

The take-off point is symbolized in some measure by the foundation of the Royal Society in Britain in 1662. Its creation had two aspects, the internal logic within science, and the external logic of the growth of capitalism. Like the other academies, founded about the same time elsewhere in Europe, it was created in part by the increasing need of scientists to communicate the results of their research activities with one another. The body of accumulated knowledge on which any scientist had to base the development and planning of his own experiments was already increasing rapidly, as were the numbers of scientists themselves. Whereas in earlier days Galileo and his contemporary physicists could keep in touch with one another by an exchange of letters once or twice a year and an occasional visit, the sheer numbers of scientists now began to make efficient communication by letter-writing an impossible task. At the same time, the speed of the advance of research made it important to learn rapidly what others were doing in the field.

The solution was the creation of the first scientific societies – themselves presaged by Bacon – and as the seventeenth century advanced these began to be set up very rapidly in several different countries. The Italian Accademia dei Lincei, founded in 1603, the British Royal Society (1662), the French Academy of Sciences (1666), the Berlin Academy of Sciences (1700), were amongst the earliest, but so rapid was the subsequent growth of academies that it has been calculated that there were some 220 of them by 1790. From the point of view of the scientist these societies were useful in that they functioned as – to quote the founders of the Royal Society – a type of 'invisible college', and a meeting place where ideas, experimental results and information could be exchanged. The societies soon took upon themselves the responsibility of publishing experimental results, obviating the need for each individual scientist to have to communicate personally with many others. Thus the form of communication which has continued down to the present day, the scientific paper, was established. This organizational breakthrough itself speeded the subsequent development of science by encouraging the exchange of ideas, by bringing together potential collaborators, and above all, by the wielding of research funds. Individuals could now actually be employed by the academies themselves on 'research contracts' to investigate specific problems. By 1709, according to Armytage, the Académie des Sciences in France employed twenty research assistants. Thus although not on a large scale, for the funds were still small, an important new principle first emerges here.

This leads to the second point about the establishment of the new academies, which was that they were far from being just informal meeting places organized by the scientists themselves, but were indeed set up directly under state patronage. The history varies, of course, from country to country, but the principle is the same for them all. Not only had a group of scientists banded together specifically to request state funds for their enterprises but, interestingly, the government of the day had seen fit to provide the money. Thus the Accademia dei Lincei was convened by Prince Federigo Cesi of Rome, whilst the French Academy of Sciences was established after a group of mathematicians and engineers had approached first a minister, Colbert, and then the king, Louis XIV, with the argument that celestial observations were necessary for the reputation of France. Before long they were in direct receipt of funds for equipment and salaries, they commissioned research, ran a botanical garden and mounted large-scale expeditions to make astronomical observations. The Royal Society in London always had a slightly less state-dominated role. It was self-instituted as a discussion group, first in Oxford and then in Gresham College, London, for a number of years before its members interested Charles II in a proposal to establish 'a College for the promoting of physico-mathematical experimental learning'. Despite royal patronage, the tradition of the Society remained one of gentlemanly amateurism, which has been a continued charge against British science, and contrasted it with the more closely state-linked academies abroad. The French Academy, for instance, paid its members a salary, thus opening a career in science to those without personal fortunes. In Britain, unless a wealthy patron was to appear to support the aspirant scientist, the door to a scientific career was open only to those with private incomes.

The academies were fostered by the state for the very direct technological benefits which they promised. Although the arguments about celestial observations and the reputation of France sound suspiciously similar to those of American prestige and the space race of which we hear so much today, the technological potential of the support of science was already becoming apparent to the politician. Thus Charles II was 'most graciously pleased' with research by the Royal Society devoted to the measurement of longitude at sea, while regarding as a 'childish diversion' the fundamental research on the weighing of air.

Religion and Science

While the explanation for the origins of capitalism must inevitably turn on the central process of capital accumulation itself, historical sociologists since Max Weber[5] at the turn of the twentieth century have continuously directed our attention to the role of religion, and in particular the role of protestantism, in serving as ideological midwife both to the nascent entrepreneur and to his sibling the scientist. Not all forms of protestantism served this function equally well. Calvinist rather than Lutheran protestantism stressed the importance of energetic, empirical and rational conduct as a means of fulfilling God's will. 'Satan', the Puritans thought with a conviction which other cultures would find startling for its vigour and certainty, 'finds work for idle hands'.

As the sociologist Robert Merton[6] has shown in an elegant essay which extends the basic Weberian insight into the essentially rational character of modern society, this new theology was signally favourable to the development of the new experimental science.* In his essay, Merton discusses the establishment of the Royal Society in Britain and demonstrates how in practical ways the protestants actually outnumbered the other religious groups among the founding members, and also how their religious orientation reinforced their scientific activity. Thus of the ten who constituted the initial 'invisible college' in 1645, only one, Scarborough, was not of protestant origin. Similarly in 1663 when the first full members of the Society were made, of these sixty-eight, some forty-two were protestant – far more proportionately than there were protestants in Britain. These cultivators of science, despite a generous handful of peers and knights, also included the new middle social classes who had engineered the Cromwellian revolution. And although the Society was called Royal, its foundations were laid in the Commonwealth period.

It was more than a tactful wish to avoid those difficulties in which Galileo, for example, had found himself, which prompted both the arch-empiricist and guiding spirit of the Royal Society, Francis Bacon, and the respected apologist for the Society, Sir Robert Boyle, to stress that science was for 'the greater glory of God and for the good of mankind'. Whilst for the diplomatic Verulam it is conceivable that this legitimation was little more than verbal deference, Boyle himself in his book *The Usefulness of Experimental Philosophy* seems less equivocal in his motivation. Nor does his practice of spending substantial sums of money to have the Bible translated into foreign languages seem anything less than genuinely devout. Another leading figure in the Society was John Wilkins, sometime Warden of Wadham College and married to no less a person than the Protector's sister. Elsewhere in the Society, it was only possible to prevail upon the modest Willughby to publish his research through insisting that publishing the wonders of nature was a means of glorifying God's works.

Thus the intellectual quest for knowledge was at least in part religious in legitimation. The college in Bacon's[8] *New Atlantis*, was established 'for finding out the true nature of all things, whereby

* This thesis is not without its critics, notably Lewis Feuer, in his book *The Scientific Intellectuals*.[7]

God might have the more glory in the workmanship of them', whilst the practical application of knowledge was humanitarian in tone '. . . and for the comfort of men'. Indeed, although Bacon is probably best known for his aphorism 'Knowledge is Power', he is careful to note the danger of knowledge, both for knowledge's sake, and also for power's sake, and to insist instead on the advantages of knowledge for charity's sake as 'of charity there can be no excess'. Thus this search for knowledge legitimized by religion and directed towards human welfare was shared as a common cultural value by the early members of the Royal Society. Indeed, there seems to have been little divorce between what in effect was pure and applied science: of the 300 problems studied by members of the Royal Society during four of its early years, up to two-thirds were problems with some practical application connected with mining and seafaring. While any such distinction between practical and non-practical science, between what Bacon called *experimenta lucifera* and *experimenta fructifera* – light bringing and fruit-bringing research – is necessarily a rough and ready one, the preponderance of the practical shows the world-centredness of the early scientists. The paradox of puritanism in action was that it was to make them more engaged with the day-to-day management of life than the many scholars who preceded them.

This is not to suggest that the scientists themselves were religious virtuosi; rather, they were religiously influenced men. The virtuosi themselves, the Calvins and the Luthers, remained profoundly anti-science. It was the second-stage protestants who secularized protestantism and gave culture both the universalism and the rational tolerance which were pre-conditions for the growth of science. The extent of the liberality of these second-stage puritans is shown by the history of John Wilkins, who although ineligible to become President of the new Royal Society because of his marriage to Cromwell's sister and his own puritan background, managed to remain influential.

Indeed the constitution of the Royal Society itself was conscientiously tolerant; in its founding charter it made room for properly 'inquisitive foreigners' to be made members, and retained during the religious tensions which accompanied the Restoration a firm commitment to continue to include Royalists, Cromwellians and Catholics alike.

Although the Royal Society's early history is perhaps the best-documented, other work suggests that similar protestant influences were at work in the setting up of the Paris Academy and Harvard University in the U.S.A. Established with the aid of Morton, the head of one of the great English dissenting academies, Harvard was directed towards scientific education. Cambridge, the university inclined towards Parliament during the English Civil War, was more friendly to science than Royalist Oxford (with the exception of Wilkins's college). In Germany both Halle and Heidelberg universities were focused on the sciences and were overtly protestant in inspiration. But, in general, although the thesis associating science with a specific form of protestantism holds, it has to be remembered that the key to this religious form is rationality, in itself a driving force for secularization rather than for religion. Thus having emphasized the significance of a deeply felt and intensely individualistic theology for creating the cultural environment in which science could flower, the success of the new science, like the success of capitalism itself, was divorced from the intentions which shared in its creation.

Despite the savagely satirical portrait of the activities of the Royal Society presented by its contemporary Jonathan Swift in his account of Gulliver's Travels to Laputa, and despite the slightly shaky early years of its history, in which it stepped gingerly between the displeasure of the universities at its activities and the exigencies of contemporary politics, the men who founded the Royal Society were conscious of the sweep of their new philosophy in its potential for world transformation. They, like Marx, felt that 'philosophers have only *interpreted* the world in various ways, but the real task is to alter it'. It is difficult in the highly professionalized business of contemporary science to recapture the *Weltanschauung* of the scientists in what Charles Singer[9] has described as the 'turbulent century'. But today, sometimes the intellectual arrogance – even *hubris* – of powerful individual scientists, men such as H. G. Wells, Haldane, Bernal or Herman Kahn recaptures the ideological certainty which cradled the early days of science.

CHAPTER TWO

Amateurs and Gentlemen: Britain in the Nineteenth Century

Despite the technological orientation at its inception, the Royal Society failed to maintain the integration of technological and scientific advance which continuously characterized the French Academy until its degeneration and transformation following the revolution of 1789. In the century following its creation we find the Academy in France embarking on a variety of technological functions, offering prizes for innovations such as powered propulsion of boats, publishing a massive twenty-seven-year, 120-part, survey of the current state of French Arts and Crafts and, in a frenzy of activity, setting up institutes such as that for the study of hydraulics. No similar activity occurred in Britain. The real question, in which lie embedded many of the structural problems of the British economy which still beset us today, is why the integration of technology and science was not subsequently continued in Britain in the way it certainly was abroad. Again and again, through eighteenth, nineteenth and twentieth centuries we find the same lamentation of the British scientists about their relative neglect and isolation compared to the firm links which were built between science, technology (the word was a German invention of the 1770s) and government and universities in France and Germany.

Such considerations were remote from the eighteenth-century Royal Society, where the intellectual ferment that had characterized it in the days of Newton, Hooke, Halley and Wren had subsided by 1730 into an over-fed, complacent calm. The eighteenth century in Britain was still the age of the amateur, the Royal Society became packed with non-scientists until the social fellows outnumbered the scientific by almost two to one and it belied its name as effectively as most London clubs today belie theirs. Research was still the prerogative of the wealthy. Thus John Flamsteed, first Astronomer Royal, although provided with a building, was expected to equip the observatory at his own expense, despite both the obvious national importance of such work, and the fact that the Royal Observatory at Greenwich at which he worked was the earliest state scientific institution in Britain, having been founded in 1675 and therefore pre-dating the next government scientific establishment, the Geological Survey, by 160 years. An estimate of the extent of amateur tradition has been provided by D. S. L. Cardwell,[1] who has calculated that of 106 leading British scientists in the eighteenth century some forty to fifty must be classified as amateurs; of the 106, twenty per cent were doctors, fifteen per cent were technologists of some sort, and ten per cent were clerics.

The Industrial Revolution and the Rise of the Professionals

That British science advanced at all during the eighteenth century owed less to the London-based and fashionable Royal Society than to the scientific societies of the northern provincial towns dominating the industrial revolution. Early in the century there had been an air of academic distinction about the Society's presidents; Sir Isaac Newton was followed by Sir Hans Sloane. But from 1741 until Sir Joseph Banks's appointment in 1778 the Royal Society was presided over by a series of undistinguished men. Banks, who remained to rule the Society for forty-two autocratic years, was of high social status and no mean scientist. Using his powerful connexions with the King, George III, and the government, he secured important public recognition both for the Society and for science. Despite this, the dominance of the aristocracy and the low status of the scientist minority had helped shift the intellectual centre of science away from the fashionable metropolis to the new industrial towns which were at the heart of the new economic order. Local societies in these towns were loosely modelled on the Royal Society, but directly geared to the contemporary technological problems in a way that the Royal Society had forgotten since the close of the seventeenth century.

The most important of these new provincial societies which were to play an influential role in the industrial revolution was the Lunar Society of Birmingham.[2] Like the other provincial societies its members for the most part were scientists, engineers and entrepreneurs, but the Lunar Society of Birmingham had the additional advantage of being in Birmingham, a town which, having mushroomed up with neither Charter nor Corporation to debar dissenters, was particularly attractive to the non-conformist commercial classes and the equally non-conformist scientists. Thus the Lunar Society, which effectively formed the intellectual centre of the scientific scene for the thirty years of its existence, provided the venue at which the engineer James Watt was to meet the entrepreneur Matthew Boulton, and was instrumental in persuading Boulton to finance the steam engine over a period of several years – when, at least in the earlier phases, Boulton lost a great deal of money. Eventually, of course, Boulton and Watt's steam engine, sold with a degree of energy and attention to consumer requirements that the National Research Development Corporation could do worse than study today, became one of the technological hinges on which the first phase of Britain's industrial revolution was to turn.

The Society itself was always tiny, never extending beyond some fourteen members, yet included Boulton himself, at whose house the early meetings took place, Dr Small, Erasmus Darwin, Josiah Wedgwood, Richard Lovell, Edgeworth, Samuel Galton and later both James Watt and Joseph Priestley. Not only were the Society's members non-conformist in religion, some – most conspicuously the chemist Priestley – were non-conformist in politics and supported the French revolution. In 1791, at the encouragement of government agents, Priestley's home, along with those of other notable Birmingham non-conformists, was attacked by a mob and both his library and his laboratory were burned. His departure to the newly independent America marked not only a happier situation for Priestley but also the end of the Lunar Society, as other members also moved away from Birmingham. The Society had, however, left an indelible mark on the making of modern Britain.

It is probably significant that, whilst the Royal Society was still the prerogative of the London-orientated aristocracy, these 'new men' of the Lunar Society were on the whole self-made men, entrepreneurs and rising professionals. It was these men above all who needed to make science and technology drive the wheels of industrialization, and they did it to such effect that these late-eighteenth- and early-nineteenth-century engineers became household heroes in a way that is no longer possible for modern engineers and technologists. We remember the names of Watt and Boulton, of Wedgwood, Stephenson, Telford and Brunel. Eventually the Royal Society, in the traditional British way, yielded to the demand for revolution by instituting mild reform and many of these men became fellows in much the same way that today, the designer of the new Severn Bridge was made an F.R.S. Yet, despite this partial, slow and unwilling expansion of state support and popular recognition in the eighteenth century, British scientific achievements were substantial in astronomy, physics, and especially chemistry. The list of British scientists – albeit largely amateurs – in the first and second rank was long indeed.

But the character of science was changing. If it could rely on some enlightened entrepreneurs and a handful of aristocratic patrons in Britain at this particular point in history, by the mid-to-late nineteenth century this was no longer the case. Meanwhile on the Continent the progress of more systematic state support for science continued. In France, the establishment of the École Polytechnique, perhaps the first attempt at a college of applied science anywhere in the world, and in Germany the foundation of new universities and technological colleges that were thoroughly professional in the education they gave, were signs of this new expansion. This was at a time when the two principal universities in England (until the emergence of Durham and University College, London), Oxford and Cambridge, remained indifferent to experimental science as a subject worthy of study and the granting of degrees.

Science and Revolution

The greatest step forward since the foundation of the Royal Society, and one which helped decisively to shift the centre of scientific excellence back from England to the Continent – to France – was the French revolution. The revolution, which changed so much, could scarcely be indifferent to science. But, as the historian Charles Gillispie[3] has argued, its liberalizing, democratizing ideology was ambivalent, on the one hand hostile to science as a symbol of high aristocratic culture and to technology as a method of emiserising the artisans and emergent working class, and, on the other, firm in its belief that science, if properly used, could be a powerful tool in the hands of the people.

Thus the first stage was that of destruction – the abolition of the academy, the 'taking over' of institutions such as the Observatory (the director was ousted by his research assistants, a close parallel to the events of May 1968 to which we refer below; *plus ça change* . . .), and even the execution of, for instance, the chemist Lavoisier at least as much because he represented 'Aristocratic science' as because he exploited the people as a 'tax farmer'. His intellectual and practical support, as a provider of gunpowder for the revolution, did not absolve him or save him from destruction.

But following the Terror and the Jacobin purges came a period of construction; the old botanical gardens were transformed into a Museum of Natural History, a new set of scientific institutes and schools were established, such as the great École Polytechnique and a series of medical faculties at Paris, Strasbourg and Montpellier. The Collège de France was revived and the Institut de France created.

The results were the building of a series of teaching institutes fundamentally different from anything that had gone before. Where the Royal Society in Britain a hundred years earlier had tentatively considered awarding scientific degrees, and rapidly withdrawn the proposal under the hostility of the Oxford and Cambridge establishment, thus holding back advance in the teaching of science in Britain virtually till the mid nineteenth century, the French Revolution had, albeit bloodily, broken the power of the old theocratic and aristocratic universities, enabling real scientific teaching faculties to be built. The École Polytechnique, for example, was to lure into teaching many distinguished scientists who would from now on extend their interests beyond research to teaching and the writing of a series of systematic textbooks, in mathematics (Lagrange), astronomy (Laplace), anatomy (Cuvier) and crystallography (Hauy).

Further, the intellectual mainspring of the revolution – the belief in a rational, liberal–democratic society fit for the growing forces of the French bourgeoisie, in which the power of Church and aristocracy were reduced – found a major place for science in its scheme of things: science and the arts were to be man-centred, not god-centred, an integrated and harmonious whole whose purpose was to contribute to the greater welfare of mankind. It was perhaps at this point that the intellectual centre of European science, which had moved from Galileo's Italy to the early Royal Society's England, passed back across the channel to France, to flower into the new chemistry and physiology which were to dominate scientific thought for a large part of the nineteenth century.

The British Road Forward

Meanwhile, objectively, as well as in theoretical hopes, the pace of events in the nineteenth century began to quicken. Following Cardwell, we can show three phases in the development of British scientific organization through the century, the first beginning after Waterloo and continuing until the mid-century, the second beginning with the Great Exhibition of 1851 and running till 1880, and associated with the interest in science shown by the Prince Consort, and the third phase lasting from the 1880s through until 1914. We can use these landmarks to get the history of the period into perspective without necessarily attaching too great a significance to specific dates.

The developments of the first period are essentially a continuation in kind of those of the eighteenth century; a continuous governmental indifference to science. We may note the existence of only one publicly financed laboratory at this time – the Royal Institution, still today in those same quarters in Albemarle Street that it occupied then, and the home for many years of a long line of distinguished researchers; Humphry Davy, the discoverer of several chemical elements and inventor of the miner's safety lamp; Michael Faraday, in many respects father of the electrical industry as well as a distinguished theoretical scientist; and in the twentieth century Sir Lawrence Bragg, researcher on the structures of complex molecules.

Although Count Rumford conceived of the Royal Institution in very practical terms, it achieved a fashionable elegance in the early part of the nineteenth century, with Humphry Davy's lectures attracting large but mainly socialite audiences. But the public interest in science stretched far beyond this fashionable concern, for the period was characterized by a quickening attempt to repair the deficiencies of public education by means of the provision of numbers of Mechanics' Institutes designed to provide a largely working-class audience with some knowledge of current scientific developments, and the expansion of the universities to include two new, more secular ones, London and Durham, both of which regarded science as an acceptable subject for the university curriculum. The campaign for educational expansion was supported by the working-class organizations themselves and by a large section of liberal and progressive opinion – such as Henry Brougham's[4] 'Society for the diffusion of useful knowledge' which published popular scientific and technical paperbacks. The demand for increased amounts of semi-skilled manpower to work the new machines contributed to the movement, but it had to fight an uphill battle against a variety of entrenched positions, not only clerical, but also the essentially conservative view well summed up in a quotation from a Quaker magistrate – 'Science and learning, if universally diffused, would speedily overturn the best-constituted government on earth' (a view supported by at least one later President of the Royal Society[5]* as well as by Oscar Wilde's Lady Bracknell, who, in *The Importance of Being Earnest*, regarded the major result of education as a tendency to riot in Grosvenor Square, predicting current upsets in that vicinity by more than half a century).

Babbage and the Decline of Science

The counter-movement was vociferous. Already, despite the indubitable preeminence of British scientists in many fields, symptoms of decline were being claimed which sound familiar a century and a quarter later: 'Is the firm and powerful voice of science to pervade the workshops of the kingdom, or shall the feeble and uncertain note of experience continue to prevail?' asked Birkbeck, the founder of Birkbeck College in London. In 1830 Charles Babbage,[7] professor of mathematics at Cambridge (and also incidentally one of the key figures in the invention of computers, speedometers,

* 'However specious in theory the project might be, of giving education to the labouring classes of the poor, it would in effect be found to be prejudicial to their morals and their happiness; it would teach them to despise their lot in life, instead of making them good servants in agriculture, and other laborious employments. . . .'[6]

operational research and actuarial tables), published a book entitled *Reflections on the Decline of Science in England and of Some of its Causes* – a title which, but for its length, we might have felt tempted to plagiarize for the present book. Apart from attacking the corrupt state of the Royal Society, Babbage was mainly concerned to contrast the lack of recognition paid to science and scientists in Britain with the situation of her main competitors, France and Germany (Prussia), where science was properly taught in the universities and where scientists could even become Ministers of State. Babbage led a campaign for the election of the President of the Royal Society to be on merit instead of social status. He lost. The Royal Society elections continued to be rigged, and in something of a huff Babbage set about forming the British Association for the Advancement of Science.

The debate which raged in Britain from the 1830s on was one which seems very familiar to us today. Certainly there were defenders of the British situation, who could point to the fact that there was no shortage of first-class scientists in Britain, in virtually all fields. Nonetheless, it was equally true that, whilst there were outstanding leading men, there was also a great shortage of plain but competent scientists needed to man the factories and research labs of the developing industrial revolution. Compared with Germany or France, it has been argued that there was less scientific activity. Fewer scientific papers were being published; fewer scientifically trained men were going into industry and hastening technological advance.

Today one is accustomed to bemoan the fate of Britain, but account for it in terms of the problems of 'End-of-Empire' and of loss of industrial power to the U.S.A. To find the arguments being expressed in almost the same words over 150 years ago is even more unnerving. After all, in the 1830s Britain was in the van of the industrial revolution. Her colonial territories were rapidly growing and her expansion regarded as a peril by France and Germany themselves.

To some extent, of course, it is probably true that such self-criticism is used as a lash to beat the politicians with, and that in the history of any country one will find the critics busily making invidious comparisons with its neighbours. Nonetheless, if the criticisms have any power in them at all, one must make the effort to provide some causal explanation. Perhaps the best we can offer at this stage is the argument that precisely *because* Britain advanced so rapidly in its industrial organization, whilst at the same time acquiring maritime supremacy and an increasing number of colonies, the need for technological innovation was less marked for a long time. Colonies provided essentially soft, politically protected markets for British goods. British ships carried them there quickly and cheaply, and the huge demand that this created throughout the whole of the nineteenth century and the first quarter of the twentieth, provided British industry with a guaranteed sale for its goods, without the need for continued technological innovation. The British manufacturer learned to produce a wide range of locally tailored goods with little or nothing to fear from foreign competition and with little incentive to invite the services of the scientist. Similarly, the colonies provided Britain with raw materials at favourable prices, obviating the need to work out more economic – and therefore technologically more sophisticated – ways of processing them. Thus Britain's uniquely structured markets enabled her to ignore the impact of chemistry in creating entire new science-based industries. Instead, the traditional approach based on the gradual mechanization of old technologies continued unchecked. What is more, the opening of these markets required primarily an efficient administration and a reasonably competent army equipped to deal with colonial battles, not European wars (with their need for technological innovation in armament). Hence the educational system became, from the 1830s onward, geared to the production of gentleman administrators and officers, not scientists. Those who became scientists (or rather 'cultivators of science') and engineers did so almost despite the prevailing ethos of the society. At least, this was true for England. Fortunately Scotland's higher educational structures were better adapted to societal needs: not only did Scots scientists tend to be university professors rather than gentlemen, but Scotland also provided the staff for the English science faculties when they were established. The extent of the Scots contribution can be gauged by the fact that of the medical graduates practising in England in 1875, seventy-five per cent graduated in Scotland. As we shall see, it was not until 1914 that the English educational ethos was challenged.

Meanwhile, with considerably smaller assured colonial markets, slightly later into the race to industrialize, and without so substantial a maritime and trading strength, France and Germany were committed to innovate or perish. To compete with the British and each other, their products needed to be substantially better, more advanced. Hence the emphasis in those countries on technology, and on a scientific education, even for administrators, quite apart from industrialists.

As a result, by the middle of the nineteenth century new types of scientific organization were beginning to appear in the German and French laboratories, coinciding with a period in which the scientific leadership in Europe was passing from the laboratories of France to those of Germany. These new forms, whose emergence has been described by the sociologist Joseph Ben-David,[8] were based on the introduction of actual laboratory practical training for students in the German universities, as opposed to the learning of theory-by-rote which still persisted in Britain and which had come to dominate even the newer French institutions. This development meant that instead of research being performed essentially by individuals plus one or two disciples, relatively large groups of students began to be formed, clustered round particular individuals or schools and working on interrelated topics – mainly in chemistry and physiology; the change in physics occurred only somewhat later.

Such a development of research led automatically to a form of organization which was to prove suitable for the emergence of industrial research also, whilst the existence of big groups made obvious the need for investment in plant and equipment as well. As Ben-David has pointed out, the situation was rather analogous to the replacement, in the industrial revolution, of master craftsmen by industrial machinery. The day of the isolated researcher was clearly limited; the future was to lie with the big laboratory.

Reforming British Science: the Bourgeoisie's Response

It was to the solution of these problems that the British Association was to devote itself. In its foundation, Babbage received the powerful support of Sir David Brewster, a physicist and a critic of government neglect of science, and of ill-organized scientific institutions and patent laws. They provided a formidable team for the launching of the British Association, and for a brief spell it looked as if it might become a powerful spokesman for organized science. Funds, raised by subscription, were used for establishing research grants and for buying equipment; politics began to intrude into its debates. Socialists such as Robert Owen were invited to its meetings, drawing an angry protest from the magisterial philosopher Whewell himself. The protests were heeded, and before long the British Association had become respectable. It has never recovered. Arranged as much as two years in advance, its annual meetings have long since ceased to be characterized by either scientific freshness or social polemic. They have become a slightly boring annual ritual. If it were not for the British Association's counterpart, the American Association for the Advancement of Science, which has managed to retain a lively multidisciplinary membership, it might be possible to argue that the day of the general scientific society drew to a close at the mid nineteenth century with the founding of the truly professional societies, such as the Chemical Society or the Institute of Mechanical Engineering. The rapid emergence of these learned societies demonstrated the actual professionalization of the scientists despite the prevailing ethos of Victorian amateurism.

But some of the criticisms voiced in its early days found their mark. Public interest in the wider spread of scientific education became more substantial. New governmental scientific agencies were founded, such as the Geological Survey of 1835, and the Laboratory of the Government Chemist of 1842. The government was also induced to give the Royal Society the (then unprecedented) sum of £1,000 a year. In 1849 a parliamentary committee of the British Association was formed, to look after the interests of science.

This growing recognition of technology at the zenith of the Empire was formally acknowledged in 1851 with the Great Exhibition. Prince Albert's fostering of the Royal Society of Arts enabled the Society to run several smaller exhibitions before undertaking the great survey of science and technology which Marx described caustically as the rejoinder of the bourgeoisie to the European revolutions of 1848. The scientific activist Lyon Playfair, in connexion with the exhibition, gave a series of public lectures on national science policy, sharply comparing the quality of German industrial research with the British situation and calling for the foundation of an industrial university to produce the needed scientists and engineers. Eventually, together with the profit of £186,000 from the Exhibition, Parliament voted an additional £150,000 to buy the South Kensington sites to establish the three

Royal technical schools which were finally incorporated in 1907 as the Imperial College of Science and Technology. The exhibition marked the public acceptance of the fact that the state had a major function to perform in the financing and organization of British research effort.

How Much Laissez faire?

From now on the debate was about how major was major. Not enough for some, for by 1856 one member of the parliamentary committee of the British Association was calling for a Select Committee 'to enquire what public measures could be adopted to advance science', whilst another called for the establishment of a government council for science. Babbage himself returned to the attack in 1851 with renewed complaints about both the status and the salary of scientists, pointing out how few posts were established and paid for with state money. Thus science was inevitably left as a pursuit of the wealthy. An expansion of state aid to science and scientists was essential. According to Playfair there were only 1,190 salaried posts available for science, philosophy and literature throughout the whole of Britain in 1851.

Needless to say, the attack on the *laissez faire* approach to science was too extreme for many. The British Association itself was divided about the prospect of a government science council, and as for state finance, the official position remained that it was preferably 'left to private associations'. Only routine activities such as the Geological Survey, or the new Board of Trade Marine Department, were properly part of the sphere of government. By contrast with the demand by one M.P. for thirty state science colleges, three – the Royal School of Science, the City and Guilds Technical College and the School of Mines (descended from the Royal College of Chemistry) – were finally established in London. These, together with Owens College in Manchester and University College, London, were hopefully to produce the scientists and scientifically minded industrialists the country needed. Meanwhile a new department, that for Science and Arts, really the forerunner of the present Department of Education and Science, with Lyon Playfair as Science Secretary, was set up. The founding of the School of Mines was itself the occasion for the class of denunciation of the deficiencies of British science with which we are already familiar, when in 1852 Playfair, lecturer in applied chemistry in the School, argued that Britain could no longer rely on cheap natural resources in an era of easy transport. Britain's trouble was that she had 'eminent "practical" men and eminent "scientific" men but that they are not united and generally walk paths wholly distinct...'

Perkin, Aniline Dyes, and the German Triumph

Nowhere is this problem more sharply demonstrated than in the famous saga of William Perkin and the aniline dye industry.[9] Perkin discovered the first of these coal-derived dyes in 1856 at the Royal College of Chemistry. Over the next fifty years they were to revolutionize the dye industry, bringing ruin to the old vegetable dyers and a host of new colours to the fabric-makers. Perkin was not slow to recognize the commercial potential of his discovery, and left the College to set up in business. Although he, and his father and brother who went into partnership with him, were novices in industrial chemistry, nonetheless the factory was successful, and the value of the aniline dyes became immediately apparent, not only to the British, but to German industrialists as well. Within six years of the discovery at least four factories had been set up in Germany to develop and produce the dyes, and within a few years, Germany entirely dominated the dye industry. Despite the efforts of the Perkin family, the fact remained that only in Germany were there sufficient technologically-minded industrialists, prepared to invest adequately in a new science-based industry, as opposed to an old-established traditional one. Perhaps even more important, only in Germany were there enough trained chemists to man the new factories. Thus, by 1879, Germany was producing some £2 million-worth of coal-tar products and Britain only £450,000-worth of the dyes which had been invented in Britain by a British scientist. Indeed, in order to find a principal for the very college at which Perkin was trained and made his discovery, the college's founders, the queen's physician, Sir James Clarke, and the Prince Consort, had found it necessary to import a leading German chemist, A. V. von Hofman, from the laboratory of the great chemist Liebig.

This extraordinary failure, despite an early researching lead, has all the signs of under-investment in innovation, and of lack of qualified manpower to drive a project through to commercial success, that we are familiar with a century and a quarter later.* It contributed to the dominance of the German chemical industry in Europe which was to continue until 1918 and beyond, resulting in such conspicuous anomalies as that by which the French soldiers' uniforms in the 1914–18 war were dyed their characteristic blue by German-produced alizarine.

We cannot really maintain the thesis that amateurism and the desire for an ivory-towered existence are part of the British national character, an immutable law of behaviour arising opaquely from an island heritage of fog and isolation. Rather, the amateurism stems critically from the intensely poor prospects of employment for a British scientist between about 1870 and 1910. At a time when scientific research was in the process of vigorous application to German and American industry, British science remained uncompromisingly gentlemanly. Thus Beer, in an examination of the German dye industry, shows the decisive role the state played in gearing the educational system to supplying the scientific manpower required by the industry, so that between 1880 and 1900 the German educational subsidy was ten times that of Britain. In this way the joint effort of industry and the state secured the professionalization of science in Germany at a time when Perkin himself was so fearful of the harm done to pure science by his venture into industry that he returned to the academic ivory tower at the tender age of thirty-three.† Thus the story of the aniline dye industry provides a classic contrast between gentlemen and players, sharper even than the earlier catalogues of woe by Babbage and his supporters.

It should not, however, be thought that all was perfect with the German system of research organization. Despite the emergence of the large researching schools attached to individual professors within the universities there were certain built-in rigidities to the German system which later developments were to make alarmingly

* Although this is perhaps the most widely known example, others exist, such as Andrew Carnegie's successful exploitation in the U.S.A. of research into steel production performed in Britain by Bessemer and others.

† It is interesting to note that Faraday himself also gave up consultancy work to go back to research although industrialists were seeking his advice. Dennis Simms, in drawing our attention to this also noted that Faraday's action 'was still held up as an example to us 20 years ago'.

obvious. Within each university, each acceptable discipline was represented by a professor, surrounded by his students; each professor was autonomous, autocratic, feared and revered as the apex of a rigidly hierarchical system. The rigidity of the system made for both the rapid development of a line of research that fell within 'the discipline' and extreme difficulty in introducing new interdisciplinary subjects which emerged as a result of the natural growth and development of science. The deficiencies of the system were subject to piecemeal reform in both France and Germany by the development of specialized research institutes, either university or non-university, designed to fulfil special research roles. Such institutes, like the Institut Pasteur in France or the Kaiser Wilhelm Gesellschaft in Germany, emerged as a new form in the late nineteenth century, but at least in Germany, they were carefully subordinated, both in power and prestige, to the traditional university.

This built-in authoritarianism of the German higher education system helped to make it an easy prey when Hitler began to oust Jewish science and scientists from the universities, but the seeds of decay were present in university syllabuses and studies that scarcely changed in the century which followed 1850. By 1900, as Ben-David has pointed out, much of the meaning of the German university course became muted: 'from something potentially creative it became part of a routine drill. University study regressed to scholastic study.' But its internal momentum was to carry it forward to the end of the First World War at least. By contrast, the reforms in the British system were, as we shall see, to revitalize it in time for 1918.

Periodic public states of complacency or concern over the state of British technological health tend to be occasioned by external and largely irrelevant factors. Today we triumph with a new atomic reactor. A state of national tragedy (at least for the popular press) descends almost overnight as a result of the announcement of the departure of a British scientist for the U.S. In the late nineteenth century similar depression or elation were produced by the big international exhibitions which followed regularly after that of 1851. Pundits anxiously used each one as a thermometer for British science. That of 1862 was regarded as proving the total superiority of British chemical manufacturing. Estimates were produced showing the growth in numbers of British scientists to as many as 45,000 (though this involved counting in members of the Horticultural Society). By 1867 all was gloom. The verdict on the Paris exhibition of that year was that Britain had fallen dangerously behind her competitors in almost all fields of manufacture. Gossip and correspondence in *The Times* led to a national conference on the training and production of scientists, under the auspices of the Royal Society of Arts. The document its committee prepared called for more science in school syllabuses, more new universities, more science examinations, with formal government recognition and help. Similar pressure, this time from the engineer Colonel Alexander Strange, through the British Association, led to the setting up of a British Association committee on the provision of research facilities. The combined effort of these, and the advocacy of the newly formed scientific journal *Nature* led to the setting up of, first a Parliamentary Select Committee, and then a Royal Commission under the Duke of Devonshire.

Of the people active in this agitation, amongst the most prominent was Strange, who, between 1868 and 1870, produced a series of papers demanding government intervention in science. He pointed out that quite a number of research areas were already government financed, such as museums, the Science and Art Department and certain specific defence projects. But this was done randomly and without coordination. For these and other questions of national importance which involved science, such as public hygiene, meteorology, etc., a Science Council was needed which could advise government, administer research grants and conduct experiments. At the head of this Council should be a Minister of Science.

Thus the agitation that led to the setting up of the Devonshire Commission in 1870 reads very similarly to that which preceded the Robbins Committee on Higher Education in 1961, and the series of reports which presaged the Labour reconstruction of the governmental scientific apparatus in 1964, which is discussed below. It may be that the mountain of agitation produced a similar mouse. The Devonshire Commission proposed that a separate Ministry 'dealing with science and education as a public service should be set up', with a Science Council to advise it, and the proposal waited a matter of eighty-eight years for its implementation. It also called for state science laboratories to be established, to encourage increased productivity amongst British scientists. In the meantime the Duke of Devonshire himself compensated for this neglect by endowing a physics laboratory at Cambridge (known after him as the Cavendish and to win world fame as the home of J. Clark Maxwell and later of Rutherford and the nuclear physics of the 1920s and 1930s, and later still of the molecular biology of Perutz, Kendrew, Crick and Watson in the 1950s). The government's response was marginal; the Royal Society grant was raised to £4,000 a year. (In this context, it is interesting to note to what extent the Royal Society had begun to become a sort of unofficial scientific advisory committee to the government.) But a request by the British Association that the state should take over tidal observations, and a deputation from the Scottish Meteorological Society with a request to the Chancellor of the Exchequer, Robert Lowe, for a grant of £300 to enable them to continue their work, were both firmly refused. Self-help was the order of the day.

Self-help or *laissez faire* struggled along in a good-to-middling way. In the following thirty years eleven new colleges were formed, whilst privately secured collaboration of entrepreneur and researcher, as in the Lunar Society a century earlier, continued to represent the best means of industrial innovation. Several firms began to set up industrial laboratories in the chemical, manufacturing, electrical and brewing industries. But still nothing existed which compared with the size of the research labs found in industrial firms in Germany and Switzerland, with their close links to university departments and research programmes on which whole groups of scientific workers could be employed (nine German dye works at this time each employed between twenty and 105 graduate chemists).

Salaries and Manpower

For Britain the structural problems remained the same. Yet another Royal Commission, this time in 1881, on technical education, heard the biologist and protagonist of evolution, T.H. Huxley, put the familiar case. 'The peculiarity of English science has been that the army has been all officers. Until within the last quarter of a century [i.e. till 1860] there has been next to no rank and file'. While in every branch of science Britain had had top scientists equal to Germany, there was not even then anything corresponding to the rank and file there was in Germany, because of the German organization and the fact that men could make a living in German universities. The reason for this are clearer now than they were to Huxley, for if the state and the universities did not underwrite scientific activity to any significant extent, nor did industry attempt to lure the scientists with high pay. Nor was the educational base on which the superstructure of science was to stand adequately secured; the first Compulsory Education Act was in 1870, but such scientific institutions as there were continued to complain of the unpreparedness of the students.

In late Victorian or early Edwardian England, the income necessary to maintain a middle-class life-style, i.e. to buy education and to have the bare decency of a domestic staff, was between £200 and £1,000 per annum. Scientists, for the most part chemists, had at the time a starting salary of £25 per annum, only a tiny minority reaching the career peak of £230.[10] George Gore, principal of the Birmingham Institute, caustically noted that where a bishop was paid £10,000 per annum, and even a general £3,000 a year, the great Faraday's official salary at the Royal Institution was a mere £200. Thus science for any man with middle-class pretensions or ambitions could only be a subsidiary activity to his main career.

Once again, the contrast with Germany reflects the weakness of British scientific support: the Prussian educational budget for the last twenty years of the nineteenth century was ten times that of the U.K. Even by 1913 there were only 300 post-graduate research students carrying on systematic scientific research, mainly at Cambridge and attached to Imperial College; even the great Cavendish laboratory could only attract about twenty-five research students. Essentially, while in Germany the universities and the polytechnics provided a broad career structure of research into industrial and pure science problems, Britain provided a narrow ladder on which a minority of graduate scientists could climb at a rate of pay which was sufficiently poor, and in research conditions of matching impoverishment, as to be a disincentive to all except the unambitious or those with private means.

This broad career structure into science and industry was supported by a considerable financial commitment on the part of the German government. For the want of any similar support the British science graduate turned away from any sort of research into teaching. In particular, arising out of Playfair's agitations and the belated recognition of the low level of technical institutions, the new polytechnics and technical colleges attracted the new science graduates, who were thus engaged in making more scientists, if not more science. Later, other dominant figures, like Alfred Mosely of South African Diamonds, impressed by the American engineers' positive contribution of bridge-building in the Boer War, added to this pressure for reform. Mosely despatched two groups, one from the trade unions and the other drawn from education, to visit the United States to find out why the American employee was apparently so much better equipped intellectually. They found that the American workman 'has received a senior and better education whereby he has been more thoroughly fitted for the struggles of after life'.[11] This unabashedly vocational slant expressed precisely the quality which gave that father-figure of the English educational system, Matthew Arnold, such distaste: 'A miscalculation of what culture really is, and calculated to produce miners and engineers, not citizens of light.' (Arnold was at the time Chief Inspector of the British school system.)

Other industrialists, like Sir William Mather, builder of the first London underground railway, provided technical in-training in their firms and at the same time argued publicly for an extension of the state's role, a pressure which resulted in a typically British piece of legislation, *empowering* local authorities in 1889 to levy a 2*d.* rate for technical colleges should they so choose, rather than *enforcing* them to do so.

Amongst the technical colleges, the London polytechnics were pre-eminent. Original research was being conducted at both Battersea and Chelsea. (The former is now the University of Surrey, the latter is a School of London University.) But these were the exceptions. As the scientist Raphael Meldola pointed out, most colleges became centres for teaching only; little time was allocated for research, subjects were taught exclusively in classes and, however zealously a teacher began, he soon deteriorated into routine teaching. 'A school of science which is not also a centre of research is bound to degenerate and to become a mere cramming establishment scarcely worth the cost of maintenance.' To give weight to this Cardwell has pointed out that of the 300 chemistry teachers in 130 polytechnics at the time only a dozen or so were carrying out research. Yet despite this critique of the existing scientific education the steady growth of numbers itself was some improvement, so that, whereas only 120 students a year had taken science degrees in London at the turn of the century, on the eve of the First World War there were almost 500 graduates being produced annually.

Meanwhile self-help continued. Where state laboratories could not be built, economic rationalization, mergers and the inexorable trend towards monopoly capitalism at last began to generate firms which were big enough to do so themselves. Lever Brothers at Port Sunlight set up a laboratory in 1889 for dealing with some of the theoretical problems raised by soaps and emulsions, whilst a merger of forty-eight chemical firms in Scotland, Tyneside and Lancashire produced the United Alkali Company and resulted in 1892 in the establishment of a central research analytical laboratory with six chemists. But the quality of these industrial scientists was still poor, so that their results – as in the development of the chemical and metallurgical techniques for British steel – were still suspect.

The government's reluctance to use its scientists was much the same. Although local government work had always been recognized as technical in character and offered employment to properly qualified specialists, central government remained chary. By the turn of the century, it employed only 200 scientists among all branches. It was ten years into the twentieth century before, at long last and under the gentle prodding of the Royal Society, under whose auspices it was initially to be run, the government set up a new state laboratory, the now world-famous National Physical Laboratory (N.P.L.) at Teddington in Middlesex, initially for the establishment of physical standards, later to be expanded into research proper as well.

At the beginning, the National Physical Laboratory was granted £4,000 annually for five years, but gradually the laboratory was able to raise its budget to some £32,000 by 1912, drawing the money mainly from industry rather than the state. Despite this self-help, by the eve of the 1914 war the British had spent £500,000 on air research through the N.P.L., compared with the Germans' £7 million. As Lord Haldane, Minister for War in the Liberal Cabinet of 1914, and later architect of the scientific reforms that the First World War helped bring about, pointed out with typical forcefulness, 'subsidies to science and education were disbursed with an equally mean hand'.

But the fact of the matter remained that none of these palliative measures could cure the apparently permanent structural disease, which resulted over these years in Britain slipping further and further behind her continental competitors, in the struggle to evolve scientific institutions adequate to maintain her in a competitive international economy. By 1914 with the onset of the First World War, Britain found herself in the ignominious position where, to quote W. H. L. Armytage: glass for range-finders, dyes for uniforms, magnetos for transport, tungsten for steel, and zinc for smelting, were all imported from Germany, whilst up to 1915 the British government was still paying royalties to Krupps for the fuses of the shells used against the Germans. Chemical glasswear was in such short supply that the government made an inventory of British stocks, in case it should be necessary to commandeer it.

Thus 1914, even more strikingly than the exhibitions of the 1860s, 1870s and 1880s, revealed the limitations of a *laissez-faire* science policy. At long last, the government was convinced – and set up a new committee. The recommendations and fate of this committee we shall trace in the next chapter.

CHAPTER THREE

The Chemists' War

War and the D.S.I.R.

War, as ever, accelerated the processes of social change. With a shock of recognition, 1914 made clear to many that, despite the facile sloganizing which announced 'We don't want to fight, but by jingo if we do, we've got the ships, we've got the men, we've got the money too', what Britain had *not* got was a chemical, dyestuffs, explosives, metal or glass industry which could provide the weapons and uniforms to support the prodigious outpouring of blood the next few years were to see. The government's ability to see the importance of maintaining even the number of science graduates, let alone to follow the radical proposals that Haldane was already making, was at first non-existent, perhaps because there was little industrial experience within the Asquith Cabinet. With the onset of war there was an immediate fall in the production of scientists and also in scientific activity. Despite their more sophisticated military potential, scientists were initially drafted into the war effort as conventional soldiers. Many, including those who offered most promise, like the brilliant young physicist Mosely, were to die. Only later were chemists withheld from the front and used in the munitions factories.

Initially, the policies, or non-policies, of the government thus demonstrated a failure to understand the scientific and technological underpinning of society. Committed to war against a state which supplied the bulk of the world's optical equipment, all the acetone – an essential material for explosives – drugs, magnetos, and the greater proportion of dyestuffs, the government was at last confronted with the painful understanding of the role of this special branch of knowledge. In 1916, Haldane said:

The necessity for the central control of our machinery for war had been obvious for centuries, but the essential unity of the knowledge which supports both the military and industrial effort was not generally understood until the present war revealed it in so many directions as to bring it home to all.

This time the alliance between state and scientist, always eagerly fostered by the state in time of war, in its insatiable search for fresh military technologies, was forced into a different relationship from the *ad hoc* arrangements of the past, even though specific *ad hoc* joint activities were still pursued, and on a larger scale than ever before. For example, the British Dyestuffs Corporation was established in 1914 with a capital of £3 million, part of which was Treasury funds. And, most interestingly, £100,000 of this was earmarked for research. What was new, however, was the establishment of science advisory committees and the beginnings of a sketchily integrated science policy, which, however much it was to recede during the lean years of the between-wars period, never quite faded into the pure ad hoc-ery of the past, which *Nature* had described in an editorial, as being: 'A sham supplemented by a few doles.'

Thus cries of woe from scientists at last met a response from government. When the Royal Society and British Science Guild formed a 'Neglect of Science' Committee which, amongst other things, criticized the predominance of the classicist in the administrative class of the Civil Service, they found that one of their most powerful allies was Lord Haldane,[1] first Secretary of State for War and later Lord Chancellor in the Liberal government, before the initial failure of the British Expeditionary Force in France forced his resignation in 1915. By September 1914, the Board of Trade had set up, under Haldane's chairmanship, a committee to 'advise the Government on best obtaining for British industry chemicals, colours and dyestuffs' – a committee which included amongst its members, ironically enough, W.H. Perkin himself, that object lesson in the previous failure of British technology. And concurrently, the Board of Education was formulating its own plan for the reorganization of British university science, so as to get flowing the two most urgently needed commodities – equipment and students.

By May 1915, the Presidents of the two Boards, of Trade and Education, were able to tell a Royal Society deputation that they were ready with a scheme, agreed by the Liberal government, confirmed by the Coalition after the Asquith government fell in June, and presented as a White Paper by Arthur Henderson,[2] President of the Board of Education, in July. At long last, science and technology were to have some sort of ministerial representation, by way of a committee of the Privy Council including the Chancellor of the Exchequer, the Presidents of the Boards of Trade and Education, and, in a personal capacity, Lord Haldane, backed by a broader based advisory council of scientists. The committee would direct Treasury funds for development of research, for support of specific proposals for individual research projects, and for setting up and developing special institutions or departments for the study of particular industrial and technological problems, and for awarding research studentships and fellowships. For its first year it was given £25,000, for its second, £40,000. The existence of a Scientific Advisory Council, appointments to which would be made on the advice of the President of the Royal Society, would assure a relative autonomy from governmental whim.

This new body was to be housed in the Board of Education and chaired by Sir William McCormick, who was simultaneously chairman of the Advisory Committee on University Grants, the forerunner of the present-day University Grants Committee (U.G.C.) and dispenser of government funds for general university support.

But already the demands of the scientists were escalating. No more dramatic incidence of the political pay-off from such demands could perhaps be foreseen than when Dr Chaim Weizmann obtained the Balfour Declaration of 1917, by which the British government agreed to the establishment of a Jewish national home in Palestine as a reward for achievements in providing a new chemical synthetic method for explosives which helped the British industry towards independence from the Germans. Nearer home the Royal Society was participating in the setting up of a voluntary Institute of Industry and Science to sponsor research and was pressing for the creation of an independent Ministry of Industry.

By 1916 the point, indeed, had been made, and it had become

clear that facilities for Haldane's Privy Council Committee at the Board of Education were inadequate. Largely as a result of Haldane's persuasion, the committee[3,4] was hived off to form a separate department – the Department of Scientific and Industrial Research (D.S.I.R.).[5] It was to form the backbone of support for science for virtually half a century. As a department of state, D.S.I.R. now had its own parliamentary vote of funds, and was, at least nominally, responsible to Parliament by way of whichever Minister held the post of Lord President of the Council.

The Million Fund and the Research Associations

The major tasks of the new D.S.I.R. were, inevitably, industrial. Whilst it continued to provide a small but increasing number of research studentships for graduates going on to take higher degrees, there were only twenty-four of these in 1917, whilst twelve post-doctoral researchers were also supported. More and more, in these early years, it became concerned with promoting technological change in industry. The major weapon chosen for this task was that of the setting up of Cooperative Trade Research Associations, in which joint research projects supported by groups of manufacturers, would receive aid in the form of government money. Independent efforts by the manufacturers – such as the rubber growers, master printers, Scottish shale oil manufacturers and silk association – had already driven some in the direction of co-operative research; this concentration and rationalization was now to be welcomed enthusiastically, in the form of the establishment of a major grant, the so-called Million Fund. As Arthur Marwick,[6] in his history of the 1914 war, has put it,

> One hundred years before, Lord Liverpool's ministry had sought release from the physical and spiritual ills which afflicted the country at the end of the Napoleonic Wars by providing one million pounds for the building of new churches. Now in the later part of another world war, Parliament again passed a 'Million Act', the money this time to be devoted to scientific research. A new deity was being enthroned.

To run the fund, the Privy Council Committee members on D.S.I.R. were set up as a Trust – the Imperial Trust for the Encouragement of Scientific and Industrial Research, which undertook to back, on a pound-for-pound basis, any cooperative research association[7] that industry set up. As such research associations have remained an important tool, albeit a weak one, of government intervention into private industry ever since, it is worth looking in a little detail at their inception from 1917 onwards, and the reasons for their relative lack of success.

The research associations, in the form proposed by the government, were to be set up as limited, non-profit-making companies, so that individual firms' subscriptions to them would be tax-free. The research associations would provide for their members a regular service of summarized information on research and development, both in general and in answer to specific questions put to them by the member-firms. On the basis of proposals from the participating firms, the research associations would be able to embark on scientific research projects subject to the approval of their advisory boards, and the results of this research would be provided free to all members of the association. All patents accruing from work of the research associations were also available to all subscribing firms. Initially the associations were to be set up on a five-year basis and the Boards elected by the participating firms, with observers from the D.S.I.R.

Thus the essence of the associations was a voluntary agreement amongst groups of, in principle, competitive manufacturers, to pool certain classes of information and activity, the inducements being (a) direct government cash grants, and (b) presumably, greater profitability through an improved rate of technological innovation. While rationality might argue such a development was in the manufacturer's interest, few, as we shall see, were prepared to embark upon the experiment with much enthusiasm. Thus, although a shopping list of industrial research was built up, starting off with the British Photographic Research Association in 1918 and taking in scientific instrumentation, the motor industry, iron, glass, fuel, forestry, radio and building – perhaps predictably, as with the present science 'glamour' industries, such as computers and electronics – the industries which in the main made use of the fund and set up associations were the new growth industries. As a result, although by 1920 twenty research associations were established, covering about half the manufacturing industries, it was still clear that the traditional industries – in particular coal and shipbuilding – could manage comfortably without science.

Meanwhile it was not long before voices protesting at the advancement of industrial profits out of public money began to be raised. Thus by 1920, Professor Frederick Soddy, speaking to a public meeting on behalf of the newly formed National Union of Scientific Workers (see below), criticized the manner in which the research associations had been set up, claiming that neither the consumers' nor the scientific workers' interests were protected. The associations, he said, enabled private industry to perform at public expense research the results of which they owned exclusively, thus helping them to profit from the results against the public, whilst the actual scientists themselves had no inventors' rights under the system, and the state, which spent half the money, had no rights to intervene at all.

Soddy's indictment might have provided a powerful case for the manufacturers acting in their own interest by setting up associations, but in fact progress was slow. Either the associations were not an effective way of problem-solving, or manufacturers were far from being the efficient entrepreneurs they were supposed to be. Between 1919 and 1923 only twenty-two research associations were licensed on grants from the Million Fund; several industries, such as the aircraft constructors, steel and pottery manufacturers, hesitated and then backed out after showing an initial interest. The reasons for this reluctance were analysed in the 1919 Annual Report of the D.S.I.R. as being due to the prevalence either of very large economic units in an industry – chemicals, for example – which carried out their own research with a jealous independence, or of very small units, almost at a workshop level, such as cutlery and pottery, where any unity of interest between many small groups was almost unobtainable. Others included under-capitalization, as in the tobacco, pin or button-making industry, where subscriptions to a central fund would represent a major overhead cost, or a feeling that there was no need for research, as in traditional handicraft industries, or the existence of trade secrets, processes perfected by one firm which the setting up of associations might result in being shared.

This comprehensive series of possible causes for failure which were really – though the D.S.I.R. was perhaps not even unconsciously aware of this – an implicit condemnation of the entire structure of British industry, simultaneously competitively fragmented and non-competitively monopolistic, and of its intense suspicion of government intervention, make it difficult to see how any associations were ever set up at all. And, in fact, when the D.S.I.R. sent out review committees, in 1923, to examine the work of the research associations as the end of their first five years approached, when they were, in principle, supposed to become self-supporting, it was found that of the twenty-two registered associations only seven had exceeded their maximum financial contribution and most barely reached the minimum. A further injection of aid became necessary, and grants were agreed for a further four to five years, on a diminishing scale, to lessen the shock of changing to self-help.

But even this was not sufficient, and several research associations were dissolved at the end of the first five years when they could not raise the necessary subscriptions for a renewal of their government grants. Even the key Glass Research Association which, with the Scientific Instruments Research Association, was considered important enough to warrant a special grant, over and above the normal, because of its essential role both for other industries and for defence, and its research-intensive nature, and which was in fact costing the government over £20,000 a year, folded up for lack of financial support from the firms concerned.

By 1928, the end of the second five-year period, the D.S.I.R.'s contribution to the associations had fallen substantially, and the number had dropped to nineteen, although the membership of those that remained had broadened, by the inclusion, for instance, of industrial consumers as well as industrial producers. It was recognized that the association would never be likely to become self-supporting, so the policy was revised, leaving self-support as an ultimate aim, but, this side of Utopia, authorizing the D.S.I.R. to continue to pay out cash-for-cash grants, subject to a five-yearly review. In 1932, when the Million Fund was at length exhausted, the costs of support fell back upon the D.S.I.R.'s yearly parliamentary vote – itself suffering from curtailment of government spending due to the Depression. But already this type of short-term research had been seen as essential, and, although work was cut back, it was no longer felt to be possible to cut research off. J.D.Bernal, in his book *The Social Function of Science*, which first appeared in 1939, made some pioneering cost–benefit calculations of the pay-off from the research associations, quoting the investigation into the appropriate quality of coke for iron-smelting which was estimated as saving £800,000 per annum, as evidence of the economic logic of applied research. Similarly, solving the problem of 'bloom' on frozen meat, Bernal estimated, had saved £300,000 per annum. Despite the evident difficulty of measuring returns on research, Bernal grossed up the total expenditure on industrial research as £400,000 up to 1938 and estimated the benefit as yielding over £3 million per annum, or, as he put it, an investment grossing 800 per cent per annum.

Even if the certainty of Bernal's perception was not shared by all, the associations continued into the Depression. Even the Utopian ideal of self-support was dropped, and the basic annual income to the research associations guaranteed, with minimum and maximum levels dependent upon the scale of support from industry. Thus the basis of the policy of support to the associations became assured, and from 1932 onwards the scale of support steadily increased, without an obvious declaration of intent; a change of policy had occurred. Government contributions in 1932 were £75,000 annually, and had risen to £170,000 by 1939, whilst industrial backing increased from £160,000 to £310,000 in the same period. By 1939, the number of associations was still only twenty-two, and only eleven remained of the original group set up before 1923, but their future now seemed secure. Indeed, the number continued to rise through the war and post-war years: there were fifteen more new associations by 1947, with a total budget four times that of 1939. Today there are over forty associations conducting research costing some £13 million annually.

On the whole, however, the criticism made by Soddy in 1920, and by the D.S.I.R. itself in 1919 when reviewing their progress, remained; whilst some associations, such as the Shirley Institute (textile industry), have built up a distinguished record of research and service, the mutual suspicion of individual manufacturers could still bedevil a project like that for a machine-tools research association as recently as 1963 (see p. 87 below).

Government Research

Meanwhile, D.S.I.R. became the chosen vehicle of expansion of totally government-sponsored research and of attempts to co-ordinate defence and civil research. Such attempts reflected the military atmosphere in which the D.S.I.R. had been originally conceived, in the midst of the 1914–18 war, and also, despite the end of the war and the disarmament negotiations, the recognition by the military that scientific research was henceforward to play a significant and ever-increasing role in the conduct of war. An early attempt to create a set of four Co-ordinating Boards, to include both military and civil scientists, for physics, chemistry, engineering and radio research, with a central staff under Henry Tizard (later Sir Henry and a major figure in the key battle over science policy in the Second World War), lasted only a few years before collapsing, as the ever-widening field of military research made the attempt at coordinating it with civil activities too diffuse and problematic. The Radio Board continued, though, and subsequently proved of immense importance in the development of radar. Meanwhile some sort of relationship between civil and military spending was maintained by enabling defence departments to contract particular projects out to D.S.I.R. for study.[8]

At the same time a steadily increasing number of D.S.I.R. research stations were set up, starting with the Fire Research Board (1917), the Food Investigation Board, the Industrial Fatigue Board and the Tin and Tungsten Board (1919). Meanwhile, the National Physical Laboratory, which had been run since its inception under the supervision of the Royal Society, was handed over in 1918 to D.S.I.R., and the Geological Survey was taken over from the Board of Education in 1919. By the mid-1920s, the Department grew more ambitious, and began extending old laboratories, such as the Low Temperature Research Station at Cambridge, and building entirely new ones, like the Torry Research Station (concerned with fisheries) at Aberdeen. What is now the Road Research Laboratory was taken over from the Ministry of Transport in 1933 after a Select Committee had concluded that the Ministry of Transport took no interest in it.

Slowly, therefore, many of the *ad hoc* pre-1914 institutions began to be gathered under one administrative roof, and the D.S.I.R.'s annual budget continued to rise, albeit patchily and unevenly, and with due respect for the limitations of Slump, Depression and pre-Keynesian governmental economics, until in 1939, on the eve of the Second World War, it stood at £930,000 annually – or about three times what it had been in 1919 – whilst the permanent staff had risen to around 2,000, compared with 900 (mainly at the National

Physical Laboratory) in 1920. A rise, of course, far from fast enough for someone like J. D. Bernal, who could point out that it still only represented a tiny percentage of anything that might be regarded as reasonable annual expenditure on science, and that, even then, Britain was spending only 0·1 per cent of G.N.P. on research and development compared to expenditure in the U.S.A. of 0·6 per cent in 1937.

Even more damagingly, the D.S.I.R. had fallen down severely in at least one major field of financing – that of university research. Only eighty-one student research grants were awarded in 1938–9 for the whole of Britain (there had been twenty-four in 1917, and fifty-six in 1920), making sure that entry into university research – or even the achievement of a doctorate degree prior to entry into industry – was still almost exclusively the perquisite of those with a private income.

Some indication of the financial problems involved for those without private means can be found in the Institute of Chemists Survey for 1920, which showed that the young chemist might expect to start at a salary of around £330 a year. By the time he was thirty-five he would reach £550 a year, and his salary would be unlikely ever to go above £800 a year. The best paid work was to be found in industry, then the Civil Service, with the schools following in third place. It has even been calculated that by 1938, the pay had deteriorated; thus starting at the same rate, by thirty-five the salary a chemist could expect had diminished by £50 to £500, and his ceiling salary was similarly lower. Given that the dominant group of scientists in the 1930s, numerically at least, were the chemists, these figures make clear the limited career potential that science could offer to those who were dependent upon their earnings for a living.

The Medical Research Council

But before considering further the effects of this continuing imbalance in hopes and rewards for scientists, we must retrace our steps to look at the other major organ of government expansion of science which dates from the First World War. The D.S.I.R. dealt exclusively with industrial science and such branches of 'pure science' which could be seen to form their theoretical base – that is, chemistry and physics. The job of support for research into biological and medical science became that of two other bodies, related to the D.S.I.R., but in some senses differing significantly from it, the Medical Research Council (M.R.C.) and the Agricultural Research Council (A.R.C.). Prior to 1911, state support for medical research had been tiny – even more parsimonious than for research in the other sciences – and limited largely to preventive medicine.*

The public health hazard of tuberculosis was the reason for the setting up of a Royal Commission in 1900 to enquire into the relationship of human and animal tuberculosis, which – a step still almost unequalled in Royal Commission annals – decided to conduct natural scientific experiments instead of merely hearing evidence and collecting statistical data, and was provided with funds to employ a scientific staff to do so. But the critical step forward came in 1911, when the National Insurance Act made provision for money to be set aside for research on the basis of 'one penny per insured person in the United Kingdom payable to Parliament'[10] – originally as part of the section referring to Sanatorium benefits, and hence for use in tuberculosis research only. It may be noted that this must surely be the earliest attempt to set a criterion of the proper rate of spending on any research – that is, it was to be related to the insurable population, and thus in some sense to research need. This concept represents a development of considerable importance, which although lost in the ensuing years, has more recently again become of interest as attempts begin to be made to provide some sort of criterion against which decisions of research policy can be based.

By 1913, a Departmental Committee on tuberculosis, set up by the Local Government Board, had recommended the establishment of a single organization for the promotion of medical research, under the National Health Insurance Joint Committee, and a Medical Research Committee was then set up with nine members, six scientists, one member of the Lords, and two M.P.s under the

* The first movement towards a broader concept of research came from that pioneer in public health measures, Sir John Simon,[9] who was medical officer successively to the General Board of Health, the Privy Council and the Local Government Board, and in 1864 obtained authority to initiate laboratory investigation as a supplement to field inquiries, obtaining an auxiliary parliamentary vote of £2,000 in 1870.

chairmanship of Lord Moulton, with the brief of framing research schemes which would be submitted to the Joint Committee for approval. These in turn were considered by a mammoth advisory council, forty-two strong, of university, medical college and Royal Society representatives.[11]

It soon became plain that the new Committee was not going to restrict itself to tuberculosis research, and its first annual report laid down that its terms of interest would include aspects of medical knowledge in the broadest sense, whether or not they had any direct or immediate bearing on any specific disease. To achieve this broadly based research attack, the Committee decided to set up a permanent central laboratory, to support permanent or temporary staff working in hospitals or other institutes (i.e. universities, amongst others), to give aid to individual investigators not directly employed by the Committee and, finally, to establish a medical statistics department.*

But the whole structure of the Committee itself was brought under review by the Haldane Committee on the Machinery of Government, and when it reported in 1918 – that famous report which left few aspects of British public and academic life untouched – the job of the National Health Insurance Joint Committee was taken over by a new Ministry of Health. As this was to be a big department, inevitably subject to political vicissitudes, Haldane regarded it as unwise to leave the M.R.C. under its potentially politically smothering wing, and argued instead for its reconstitution as the Medical Research *Council* under a Privy Council Committee with a status analogous to that of the D.S.I.R. This proposal was accepted in 1919 and carried into effect in 1920, when the M.R.C. was set up in a form which has since been little changed, with the Privy Council Committee for Medical Research, under the chairmanship of the Lord President and including the Home Secretary, the Minister of Health, and a Medical Research Council of eminent scientists, again, like those of the D.S.I.R Council, to be appointed with the approval of the President of the

* In 1914 the Mount Vernon Hospital, in Hampstead, was chosen to form the central laboratory, although largely because of the intervention of the war it was not occupied until 1920. Meanwhile, the war itself, and the thorough shake-up that other scientific institutions were undergoing affected the working of the M.R.C. as well; topics of research were switched to 'war medicine' – the effect of chronic TNT poisoning on explosives workers, the control of 'gas gangrene', the search for antibiotic and antiseptic agents.

Royal Society. There was to be a chairman of relatively limited tenure, but a permanent secretary.[12]

While the chairman has generally been a non-scientist – often a retired political figure – and the scientific membership of the Council has turned over with some rapidity, the secretary has been a permanent career appointment of a medical scientist. Because of this permanency much of the power of the M.R.C. has resided in the secretary himself, of whom there have been only four between 1920 and the present time.* In this stability at the top the M.R.C. has differed substantially from the D.S.I.R., even though in formal terms the two councils were similarly structured.

While the D.S.I.R. has always had something of the characteristics of a government department, civil-service-manned, the new M.R.C. did not move in this direction, but retained a high degree of professional autonomy. Despite the gloomy tone of the first post-war M.R.C. report, lamenting that since the Armistice research had virtually 'disintegrated for lack of funds', the changeover between the old Medical Research Committee and the reformed M.R.C. in 1920 took place smoothly and with no major policy changes. Although funding by means of 'a penny a head' was replaced by parliamentary vote in parallel with D.S.I.R., thus abandoning an interesting concept before it could be adequately tested (today, M.R.C.'s finances approach 5*s*. per head of the British population), the policy of support for a central laboratory and individual workers in hospitals and universities was unchanged.

Unlike D.S.I.R., most of whose research was carried out in government research stations, such as the National Physical Laboratory, or in the research associations, M.R.C.'s in-house research institutes till 1950 consisted only of the Mount Vernon laboratory and expansion was slow. In 1922 a programme of virus research into dog distemper, partly funded by the fox-hunting fraternity, following an appeal in the magazine *The Field*,[12] resulted in the purchase of another site on which to breed infection-free dogs and ferrets, on the outskirts of London, at Mill Hill. This site was later expanded into the National Institute for Medical Research, as the Mount Vernon laboratories became too small,

* They were Sir William Fletcher (secretary of the previous Medical Research Committee) until his death in 1933, Professor Edward Mellanby until his retirement in 1949, the pathologist Sir Harold Himsworth, until his retirement in 1968, and currently Dr J. A. B. Gray who succeeded Sir Harold in 1968.

but a second war intervened before these new laboratories could be occupied.*

Subsequently a third M.R.C. establishment, at Carshalton in Surrey, was created and the building of a fourth, the Clinical Research Centre at Northwick Park, Harrow, is virtually complete. These in-house establishments maintain a permanent staff of M.R.C. employees, with room for temporary workers. But most of the scientists employed by M.R.C. are still grouped in small units, of eight to twenty workers, attached to university departments and hospitals; working directly under individual research leaders, to whom M.R.C.'s policy is to give considerable freedom of research choice.

The consequence of this has been that M.R.C.'s interests have progressively broadened to take in virtually the whole of biology, from tuberculosis and virus diseases in the 1920s, vitamins and chemotherapy in the 1930s, antibiotics in the 1940s and fundamental research in biochemistry, biophysics, genetics, molecular biology and psychology since the Second World War. Perhaps relatively under-emphasized has been a role in preventive medicine and larger aspects of public health.

The one aspect of biological research not regarded as falling within the aegis of M.R.C. was agriculture, and this was in due course made good when, in 1931, a third council, the Agricultural Research Council (A.R.C.) was established. Like the earlier two, it was set up with a Privy Council Committee and a scientific Council, and in structure and policy it has occupied a somewhat intermediate position between that adopted by D.S.I.R. and M.R.C., maintaining its own research stations and setting up a limited number of university-based groups working on specific problems.† But in scale of financing, power and prestige, it has always ranked third behind D.S.I.R. and M.R.C., even though agriculture has been an area of research in Britain where for many years there has been no apparent shortage of funds or anguished

* The tradition of longevity displayed by M.R.C.'s secretaries has been matched by that of the directors of the National Institute, of whom there have been no more than three, Sir Henry Dale, Sir Charles Harington, and Sir Peter Medawar.

† In fact the A.R.C. is rather more complex. Some of the English Institutes are private companies, like Rothamsted (founded in 1826), others, like Babraham in Cambridge are wholly funded. In Scotland the Institutes are funded by the Department of Agriculture but directed by the A.R.C.

cries of research starvation, and indeed, in recent years there have been suggestions that there may in fact be too much agricultural research in hand, compared with other areas.

The Scientists Organize Themselves – Planning and Freedom in Science

Just as scientific affairs began in the years between the wars to occupy an increasing amount of governmental administration, so the scientists themselves began steadily to be drawn into an examination of their relationship with the rest of society. Some, particularly the more senior scientists, were able to work through the Establishment, in conjunction with Lord Haldane, not only a Liberal peer and politician, but also brother of the physiologist J.S. Haldane and uncle of J.B.S. Haldane, equally prominent as a physiologist and a Marxist intellectual. An example of such an approval was the 'Neglect of Science' Committee, set up at the height of the war, to which we have already referred, which criticized the lack of scientists and the predominance of classicists in the ranks of the Civil Service administrators, a point which was equally forcefully made by the Institution of Professional Civil Servants itself in its evidence to the Haldane Commission. At the same time, the physicist J.J. Thomson ran the Prime Minister's committee on Science and Education, arguing for an educational programme relating science to society in a way that only some of the newer universities in Britain manage to do even today.

But for most of the rising numbers of industrial, academic and government scientists, who had begun to chafe against the financial and status barriers to science as a career, recognition that theirs was a necessary profession, vital to the war effort, but one to which limited value was yet attached by society, helped to increase the scientists' consciousness of themselves as a professional group, with a specific set of values and problems. This increasing group consciousness found natural links with the tradition of the scientist as something of a radical, in the sense that his professional scepticism frequently spills over into a generalized willingness to question the basis of society. As membership of the Royal Society, which might have provided a forum for the discussion of public policy and science, was *élitist*, and hence excluded the majority of scientists, and the British Association was less than vital, some new grass-roots organization seemed called for.

The Rise of the A.Sc.W.

This need was expressed when, early in 1917, a movement to radicalize the scientific profession as a whole began to take shape, heralded by two special supplements in the *New Statesman* arguing the value of organization to professional workers, partly in their own interests, partly because their services would be needed in the post-war reconstruction. In the same year, a group of university, government and industrial scientists met to set up a professional association for scientific workers – the National Union of Scientific Workers (N.U.S.W.). Their manifesto argued that:

> One of the main reasons why Science does not occupy its proper place in the national life is that scientific workers do not exercise in the political and industrial world an influence commensurate with their importance.

As one step towards achieving this the Union 'might hope to put forward Parliamentary candidates of its own'. By 1918, N.U.S.W. was formally registered, with a membership of about 500 and Major A. G. Church as General Secretary.[13]

But it almost immediately ran into internal conflict, between those of its members who saw its role as essentially that of a professional association (like, for instance, the Association of Chartered Accountants) and those who regarded it as a union proper. At the same time stresses arose between it and other unions and associations set up to organize engineers and other industrial scientists.

From 1920 on, the N.U.S.W. began to voice increasingly loudly its critique of science policy, influenced heavily by the rising group of radical scientists. These included not only the respectable, like the physicists Professors Soddy and Barstow, but also the less so, like the iconoclastic, erratic, but brilliant H. G. Wells. Wells's early passion for science fiction had long settled into a clear-headed vision that the ideal future organization of the world was through a world government, and that science must play a major part in creating it, either destructively, by the horror of more scientifically waged wars which would force a despairing world under the heel of a technocratic dictatorship (the Air Dictatorship, he once called it), or constructively, through an open conspiracy of scientists and intellectuals who would reshape the world in its own best interests.

Meanwhile, in the short term, the influence of such men began to shape the N.U.S.W.'s thinking as it began to call for a positive use of basic scientific research, directed by the government towards social advance, or deploring the setting up of the research associations by D.S.I.R. in a manner which protected neither 'the interests of the consumer, the merchant, nor the scientific worker'.

H. G. Wells, Major Church, and Professor Dame Helen Gwynne-Vaughan, all stood at the 1923 election. Church was elected, although he had not stood as official N.U.S.W. candidate, and was given a vacancy on the M.R.C., later becoming Parliamentary Private Secretary to Sidney Webb in the first Labour government. In and out of Parliament Church continued to press for the establishment of a Minister of Science, and for a greater interest by the House in scientific affairs. But despite the militancy of the Union's policy, the continued demands for increases in pay, and steadily sharpening critique of the place of scientists in British society, its membership was slow to rise. Only ten per cent of those 10,000 scientists estimated to be eligible for membership had enrolled by 1927, partly because of the reluctance of many scientists to join a union as opposed to a professional association, and partly because of the politically radical line which N.U.S.W. maintained.

An appeal for membership over the name of twenty-one eminent scientists, including J. B. S. Haldane, H. G. Wells, Julian Huxley, Sir William Bragg the crystallographer, and Sir Richard Gregory, editor of *Nature*, claimed that the Union should be entirely non-political, and concern itself with drawing up a code of professional ethics and a central register, and this move back towards the idea of a professional association was formalized later in 1927 when the name was changed to the Association of Scientific Workers (A.Sc.W.), and its rules changed to bring it outside the scope of the government's definition of a trade union.*

* The difference is indicated by the rules of Association, which then read:

(*a*) to promote the development of science in all its aspects and to maintain the honour and interests of the scientific profession, and

(*b*) to restrict the practice of science for remuneration to persons possessing adequate qualifications.

This may be opposed to the old first rule 'To regulate the relations between scientific workers and their employers'.

610 new members were recruited in the year. But, in fact, the advantages of the change in rules were short-lived. Professional scientists were still suspicious of joining, preferring the Association of University Teachers (A.U.T.) or the Institution of Professional Civil Servants (I.P.C.S.), and industrial scientists demanded concrete results – the entire Siemens Branch, for instance, resigned *en bloc* in 1929 when A.Sc.W. failed to achieve recognition there, and even by 1935 membership was below 700, and the journal, *The Scientific Worker* was not published for two whole years.

By this time, the A.Sc.W. was seeking 'to do for the scientific world what the British Medical Association and the Law Society have already done for the medical and legal professions'. Its one notable success at this period was the establishment by Church, with Gregory's aid, of a Parliamentary Science Committee, as 'an authoritative body, able to present to Parliament and the country, the collective opinion of the scientific community on matters affecting the country's interests'. Essentially a parliamentary club enabling scientists to meet and to talk with parliamentarians, but prized as such on both sides, it was to be reorganized in 1939 as the Parliamentary and Scientific Committee, and continued to grow in prestige in the years after the war, till today it has upwards of 130 M.P.'s and sixty peers as members; it has, however, largely confined itself to relatively non-controversial discussion meetings.

Meanwhile, from 1936 onwards, the A.Sc.W. began to grow again. It supported – along with groups within the Royal Society and the British Association – the formation of the Academic Freedom Committee, set up to help the increasing numbers of refugees and scientists who fled from Nazi Germany as the persecution of Jewish scientists began to increase in vigour. It published a review of the effect of the Depression on the state of science in Britain. It set up student branches with nominal subscriptions. Thus it began to swing back towards its earlier, more radical line.

Bernalism and its Enemies

New names began to rise to the forefront of A.Sc.W. activities, the mathematician Hyman Levy, the physicist P.M.S. Blackett, and the biochemist David Keilin, were all vice-presidents in 1938–9 and Chairman of the Executive was J.D. Bernal. But the radicalism of the A.Sc.W. was but one expression of a 'growing awareness of social responsibility among the rising generation of scientific workers', as both Presidential addresses to the British Association and letters to the weekly *Nature* testify. The names of the scientists leading this movement included the biochemist Sir Frederick Gowland Hopkins (whose Cambridge laboratory sheltered many of the refugee German Jewish biochemists from Sir Hans Krebs to Professor Ernst Chain), Sir John Boyd Orr, Frederick Soddy, Sir Daniel Hall, Julian Huxley, J.B.S. Haldane and Lancelot Hogben. At this period a letter from twenty-two Cambridge scientists protesting against the 'prostitution of science for war purposes' was published in *Nature*. Cambridge was the location of the most militant of the scientists, the Cambridge Scientists' Anti-War Group going so far as to picket military bases. Rather more respectable in flavour was the London-based Tots and Quots Club. Solly Zuckerman, C.P. Snow and Ritchie Calder were all members. It must not be assumed, though, that there was no counter-movement. Ronald Clark in his biography of J.B.S. Haldane, quotes an exchange with the biophysicist A.V. Hill, who commented in *Nature*: 'If scientific people are to be accorded the privileges of immunity and tolerance by civilized societies, however, they must observe the rules.'

Haldane's response was to wonder if Hill had 'done a service to science by penning a sentence which might be interpreted as meaning that his profession should only be tolerated in so far as it is muzzled.' Hill's reply was unequivocal:

> I should not condemn men for studying human diet, but the motive should be the discerning of scientific facts, not the demonstration that the British working class is underfed. . . . A reputation gained by scientific achievement, and the immunity accorded to scientific pursuits, should not be lightly used to extort consideration in other respects.

Bernal's book, *The Social Function of Science*, was published at this time, and with its powerfully argued case for the planning of science within society, the need for adequate investment in science and proper use of scientific manpower, gave rise to widespread and vigorous debate. *The Social Function of Science* (and J.G. Crowther's *The Social Relations of Science*, published a few years later) set out a number of premises about the interaction of science and society that seem today less threatening than they did at the time.

Although these premises are now more or less common ground between advanced industrial societies whether socialist in economic form or not, as we shall show in the following chapters, in 1939 this was far from being the case.

Bernal's book was regarded as an attack upon the entrenched position of academic liberals. A 'counterblast to Bernalism' was promptly issued by the Cambridge don J. R. Baker,[14] claiming that Bernal threatened to dragoon scientists into slave teams to undertake socially approved research, and ruthlessly to stamp out their individuality. Sir Solly Zuckerman recalls a histologist who said of Bernal at the time: 'I know what he's after: he's going to tell me that I dare not ever again use gentian violet as a stain for my sections, and that from now on I shall have to restrict myself to methylene blue.' The philosopher of science, Michael Polanyi, set up a 'Society for Freedom in Science' which flourished for a while during the war, to attack the concept of 'planning' in science.[15] Another leading exponent of this viewpoint was Karl Popper.

But in fact, Polanyi's polemic, and much of the organized, though not the intellectual opposition to the concept of planning of science was swept away within a year of the appearance of Bernal's book by the war itself. The pragmatic need to establish relevant priorities in the performance of research and the allocation of funds, which had seemed so heretical to the vested interests of apologists of academic freedom when first advanced, was taken for granted by the scientists at war.

The sense of embattled participationwas reflected in Zuckerman's anecdote of how Allen Lane, the publisher of Penguins, agreed to produce within a fortnight a book – *Science at War** – arguing how best to speed the translation of scientific discovery to practical advantage in the national interest, provided the scientists concerned – Zuckerman amongst them – could write it within a similar period. Both sides kept their bargain.

In such a climate the A.Sc.W.'s membership rose fast, especially amongst industrial scientists. In 1940 it was re-registered as a trade union, and in 1942, with a membership of 4,500, it was affiliated to the T.U.C., and its composition from then on gradually changed towards an overwhelming preponderance of technicians and industrial scientists, although a hard core of researching scientists, generally those politically committed to the left, re-

* A product of the Tots and Quots Club.

mained. Blackett himself became President after the war, editing a second Penguin – *Science and the Nation* – which appeared in 1947, with plans for the post-war reorganization of British science to achieve economic stability and scientific efficiency. Blackett said in his introduction:

> ... [the authors] are frankly and proudly partisan in our attitude to the main social tasks of today ... we find little to admire in those of our scientific colleagues who, faced by the great social problems of our time, are so frightfully scientific that they are unable to make up their minds on which side they stand.

But this brave alignment could appeal to but few scientists. A.Sc.W.'s dual role – of a platform for the socially committed scientist and a technicians' trade union – gradually resolved itself in favour of the latter, despite a verbal intransigence in its policy statements. Although still politically to the left on broad issues, in its recommendations on science policy it became less and less radical; its science policy committee was even wound up for a while in the early 1960s, and in the great debate which preceded the transformation of British science policy in 1964 its contribution was remarkably mute. By 1968, and now some 22,000 strong, it had taken the final logical step in this progression away from its original concept, amalgamation with the militant and industrially more powerful technicians' union, A.S.S.E.T., to form the new A.S.T.M.S. – the Association of Scientific, Technical and Managerial Staffs – with a membership of 85,000, but inevitably, with little appeal for the professional scientist, whose conditions of work continued to be dependent largely upon negotiations by the Association of University Teachers and Institution of Professional Civil Servants. Thus the rise and fall of the attempt to create an all-scientists' union or association came to a halt in 1968. There is no reason why A.S.T.M.S. should not succeed as an active technicians' union, but unless it can reforge an alliance with the radical scientists of the 1970s it is unlikely to find itself a role as a spokesman for science arguing the need for the transformation of British society.

CHAPTER FOUR

The Physicists' War

Science and War reflected, as we have seen, the sudden change in the intellectual environment that the outbreak of the Second World War produced. This change was evidenced by the recognition by the politicians – even more marked than in 1914–18 – that war had become a scientific affair. Thus, as Stafford Cripps, then a member of the War Cabinet, said in 1941:

> I think our main difficulty with regard to the proper utilization of the scientists in this war has been the failure to realize at a sufficiently early stage that this was going to be a truly scientific war and that the battle would not be won merely by the physical ascendancy of our race, but by the ingenuity of those who have been trained in our schools, technical colleges and universities.

Cripps was right: it took a year or more from September 1939 for it to be generally recognized that this was to be the physicists' war *par excellence*, even more perhaps than 1914–18 had been a chemists' war. And the full realization of the role of the physicists, of course, only came in 1945 with Hiroshima and Nagasaki.

The story of British science and the war has by now been told many times in the form of memoirs and biographies of the participants, such as Tizard and Cherwell, in dramatic (some might say over-dramatic) form by Lord Snow in his lectures and novels, in the official war histories and in the accounts by Robert Jungk and others of the scientists and their heart-searchings involved in the development of atomic weapons, and the role of the 'boffins in the back room' that have been given by Ronald Clark.[1] Three themes of general importance arise in these war years and mark the way for what was to come subsequently. These are (*a*) the rapid development of war research and the procedures whereby aspects of this research – such as the decision to develop atomic weapons – remained deliberately hidden from parliamentary scrutiny, (*b*) the growth of centralized bodies for scientific decision-making which became necessary because of the huge increases in investment in research and development the war brought about, and (*c*) public recognition of the need to lay down plans for the post-war retention of many of these structures in the shape of permanent governmental policy-making bodies for the conduct of research and development. These themes are really also those of the general public recognition of the importance of science and its effects upon society as a whole. We can consider each of them separately.

The Emergence of War Research

So far in this history we have not found it necessary to say very much about war research – now generally, somewhat euphemistically, referred to as defence research.* Certainly, at least until 1914–18, what activity there was in the back rooms of the various war ministries was not of a level which could really be dignified by so grandiose a title; despite the long-term interest in scientific research of the Admiralty, for instance, under whose auspices the first of all British state-aided institutions, the Royal Observatory, at Greenwich, had been set up in 1675. By the time of the 1914–18 war, perhaps because the navy was the senior service (it cost some £51·5 million to run in 1914 as against the army's £29 million), the Admiralty was quick to set up its own Board of Inventions and Research, recruiting such eminent scientists as Professor J.J. Thomson, Sir Charles Parsons and Dr G.T. Beitby to serve on the Board. The terms of reference, quoted by the historian Arthur Marwick,[2] were:

(i) to concentrate expert scientific enquiry on certain definite problems, the solution of which is of importance to the naval service;

* Our son Simon has pointed out to us that George Orwell, in *1984*, attains the final euphemism – 'Ministry of Peace'.

(ii) to encourage research in directions in which it is probable that results of value to the navy may be made by organized scientific effort;

(iii) to consider schemes of suggestions put forward by inventors and other members of the general public.

(The last is the catch-all category which government under pressure tends to invoke, as for instance in the recent case of the *Torrey Canyon* incident. In the First World War it produced schemes for catching Zeppelins by magnetism and for electrical death rays.)

But, *pace* the navy, the rapid development of new war technologies, such as the aeroplane, the tank and the machine-gun, and of new techniques in the production of explosives, was probably the most salient contribution of the First World War, with the addition, perhaps, of the development of chemical warfare methods, poison gases and the like, and their potential antidotes, which had occupied some time and ingenuity. The Chemical Defence Experimental Establishment, for example, was established at Porton in Wiltshire in 1916. But the innate conservatism of the military and the genuine hopes of moves towards peace and disarmament in the 1920s, culminating in the signing of the Geneva Protocol of 1925, certainly helped inhibit active war research in Britain. Indeed, in 1918, the policy was adopted of 'pre-supposing peace' for a period of ten years ahead, which was renewed year by year until the 1930s. This meant, for example, that the co-ordinating Board on Defence Research which D.S.I.R. had set up in 1919 under Henry Tizard, was disbanded in 1928, although there remained, of course, Directors of Research within each of the three Service Departments.

It was not until the 1930s that the changed political climate, which made it clear that there was now a real risk of war once more, began to reflect itself in tentative moves towards a more substantial research activity. Strategists such as Churchill, even out of office, together with his scientific adviser, F. A. Lindemann, the physicist Professor of Natural Philosophy at Oxford, unsuccessful Conservative Parliamentary candidate and later as Lord Cherwell,[1] *éminence grise* of British wartime science policy, were convinced that the major threat, and hence most important research area, was the air. Indeed they were probably right.

The overriding theme of the 1930s was research into the development of accurate means of navigation for fighters and offensive bombers and rapid detection methods for incoming enemy bombers. The revelation in the R.A.F. exercises of the summer of 1934 that Britain was practically defenceless against bombing from the air led to the setting up of a committee of scientists and service chiefs–the committee for the Scientific Study of Air Defence – under Tizard, which also included amongst its members the physicist P.M.S. Blackett and the biophysicist (and M.P. for Cambridge University) A.V. Hill. It was this committee which led to the support of the development of radar by Robert Watson-Watt, first at the National Physical Laboratory and later transferred to the Air Ministry, and to the setting up of a chain of radar stations round the British coast. The pre-war years of this committee were marked by the rivalry between it and the parallel activities of Lindemann and Churchill, who accused Tizard, along with the rest of the British war establishment of the time, of 'defeatism'.[3] These years of pre-war bickering and committee manoeuvring between Tizard and Lindemann culminated, when Churchill became Prime Minister, in the virtual squeezing out of Tizard from his various advisory posts and his replacement by Cherwell; later when Labour came to power in 1945 Cherwell followed Churchill into opposition and Tizard returned to the centre of the science policy stage.[4]

But the fascination that this politicking has had for later historians has perhaps obscured the fact that on the whole the differences between the two were at the level of personal animosity and tactical disagreement. On the broad matters of the strategic role of science in contemporary war, in both defence and offence, they were agreed. Equally both were comparable in that they were happy with the role of an essentially back-stage scientific adviser. Neither argued at all for the democratization of the role of science advice *per se* – only as to who was to be the adviser. Nor should it be thought that Tizard himself was in any sense a man of the left, even though he found service under a Labour administration more congenial than that under the Conservatives. Whilst in terseness of style and personal manner he appears in retrospect to have been rather similar to Clement Attlee, it seems to have been purely fortuitous that he found himself linked with Labour; in this he was quite distinct from the entrenched high conservatism of Cherwell, or the open social-democratic commitment of Blackett.

But to return: war, of course, accelerated the development of radar and the setting up of a number of further Air Ministry units such as that on telecommunications, and there was a steady influx of university scientists into war research and development. Many, such as Blackett and Hill, were already deeply involved, but new names, like John Cockcroft, later to work on the atomic bomb and to become Chairman of the Atomic Energy Authority, and Solly Zuckerman, then an Oxford anatomist whose long career in government began with his investigation of the effects of bomb blast on human victims, now began to appear. The ideological aspect of the war made it possible for even those who opposed science in war in principle, like Bernal, to became involved.

By 1940 Churchill had set up a Ministry of Aircraft Production under Lord Beaverbrook and all the Air Ministry scientific effort, from the Directorate of Scientific Research downwards, was transferred. This transferral meant incidentally the final demise of the Tizard Radar Committee, and when shortly afterwards Tizard resigned as Scientific Adviser to the Chiefs of Air Staff, it was no more than the inevitable recognition that the ascendancy of Churchill brought with it that of Cherwell as well.

The same period saw the setting up of a new branch of war science, christened Operations Research (O.R.), as an attempt to apply the methodology of the natural sciences to the improvement of the efficiency of war and, later, industrial activities. By 1941, all three of the armed services had their own Operations Research teams – the Admiralty's headed by P.M.S. Blackett – and one of the most quoted of wartime policy clashes employed the techniques and calculations of Operations Research on how bombers could most effectively be used. Cherwell, with Churchill's approval, argued for their use in saturation bombing of the German working class on the grounds that this 'de-housing' policy would cause death, loss of morale and economic disruption. Blackett and Tizard calculated that on a cost-effectiveness basis the use of bombers to escort ships instead was more economic.[5] The operational life of a bomber flying sorties over Germany would be very low. In the event they were overruled; political calculations triumphed over operational research and 'de-housing' became the official rationale of the British strategic air offensive until almost the last days of the war. By then, the accuracy of the O.R. calculations was apparent to all but the most obdurate.

But dominating all of these British war research activities, we can now see with the benefit of hindsight, were the moves towards the development of atomic power. The possibility that a self-sustaining nuclear fission reaction might take place in uranium was recognized in the middle of 1939 in Britain, the U.S. and Germany. Both Tizard in Britain and Einstein in America argued the likelihood of the Germans being able to exploit the reaction first, and in both countries intensive research was set in progress. In fact, as the Allied investigating teams sent to Germany after the war found, the Germans were really quite far from success, for a variety of reasons.[6] One major reason was the Nazi persecution not only of the Jewish scientists but of their science as well, which pressed directly on Jewish – that is Einsteinian – physics, and which reduced German science to a low ebb from which it has taken many years to recover. It resulted in the expulsion of many scientists who were, like Rudolf Peierls and Otto Frisch in Britain, and Einstein himself in the U.S., later to play a major part in the U.S. and British atomic research effort. Other reasons included faulty research choices and a genuine uncertainty in the German research effort as to whether they were trying to produce nuclear fission for use as a potential bomb or merely as a source of power, an uncertainty which resulted in the relatively low priority atomic research was given as against, say, rocketry. But it was also true that, even if the Germans had had the research success that the British achieved, they, like the British, would probably have lacked the industrial potential to perform some of the crucial separation steps to isolate the active isotope of uranium. Indeed, the history of the atomic bomb – and that of penicillin – are two early examples of projects whose development was to prove to be beyond the potential of what were recognized after the war as 'second-rank nations'. Both Germany and Britain lacked the industrial potential to exploit their laboratory-made basic science discoveries.

The early political reaction in Britain to the potential of the atomic bomb was sceptical; against the enthusiasm of the scientists, Churchill wrote to the Secretary of State for Air urging him to put down any 'scare' about a nuclear weapon, as it was unlikely ever to be built. Thus the early British research was only semi-official; pilot projects at Imperial College and Liverpool by Thomson and Chadwick, and by the 'enemy aliens' Peierls and Frisch at Birmingham. A letter from the latter two to Tizard led to the setting up of a new committee under Thomson including A.V. Hill,

Chadwick and Cockcroft, with Peierls and Frisch as 'visitors'; this committee later became famous as the 'Maud Committee' which was eventually to be transferred to the Ministry of Aircraft Production. Research was still on a small scale and in university departments, but industrial involvement began early in 1941 when collaboration between the Maud Committee and the Imperial Chemical Industries (I.C.I.) Research Group under Sir Wallace Akers began. The major problems were now largely engineering ones and development was beginning to prove expensive. I.C.I.'s involvement became increasingly important as government funds proved tight, and a meeting in April 1941 – perhaps the lowest point of the war for Britain – between government and I.C.I. representatives, resulted in an agreement that I.C.I. take over from the government the building of a reactor in return for helping the government produce a bomb.

The case for both a reactor and a bomb were vigorously pressed by the Maud Committee, but the enterprise was now in danger of becoming so large as to overbalance the rest of the Ministry of Aircraft Production's research, and in October 1941 the entire project was transferred (by Sir John Anderson, Lord President of the Council and hence titularly in charge of the Civil Research Councils) to D.S.I.R., which formed a new Division, discreetly called Tube Alloys, attached to the Ministry of Supply, to handle it. Wallace Akers of I.C.I. was brought in to run Tube Alloys, with a budget of £100,000 for the first six months, and all the Maud Committee's research groups were transferred. Decisions to embark on the construction of full-scale uranium isotope separation plants in Wales and at Chalk River, Canada, were made. But already the project was escalating to an unsupportable degree. International collaboration would clearly be needed, and in October a secret approach was made to the U.S. through Vannevar Bush, Roosevelt's scientific adviser. Roosevelt responded in a letter to Churchill suggesting that there be joint efforts on the project, and, following a series of transatlantic visits, a decision was made in June, 1942, to build a bomb in America on the basis of shared results and information. From this time on, the fate of the British research was tied to that of the Manhattan Project and the work of Tube Alloys was reduced.

This collaboration with the U.S. on research projects was not confined to atomic research; in return for U.S. participation in the war a very deliberate decision was made by Churchill, partly on A.V. Hill's urging, to exchange defence information, as early as July 1940; that is, before the U.S. had even entered the war. In August, 1940, Tizard was despatched with a scientific mission to the U.S. with instructions to 'tell them what they want to know and give all assistance on behalf of the British Government to enable the armed forces of the U.S.A. to reach the highest level of technical efficiency'. Several vital military secrets – in particular proximity fuses and the key development in the new British radar, the cavity magnetron – went with the mission as part of the deal, and when it returned, in October 1940, one member, G. P. Thomson, remained in Washington at the head of a new British Commonwealth Scientific Office through which further exchanges would be made.

The most conspicuous development that went across the water in this way was, of course, the transference of the development of penicillin from the Oxford laboratory of Florey, Heatley, Abraham and Chain to the industrial laboratories of the U.S.A. The penicillin problem was that British facilities for producing it on more than a tiny laboratory scale were lacking, and the unpatented project was farmed out for the development of production techniques to the U.S. pharmaceutical companies. One result of this was that the manufacture of penicillin on a large scale rapidly became possible. A second result was that the U.S. now held all the patents in its manufacture and after the war Britain was forced to buy back the material she had once parted with as part of a wartime information exchange.

Indeed, in some respects the technical collaboration with the U.S. was always a little one-sided, reflecting the weakness of the British political bargaining position. Even before the war ended a process of 'freezing out' of British scientists from the Manhattan Project had begun and the U.S. press release following Hiroshima and Nagasaki so played down the British role that a counter-statement, outlining the British work, was put out by the Directorate of Tube Alloys together with statements by Churchill and by Attlee, by now the new Prime Minister, in August 1945.[7] This freezing out culminated in 1946 with the passage in the U.S. of the McMahon Act which forbade *any* sharing of atomic secrets by the U.S. with any other power, including Britain. This history is one of the emergence of America from isolation, and so gathering to herself military science as part of the essential apparatus of a first-class world power.

By this time, a major controversy was already raging among the scientists over the decision to drop the bomb.[8] Arguments as to whether it should have been dropped over the sea as a demonstration, or at least only on one and not two cities in Japan, split both the political world and the scientific community. Many of the physicists had thus become locked in an ethical and political conflict which was to last until the present day. Thus concern over British participation in the development of the bomb and the extent to which future research was to come under democratic control became obscured in the general issues of control, disarmament and secret research that had been raised. It is clear, though, that Churchill was asked for, and gave, his formal consent to the use of the bomb, during the Potsdam Conference which followed Germany's surrender, but that the British Chiefs of Staff were not consulted. Both Churchill and Attlee seemed to have believed – with hindsight it would appear somewhat naïvely – that the information would continue to be shared between Britain and the U.S.A. against the rest of the world after the war. Thus in a 1945 debate,[9] Churchill defended Truman's decision to keep the atomic secrets in the U.S.A. and U.K. and not share them with the rest of the Allies as 'a sacred trust', a comment that runs wryly by the side of the McMahon Act passed in the following year. Probably it was too soon after the heroic period of the war for British politicians to recognize that the workings out of 'End of Empire' were upon them.

But interestingly in view of what was to follow, Churchill went on trenchantly to define the need for control of research:

> Whatever is decided on these matters should surely be decided by Parliaments and responsible governments and not scientists, however eminent and however ardent they may be. . . . It is the duty of scientists, like all other people, to serve the State and not to rule it because they are scientists.

This sentiment makes strange reading, except in so far as '*L'état c'est moi*' held, when placed alongside Churchill's own method of seeking scientific advice from one privileged figure – Cherwell – and indeed in view of the fact that from 1945 onwards British atomic research continued towards the development of what became known, in the jargon of the late 1950s, as a British 'independent deterrent' without even the semblance of parliamentary scrutiny. Churchill himself claimed not to have known that British atomic research was continuing under the Labour government until he took office again in 1951, although one may perhaps wonder if his surprise was more than political licence. Search through the parliamentary records finds him, whilst still in opposition, early in 1951, attacking the Labour government for its failure to produce an atomic bomb in the five-and-a-half years since the war, a charge against which Attlee rather ambiguously defended himself. The first clear statement that research was continuing was made by Churchill in 1952:[10]

> I was not aware until I took office that not only had the Socialist Government made the atomic bomb as a matter of research, but that they had created, at the expense of many scores of millions of pounds, the important plant necessary for its regular production. . . . They preferred to conceal this vast operation and its finances from the scrutiny of the House; not even obtaining a vote on the principle involved . . .

The sum which the Labour government had managed to 'slip through' the accounts in this way was, Churchill revealed later, in October 1952, at the time of the first British bomb test, a little matter of £100 million. Thus, with the participation of both Labour and Conservative Cabinets (and there is even some doubt as to whether all the Cabinet were involved), but not that of Parliament, Britain entered the nuclear age.[11]

The Mobilization of Science

So far we have concentrated on the actual development of new technology which the war stimulated and in the evolution of defence research structures to cope with them. But the involvement of science in the war was at more levels than these; a total war implied a total mobilization of science too. As far back as 1938, the Royal Society had prepared a memorandum on 'peacetime organization for voluntary training of scientific workers for service in case of a national emergency' which, passed by way of the Prime Minister to the Ministry of Labour, had led to the setting up of a Central Register of scientific and technical personnel who could be called upon in an emergency. Thus by the beginning of the war, there was a fairly comprehensive register available of qualified scientists and engineers – which, apart from anything else, now provides a useful statistical source of information, revealing, for instance, that by 1940 there were 1,175 physicists in Britain (compared with 4,000 in the U.S.A.).

Meanwhile mobilization was pushed a stage further when Sir Lawrence Bragg (Director of the Cavendish Laboratory, Nobel prize-winner and son of Sir William Bragg, then President of the Royal Society), suggested that university teaching staff and students should put themselves at the disposal of the Services Research groups as supplementary staff. The result would be, as Bragg said, that 'the teaching work and research at the universities would be crippled, but I think we must face that in this emergency'. A modification of this policy was eventually adopted.

Thus the onset of war found British scientists in a greater state of readiness, and British government in a more responsive frame of mind to their use than had 1914, and the disappearance of qualified manpower into the maw of the armed forces was relatively checked. From the high scientific pundits to the man at the bench there seems to have been a general willingness to ask how they could contribute as scientists. Penicillin, for example, was developed to help with the treatment of wounds, and although scientific priority is of immense significance, so that the names of Florey and his co-workers are both scientifically and publicly renowned, as one biologist commented, 'It wasn't a miracle. Someone had to get there first, and for the biologists wounds were clearly *the* important problem of the war.' Indeed, there is little doubt that Britain made greater and more efficient use of her manpower resources during 1939–45 than ever before or since and, for that matter, coordinated her resources with a greater degree of success than the totalitarian and hence ostensibly more efficient Nazi society in Germany.

Mobilization of the scientists was mainly confined to university scientists who found themselves seconded to a variety of units, departments and activities often remote from their original research activities. A different decision was made by D.S.I.R.[12] when in 1939 it was agreed at Cabinet level to maintain the Department and its research stations as units and not to disperse its staff to the Services. It was also agreed, bravely, not to cut back on non-military research provided it could be shown to be essential to the maintenance of the life of the nation. In the event, D.S.I.R.'s budget was virtually frozen at around £600,000 a year, for the duration of the war, while prices rose. Thus the Research Boards and the Geological Survey worked comparatively as normal throughout the war; only the National Physical Laboratory was split up by taking the radar research team into the Air Ministry.

D.S.I.R. even increased its scientific staff, from 2,153 in 1939 to 2,772 in 1945 – including, of course, the Tube Alloys group working on the bomb, which was separately funded – and the number of government research and development contracts with industry also rose sharply. By December 1942 the Ministry of Supply had 186 research contracts in 114 different firms and sixty university teams working on specific projects in sixteen universities.

Similarly, the number of research associations and their funding rose dramatically during the war, with a quadrupling of funds and fifteen new associations formed between 1939 and 1947. Because of economic pressure, attempts were made to finance research associations by statutory levy – a scheme which had been rejected several times before the war. Most industries tried voluntary levies with some success, but one, cotton, obtained statutory powers in 1940 for a compulsory levy on all cotton imports. Legal measures to secure industrial research facilities in other industries were eventually granted to the Board of Trade in 1946, due in part to the powerful advocacy of Herbert Morrison.

The Coordination of Government Science

The improvised air with which committee on committee was created in order to deal with the war pressure on research, mirrored in the quotation from Stafford Cripps given earlier, revealed a grave weakness that still existed in the policy-making apparatus, that of the lack of any body which could coordinate the many branches of scientific activity in which the wartime government now found itself engaged. This problem was foreseen at an early stage: seven weeks before the outbreak of war, the President of the Royal Society (Sir William Bragg), had written to the Minister of Coordination of Defence (Lord Chatfield) proposing, with that modest certainty that seems characteristic of all Presidents of the Royal Society, to form 'small groups of representatives of the various branches of science . . . from leading members of the Royal Society who naturally are in close touch with the main body of its Fellows'. Such a group would then study the activities of governmental science organizations, suggest improvements, point out deficiencies and convey potentially valuable scientific ideas to the Committee for Imperial Defence. This advisory group would be without executive power, but would act as a channel between the government and the scientific community.

This ambitious proposal was met with polite inaction by the Ministry, and Bragg then reduced it to one that the two Secretaries of the Royal Society should be attached in some appropriate manner to the War Cabinet. This proposal was apparently considered, but rejected at Cabinet level on the grounds that they already had access to all the scientific advice they needed and that Bragg's proposal would merely overlap with existing machinery.

The Royal Society tried again a year later, when Churchill was Prime Minister, and was eventually allowed to set up its Scientific Advisory Committee under the chairmanship of Lord Hankey with the Secretaries of the Royal Society, D.S.I.R. and M.R.C. attached. The brief of the Advisory Committee was 'to advise the Government on scientific problems *referred to it* . . . and to bring to the notice of the Government promising new developments of importance to the war effort'. This was a considerably more limited role than the Royal Society had originally demanded and it still deliberately left the scientists without power to influence decisions at the highest level. This task was left to Lord Cherwell. Indeed even this slightly soggy sop to scientific demands was obviously acceded to only somewhat reluctantly by Churchill who rather darkly warned the Committee not to exceed its defined role – 'Don't meddle with our innards'.[13]

This limited role attracted mounting criticism from outside the government. Partly as a result of a speech by Tizard to the Parliamentary and Scientific Committee urging more coordination of scientific effort and a voice for scientists in the making of strategic decisions, the Parliamentary and Scientific Committee sent a deputation in July of 1942 to the Scientific Advisory Committee asking for more effective scientific organization. The government's response was given in a House of Lords debate by Lord Snell:

> No set of men, however eminent, could be allowed to put their judgement before that of the Minister unless serious inroads were to be made into

the doctrine of Ministerial responsibility, upon which the normal working of our democracy rests.[14]

The Parliamentary and Scientific Committee's reply was a motion supported by 145 members of all parties, and championed by Professor A.V. Hill in the House of Commons, calling for a full-time Central Scientific and Technical Board to coordinate research and development for war. The result of this was three new appointments of full-time scientific advisers to the Ministry of Supply made, according to that Ministry, 'with a view to completing the existing organization for research and development'. And with this, until the end of the war, the critics had to be content.

CHAPTER FIVE

The Aftermath: Science and the End of Empire

Post-War Pressure for Reform

Despite the war mobilization, the field of scientific and technical research was as a whole left without effective coordination, and the only scientific advice available at Cabinet level was that of Lord Cherwell, by 1942 Paymaster-General with a seat in the Cabinet. The organizations that existed did so in comparative isolation, with contacts between them largely at the personal level through the scientists involved. They included:

(i) The Scientific Advisory Committee to the War Cabinet, the result, as we have seen, of the pressure from the Royal Society, with Lord Hankey as Chairman and Clement Attlee (Lord President of the Council) as President.

(ii) D.S.I.R. and its various research boards and associations, together with M.R.C. and A.R.C., also under the Lord President of the Council.

(iii) An Advisory Committee on Scientific Research and Technical Development, which had been set up in 1939 at the Ministry of Supply, with a direct concern in weapons research and hence heavily orientated towards engineering and technology; amongst its members were Cockcroft, Hill and Tizard.

(iv) The Services Research Establishments, mainly devoted to the improvement of existing weaponry.

(v) Ministry Special Committees such as the Tizard Committee, the Maud Committee and so forth.

(vi) The Central Register of Scientific Manpower under the Ministry of Labour.

It must be recognized that, of these bodies, the distinctly new ones, the Advisory Committee and the Central Register, had developed to no little extent as a result of pressure from the scientists themselves by way of the Royal Society. This pressure reflected a larger and more general concern amongst politicians as well as scientists about the growth of British science, whose strength and weaknesses the war was rapidly revealing. By 1942 the A.Sc.W. was beginning to publish policy statements about the need for a vigorous post-war scientific administration, whilst from the government side a special committee under Sir Alan Barlow[1] of the Treasury was appointed to look into the longer-term needs of science. It reported in 1943 on the need for strengthening the central scientific administration and rapidly increasing the number of available scientists and engineers and improving their pay and status. In the past, it concluded, both salaries and promotional opportunities had been inferior for government-employed scientists, some of whom at least should have opportunities similar to those of the administrative class of the civil service – a conclusion not too dissimilar to that arrived at by the Fulton Commission[2] twenty-five years later.

The period 1943–6, which saw the emergence of a profound feeling that changes amounting almost to a revolution were needed in many aspects of British society, also saw the publication of a series of plans and proposals for the future and the sweeping Labour victory of 1945. This period also marked the coming together of the various pressure groups for science policy reform, to demand that the moves towards centralized policy which the war had enforced should be strengthened in peacetime. From as early as 1945, the Labour government was under pressure from Barlow at the Treasury and Herbert Morrison, then Lord President of the Council, and hence in titular charge of the Research Councils, although, as we have seen, their evolution had in fact led to a great deal of autonomy from effective political control. As Morrison said in one of the earliest post-war debates on science:

> Science had contributed enormously to the winning of the war . . . the Government . . . are . . . desirous that science shall play its part in the constructive tasks of peace and of economic development.

The first step was to clarify the wartime arrangements by the establishment of two science advisory committees, one for civil and one for defence research. In fact, a further year passed before the committees were eventually set up, with Tizard as chairman of both. The rationale of combining the offices of chairman of the Advisory Council on Science Policy[3] (A.C.S.P.) and the Defence Research Policy Committee in one man seems to have been derived from the possibly unique range of experience that this particular chairman, Tizard, brought with him; but that it would also help secure coordination, the lack of which had been such a steady source of complaint during the war, was almost certainly realized. It did not outlast the reign of Tizard and the Labour government, however.

The new A.C.S.P. under Tizard contained representatives of the Research Councils, the University Grants Committee, Barlow from the Treasury, several academics who had already played an advisory role during the war (such as Zuckerman, now Professor of Anatomy at Birmingham, and who by the following year, 1948, became Deputy Chairman – a post he retained until the abolition of the A.C.S.P. in 1964) together with a number of industrialists. In principle, the A.C.S.P., with the task of advising the Lord President in respect of the formulation of scientific policy, and explicit responsibility for surveying in particular manpower, industrial research and productivity and governmental organization of the Civil Service, would have been precisely that coordinating and powerful policy-controlling body which had been demanded.

The practice, however, was to prove otherwise. What was so damaging was the 'A' of the A.C.S.P.; the Council was purely advisory. It was not so much that that the scientists came into conflict with their political masters, but with the Civil Service. The Secretariat of the new Council seems early to have run into opposition from those mandarins within the Civil Service – particularly within the Treasury – who resented the passage of power into the hands of an essentially non-Civil Service body; it was, for the eighteen years of its life, to be hampered by an inadequate machinery for either obtaining information on which to base its advice, or having its advice heeded once given. Within a short while of its establishment, criticism of its impotence was already beginning to be heard. The range of problems presented by British civil science was all too clearly too great for a part-time committee of thirteen.

At least in the early days though, it did not concern itself with atomic energy. Sir John Anderson's wartime committee for Tube Alloys was reformed in 1945 and elliptically named the Advisory Council on Atomic Energy. This lasted but a short while, however, at least in part because of an apparent determination to retain personal control over the atomic energy programme by the Prime Minister, Attlee. Although by 1950, an atomic energy committee of the A.C.S.P. was in existence to advise on the setting up of a Nuclear Power Programme, the anomalous position of atomic energy was not clarified until 1954.

Below or adjacent to the A.C.S.P., the Research Councils – to be joined in 1949 by a new one, the Nature Conservancy – continued much as before. No attempt was made to question the suitability of continuing a system of administering science in which fund allocation remained in the hands of autonomous and virtually self-electing Councils; indeed, the principle of 'freedom from political control' which was established in the structure initially laid down by Haldane, was firmly reasserted. Investment in both the Councils' own units and research associations and the funding of university research, continued to grow until the drastic effect of the rearmament programme of 1950 took its toll of industrial as well as governmental financing. Thus civil science spending, by the Research Councils and elsewhere, rose by nearly five times between 1945 and 1950, from £6·5 million to £30 million, including £8 million for aviation and atomic energy. It was left to the incoming Tory government to check this rise temporarily in 1951. Meanwhile, the expanding nuclear power programme was beginning to monopolize top quality research workers and, even more important, research engineers.

One new development, very much a brainchild of Blackett, was a new body intended to bridge that long-bewailed gap between invention and innovation, the National Research Development Corporation (N.R.D.C.).[4] This body, somewhat anomalously located under the Board of Trade, was intended to provide a means of financing potentially promising research that industry either could not or would not support. The argument which backed its establishment, with an initial capital of £5 million over twenty years (increased to £10 million in 1958 and today £50 million) and a financial latitude by which it was required to do no more than eventually break even, taking one year with another, was that many potential inventors and their inventions remained unexploited because of the reluctance of industrialists to finance them, or the shyness and inability of universities and scientists to become involved with industry. N.R.D.C. was to act as a marriage broker, bringing inventor and industry together, and, if necessary, financially endowing the match. This was in many respects a sensible attempt to draw the lessons of penicillin, or for that matter the dyestuff story itself. But, for reasons that will become clear later, it was never to prove the successful matchmaker that Blackett had hoped for.

The success or failure of the second of the two central advisory committees, that on defence, was less immediately conspicuous to the outside world. Despite the measures of disarmament that Britain undertook immediately following the end of the war, spending on defence and on defence research was never to fall significantly again. Defence research spending (initially administered through the Ministry of Supply – later the Ministry of Aviation) rose from £34 million in 1945 to £63 million in 1950, *before*, that is, rearmament gave it an additional boost. One of the other post-war reconstructions of the Labour Party was the establishment of a Ministry of Defence *per se*, a Ministry which was initially retained by Attlee himself. The role of the Defence Committee[5] was to advise the Minister on matters connected with the formulation of scientific policy in the defence field, a task later redefined as 'all scientific and technical matters which may affect the formulation and direction of defence policy'. It thus became responsible for overseeing the whole defence research programme and for the allocation of inter-service priorities. The Committee was chaired by the Chief Scientific Adviser to the Minister of Defence, then Tizard; the job later fell to Zuckerman. It was also to include representatives of the Chiefs of Staff and their scientific advisers for each of the services. In its own way, this Committee probably worked better, at least in the early years, than did the A.C.S.P., although it found itself in the position of having no control over one particular area of military research, nuclear weapons, due in part to the diffident approach of the Attlee government to the clear-cut establishment of a policy towards either civil or military atomic power.[6] This semi-autonomous solution for the organization of the atomic energy programme became a standard governmental response both in Britain and abroad.

Within these limitations, the Defence Research Policy Committee's job was to undertake broad reviews of the whole defence research and development programme and to attach priorities to the different projects with which it had to deal. Increasingly in later years, as defence research has become more and more expensive, and overall defence policy has fluctuated according to the financial and political exigencies of the time and the personal predilections of a series of rather transient Defence Ministers, its role has been a difficult one. Typically, the political situation has changed more rapidly than the scientific, and it was many years into the 1950s, when defence research already amounted to eighty per cent of all government spending on science, before the recognition of the financial limitation on defence research added to the Defence Committee's brief that of 'keeping under review the defence research and development programme so as to ensure that it is appropriate to current defence policy *having regard to available resources*'.[5] (our italic).

An easier task to set than to achieve, despite a defence research budget which by 1961 had climbed to £240 million. The problem of the rigidity of the defence research programme was only officially commented upon after a series of reversals of defence policy in the 1950s had led to the public recognition that hundreds of millions of pounds had been wasted on cancelled projects. As one of Sir Solly Zuckerman's later committees (that on the Management and Control of Research and Development) put it in 1961:

> Some major projects on which staff are now working are not likely on average to be completed before at least five years. . . . It is inevitable that the bulk of the current programme should reflect past decisions rather than those which might be taken today.

And the Defence Research Policy Committee's history suggested to the Zuckerman Committee that it had not so far been able to play the full part expected of it despite its formal responsibilities. Although the main account of its workings is still shrouded in the mystery of official secrets, this slight lifting of the veil by no means allays all the doubts which have been raised about the management and conduct of British defence research.

Thirteen Wasted Years?

The fall of the Labour government in 1951 did not have any immediate effect on the development of science policy other than the final departure of Tizard (who died in 1959), who was replaced as chairman of the A.C.S.P. by Sir Alexander Todd, the Cambridge chemist. Cherwell reappeared briefly, apparently somewhat at Churchill's persuasion and against his own wishes, as he was already a sick man and died not long after (1957). Spending on all fields of research and development continued to rise year by year by an average of thirteen per cent; the post-war exponential growth phase was well under way.

What happened under the Conservatives, was, in a way, rather more subtle. The Labour administration of 1945–51 had begun to forge the instruments of science policy, but already by 1951 their deficiencies were increasingly apparent. Their natural evolution should have led rapidly to the developments which, in fact, were virtually postponed for a decade. The science policy apparatus of 1947 had been, by comparison with that of the rest of the Western world, well ahead of its time (as will be apparent in Chapter 6). The virtual abdication of responsibility for the further evolution of this apparatus by the new government meant that when the reforms did occur, ten years later, much valuable ground had been lost and Britain had slumped still further into that slough of post-imperial despond, political poverty and economic stagnation which neither the Conservatives, nor subsequently the Labour administration of 1964, proved capable of shaking off. Meanwhile, the growth of science and technology which continued unabated over the whole period, meant that the virtually autonomous research administration which had been set up, via the Research Councils, the Atomic Energy Authority and the increasing amounts of public money being channelled, through the defence departments, into private industry, notably the aerospace firms, had resulted in the development of vast researching empires, overlapping, non-coordinated, and essentially insensitive to political or parliamentary control. The profound effects of this ideological commitment by the Conservatives to *laissez-faire* policies will become apparent as this account proceeds.

Throughout this period, the A.C.S.P. continued to issue dire warnings of what would happen without a proper foundation of policy, as in this extract from its 1954 report:

> If resources were unlimited, it would be possible to have a very large programme in both the defence and civil fields. But in our view, resources devoted to civil research and development have been, and still are, far too small for a country whose competitive position in world trade is dependent upon the economic development of new products and new processes.

The problem of priorities was indeed increasingly to dominate thinking as the decade wore on. Presumably the Defence Committee was saying the same thing – at least one hopes it was – but, if so, its advice, too, was but little heeded. About the only commitment to a research and development strategy which remained unequivocal was that to the development of nuclear energy for both military and peaceful purposes, which began to eat up an increasing proportion of the science budget, both civil and military, from 1954 onwards. The single-minded resolution with which this objective has been pursued by British governments since the war, compared with their faltering if extravagant approach to aerospace and hesitant approach to computers, does not seem to have been remarked upon as the strangely fixed lodestar it has proved. Whether the objective was ultimately chimeric is perhaps too early to tell, so far as the civil programme is concerned (though see p. 122 below); the expensive absurdities of the defence programme and its basis on an essentially undeliverable independent nuclear deterrent stands as a monument to political determination if not to political wisdom.

The pursuit of this hope of atomic energy led to the establishment in 1954 of the Atomic Energy Authority (A.E.A.), a relatively rare institution in Britain in that it is a public corporation, neither a nationalized industry nor a government department, a model which was used very successfully for the New Town policy and more recently (1968) in the transformation of the Post Office. It was free from day-to-day governmental control, subject to the fact that its 'overlord' minister was Lord President of the Council,* and its expenditure was met out of annual parliamentary votes; its

* Responsibility for the A.E.A. was taken by the Prime Minister for the duration of Lord Home's presidency of the Council and was only returned in 1959 when Lord Hailsham became President.

income rose from £47 million in 1954 to £106 million in 1958. Its powers in the field of atomic energy were, and are, comprehensive, covering the production, use and all forms of research into atomic energy and radioactive substances. Its major tasks are to provide fissile material for the defence programme, to conduct basic and applied research and development in its own establishments (such as Harwell, Culham and Aldermaston) for the nuclear reactors which were set up over the following years by the Central Electricity Generating Board, and to develop and produce atomic weapons and components.

The Authority itself consists of a full-time chairman and deputy chairman and ten other members (four full-time), the work being divided into a number of semi-independent divisions, each with a considerable measure of autonomy. This autonomy is also retained by the A.E.A. itself against the Minister of the day, by virtue of the fact that the Chairman of the A.E.A. (initially Sir Edwin Plowden, later Lord Penney, designer of Britain's first atomic bomb, and now Dr John Hill) is himself the government's principal adviser in the field. Consequently, there has been little or no challenge to the validity of the A.E.A.'s judgement on appropriate research lines and policies. For a long time the publicity given to the success of the nuclear generating stations that have begun to spring up around the country since the late 1950s dampened any potential criticism of the work of the A.E.A., not least because its total budget and the number of staff it employs have been regarded as classified information, not apparently released even to the Zuckerman Committee in 1961. These issues became more open, however, when the relative lack of export success by the British nuclear industry and A.E.A. became a matter of public debate in the later 1960s (see next chapter).

Apart from the setting up of A.E.A., the 1950s saw little change in the administration of civil science, with the exception of an internal reconstruction of D.S.I.R., which for some years had been pressing for a reasonably firm budgetary allowance over more than just a year-to-year basis, a policy accepted in 1953.[7] Thus in 1954 a 'five-year plan' forecast £6 million of new buildings, a yearly staff increase of 200 scientists and technicians and a steadily rising income, forecast to reach £6·5 million in 1958–9. The forecasts proved underestimates, even allowing for inflation. A second five-year plan, in 1959, estimated for a total expenditure to 1964 of

£61 million, nearly double that of the past five years, but so rapid was the expansion rate that by 1960 five-year forecasting was abandoned; instead forecasts were to be made each year for the next two, and only tentatively for the next five. By 1964, the D.S.I.R., before being reorganized as the Science Research Council, was spending some £30 million annually.*

Meanwhile several new techniques were developed to inject a little more life into the research associations. Financial provisions for some of the associations were liberalized in 1962, whilst a new system of providing 'ear-marked' grants for selected projects, judged to be of potential national significance, came into force in 1963, and efforts began to be made to break what has consistently been seen as one of the major barriers to innovation in industry – that of the inefficient distribution of information. 'Information scientists', a new specialism, closely related to that once known as librarians, had for some time been pressing for the establishment of 'Offices for Scientific and Technical Information' to be set up, and by the last years of D.S.I.R.'s life, it had begun to respond to this pressure.

Gas-lights in Richmond Terrace

Despite the enormously increased scale of scientific spending as the 1950s wore on, both political parties were slow to see the implications. The structure of the Research Councils and the A.C.S.P. remained untouched, throughout a period equal to a threefold expansion of the total scientific budget. One of the few observable reforms that presaged what was to come was that in

* This rapid expansion led to some minor changes in the organization of the D.S.I.R., proposed by an investigating committee under Sir Harry Jephcott, sometime research director and managing director of Glaxo, the pharmaceutical firm, which reported in 1955. In 1956 these reforms were put into effect, replacing the old Advisory Council which had run D.S.I.R. since its inception by a Council for Scientific and Industrial Research, a corporate body, on the lines of those of the M.R.C. and A.R.C., but still under the Lord President of Council as the directly responsible Minister. The new Council began life with Jephcott himself as Chairman, and the chemist Sir Harry Melville as Secretary. But apart from the formal tidying up reflected by this change, it is doubtful that it caused any major alteration, either within D.S.I.R. or, more critically, in its relations with the outside world.

1956 a manpower sub-committee[8] of the A.C.S.P. was created under Sir Solly Zuckerman, with the task of surveying the current manpower figures for scientists and technologists, and projecting them into the future. They calculated that there were then more than 145,000 scientists, technologists and engineers in Britain, or six per thousand of the working population. The increase was now becoming very rapid. Between 1956 and 1959 there was an estimated growth in numbers of nearly twenty per cent in scientists and engineers, for instance, and this growth rate, of about six per cent per annum, has continued ever since. Nonetheless, the rate of production of qualified manpower was still inadequate. This shortfall, against which successive governments had been warned ever since 1945 by the A.C.S.P., was not met even by the substantial expansion of university and technical college places that had taken place, so that by the end of the 1950s the annual output of scientists and engineers stood at nearly 15,000 – three times the pre-war level.[9] The rate of production of scientists in Britain was still low by comparison with the U.S.A. or U.S.S.R., and led to a continued difficulty amongst industrial firms in filling vacancies. According to the Federation of British Industries, the overall vacancy rate was thirteen per cent in 1959 – and as much as twenty per cent for engineers.

Despite this shortfall, the Manpower Committee, which now produced a regular series of reports, felt by 1961 that the supply of scientists would be roughly 'in balance' by 1965. It was working, as the census figures published for 1961 later revealed, on data which sharply *underestimated* the total of qualified manpower in the country. Yet despite this, and despite the fact that the growth in production of scientists continued to exceed all predictions – as it had done, indeed, since 1945 – demand continued to exceed supply. Whilst the sanguine assumption that the country would be 'in balance' with respect to its scientists and engineers did less damage than the prediction by the Willink Committee,[10] first made about the same time, that the nation was overproducing doctors, which led for a period to the virtual abandonment of plans to expand the medical schools, nonetheless the Zuckerman Committee's manpower predictions certainly helped induce a less than wholly desirable feeling of official complacency in the late 1950s and early 1960s that was not really broken until the much more dramatic plans for growth in the numbers of university places proposed by the Robbins Committee became public in 1963.

The 1959 election was fought with barely a mention of the role of science and technology, bar the statutory nod to the age of automation, atomic power and the need for 'the full use of modern technology', in the party manifestoes. But buried within the Labour Party policy documents was the hint of the need for a Ministry of Science and a Royal Commission to re-examine the Universities and higher education. These proposals, apparently, were watered-down versions of those made by a group of senior scientists sympathetic to Labour which had been meeting informally to consider science policy problems since 1956. Both these proposals were promptly adopted by the victorious Conservatives. The Robbins Committee on higher education was set up, and a new Ministry for Science was announced, with Lord Hailsham (now Mr Quintin Hogg), at its head. It might be thought that at last, a hundred years and ten scientific doubling periods after William Teeling and the other parliamentary advocates of the British Association had first demanded a Science Ministry, their case had at last been met. But it was not to be so.

It was at once made clear, that what had been set up was not a Ministry *of*, but a Ministry *for* science. The distinction was more than semantic. It meant, as Sir Hugh Linstead,[11] Chairman of the Parliamentary and Scientific Committee, put it, that the Minister's job was to *foster*, but not to *own* science, as opposed, say, to Ministers *of* Health or *of* Education. The job of the Minister was as an overlord. As Hailsham himself put it:

> The structure of the office of the Ministry of Science is federal in character. In this it differs from almost all other government institutions. This is because science, oddly enough, must be done by scientists and not by politicians or Civil Servants. By scientists I mean, of course, mainly actual scientists, with laboratories and factories, and not only men with brilliant science degrees brought into administration. . . . The Minister himself has a small office of under fifty. [A bus-load of Civil Servants, he was to describe it elsewhere.] This is not only because his name is not Lord Parkinson.[12]

The implications of this were clear. They remained deep-rooted in the Conservative Party's and Hailsham's ideology. Science was an activity of scientists, essentially as unplannable as Polanyi had argued in 1940. Fundamental science should be associated with universities. Government institutes should be mainly concerned with applied research. Defence research was, fortunately, the problem of another department. Industry should be encouraged to expand its own research facilities. But all on a level of what might be called the exhortatory style of government action by request and hope. This ideological approach was never seriously challenged within the Conservative Party, except perhaps by Aubrey Jones, at one time Minister of Supply and a firm believer in centralized technocratic control of the economy in general and 'French-style' planning. Jones continued to voice this opposition to the prevailing conservative ethos as a back-bencher for several years, before ending up, under Labour, as chairman of the Prices and Incomes Board.

In general, though, this euphoria about government by consent spread downwards from the Minister. In 1961, a 130-page report on the 'Management and Control of Research and Development'[5] was produced by the committee under Sir Solly Zuckerman, after a comprehensive review of all government research establishments, which concluded that fundamentally all was well with government-sponsored research. The committee's strongest conclusion was that some research projects could not be justified and that the Directors of research establishments should consider carefully before embarking upon them, and should ensure that a rough time-table of progress should be maintained. When it is considered that the period covered by this committee included such scandals in the administration of defence research as the £100 million lost on Blue Streak following a six-fold escalation in estimated costs, the propriety of these delicate conclusions may well be pondered.

In essence nothing was initially changed by the establishment of the Minister. Lord Hailsham still retained his several other titles (at one stage he had five government posts simultaneously), and his major role as Minister for Science, that of overlord to the Research Councils, had, of course, originally been vested in one of the posts he still retained, that of Lord President of the Council. As one sardonic scientific civil servant remarked, Richmond Terrace, containing the Minister's office, was still lit by gas lamps. Nonetheless, it is certainly true that, as his period of office went on, Hailsham found himself with steadily growing powers – almost despite his own inclinations. The need for more committees, better advice and an increased secretariat became pressing. And in 1963 one major change occurred, foreshadowing the integration that was to come later, when ultimate responsibility for the University Grants Committee was removed from the Treasury and placed with Hailsham in his role as Lord President of Council.

But the establishment of the Ministry at least served to focus public debate on the implications of the links between science and government. The Labour Party put out an immediate counter-proposal, that the Minister should be a senior Cabinet Minister, responsible for all scientific departments, including N.R.D.C., and a manpower register, with effective powers to coordinate, control and plan science and technology, advised by a new scientific and technical planning board of leading scientists. Having thus publicly committed itself in 1961, the Labour Party then went into a private policy session that lasted it through the remainder of the years before the 1964 election, with only occasional rumbles of steam being allowed to escape into public view.

Robbins – 'More Means Worse'?

Meanwhile the Robbins Committee ran into new problems, one as old as science, and one a new one, arising from the complexity of the modern world. The first was to decide where science should go in their scheme of things. Where should the Ministerial split be made? Industry locked into technology, technology to science, science to the universities and the universities to secondary and primary education. One Ministry could obviously not be expected to control all this effectively, but any split that one considered would inevitably create opposition as the wrong choice. On the one hand, it was argued that schools and universities were all part of 'education' and should be integrated to ensure that two classes of educational citizen did not develop. On the other hand, any attempt to split off science from the universities, would be seen by an army of outraged academics as an attack on that most powerful of vested interests 'academic freedom'. At the same time, one could not divorce technological research from its industrial links, nor should one, perhaps, divide it from pure science if one was not to accentuate the gulf which was generally recognized as one of Britain's most acute problems. The only certain outcome of this embarrassing dilemma is that whatever the Robbins conclusion, the result would have been a storm of protest. This question was initially incidental to Robbins's main problem, which was to decide on the rate of expansion of the universities over the coming few years, although it became more important as the Committee's deliberations wore on. However, solving the problem was not made any easier in that the Robbins Committee neither asked itself what the universities were for, nor at a more mundane level did it number a single scientist amongst its members.

The second question was more central, and this was to try and arrive at some sort of figure for the country's projected manpower needs in the years to 1970. If the universities were to expand at the right rate, a way had to be found to predict what output of science and technology graduates they should be producing each year between 1960 and 1970. The issue was not as simple as that, though, because an expansion in the teaching of science and technology in universities required new qualified scientists and technologists as university teachers, whilst to ensure an adequate number of would-be scientists, an increase in the number of schoolchildren studying the subject was also demanded. These interlocked problems led Robbins into an attempt to create comprehensive 'models' of the educational system, envisaged as a sort of reservoir into which streams of children poured at one end and a flow of graduates trickled out at the other. The number of children entering was more or less fixed; all the regulation had to be done at the outflow end of things.

Robbins reported in 1963,[13] and after considerable internal discussion essentially came down on the side of the creation of two new Ministries, one for schools, and one for the universities plus science and technology (Ministry of Arts and Sciences). There was (predictably) an immediate outcry from the educationalists, who claimed that a division between Ministries of higher and lower education, with the additional prestige of science and technology being attached to the former, would be disastrous for the schools and leave them to be treated as second-rate citizens. But this was a minor point of dispute compared to the larger one of the substantial expansion in numbers of university places that Robbins demanded. Recommendations included an increase in the number of full-time students in higher education of over eighty per cent to 340,000 by 1980, with a corresponding increase in the number and size of universities and elevation of the colleges of advanced technology to full universities. These recommendations ran headlong into the intensive fire of *The Times* and entrenched conservative political and university opinion, which all subscribed, more or less emphatically, to the proposition that whatever the manpower needs of the country, as far as the universities were concerned, 'more meant worse'. In this major battle the minor fight over who should get science and technology was temporarily submerged.

In 1964 the government announced its acceptance of the Robbins targets for university places and an immediate supplementary grant of £56 million over the next three years, but meanwhile something still had to be done about science. Scandals in the management of research and development projects, like the ill-fated Blue Streak rocket, were embarrassing. The failure of the continued and massive government investment in the aircraft industry or atomic energy to produce commercially viable products, and of the Research Association to foster industrial research was becoming apparent. As Hailsham said of the machine tools industry:

> I thought we had at last got a proper Research Association going . . . but . . . I had the gravely disappointing news that one of the largest and best established firms had refused to join on the grounds that they had established a research body of their own . . . [which] proved to be little more than a prototype testing station . . . the management of that firm had insufficient realization of what we even mean by research when we talk about it.[12]

Complex scientific–political problems kept arising, such as the extent of British participation in the space research field, which were met by a set of varied and ill-coordinated *ad hoc* advisory committees operating outside the structure of the Research Councils proper. At the same time, the exponential growth of the science budget continued practically unchecked. Nationally research-and-development expenditure rose from £478 million in 1959 to £757 million in 1964, an overall growth rate of eight per cent. But this figure created some important changes in the *proportion* of funding by the different sectors. Thus whereas in 1959 the government had paid for sixty-six per cent of all research and development, by 1964 this figure had declined to fifty-six per cent, and the proportion carried by private industry had gone up accordingly. Equally the proportion spent on defence had declined from seventy-four per cent of government spending in 1959 to sixty per cent in 1964, whilst that on the civil service had increased.*

* Statistics derived from annual reports of A.C.S.P.

Part of this alteration was caused by a simple reclassification; thus some of the defence projects, supported by the Ministry of Aviation, had been reclassified as civil – like Blue Streak, for example, resurrected as Britain's contribution to the European Launcher Development Organization (see Chapter 9) – but nonetheless a very real increase in university and Research Council spending had occurred. Thus a significant alteration in the balance of research activities was becoming apparent. At about the same time came the first of what were to become a regular series of crises about the emigration of British scientists to the U.S.A. – to be immediately christened by the press as the Brain Drain (see p. 203 below). Matters were not helped by Hailsham's inept handling of public criticism, and his dismissal of the brain drain problem as an indication of the superiority of the British over the American educational system. Academic anger mounted, and the award of an honorary degree to Hailsham was temporarily blocked at Cambridge by a group of militant dons. Others expressed their concern at the starvation of funds for university science, and the parliamentary opposition promptly jumped on to this band-wagon too, with R. H. S. Crossman, then Shadow Minister for Education, promising that the Labour Party would immediately increase university science spending by £35 million.

The Trend Report

All these factors combined to generate the government's response, partly at the suggestion of the A.C.S.P., which was not unaware of its own inadequacies; yet another committee of inquiry into the organization of civil science, this time under a Treasury official, Sir Burke Trend.[14] (This tendency to locate committees of inquiry into civil service and governmental structure in the Treasury is deep-rooted; the Barlow Committee of twenty years before will be recalled; whether the practice will survive the Fulton reforms of the Civil Service, proposed in 1968, remains to be seen.) The committee was set up in March 1962, and after forty-four meetings, finally reported in October 1963.

Widely expected to produce merely a few palliative administrative reforms, the report in fact took note of the wind of change which was blowing during the year of its preparation, and arrived on the political scene at precisely the time when it was becoming apparent that the Labour Party would fight the 1964 election on a 'scientific' platform. It thus became immediately embroiled in a political battle. The report was significant, in that its writers, by stretching their terms of reference to the limit, had managed to produce the first governmental attempt to describe comprehensively the untidy mess of British science, and the *ad hoc* quality of its administration. It made clear that the appointment of a Minister for Science had scarcely altered the position, because of Lord Hailsham's deliberate abstention from the use of even such marginal powers as he possessed. Nor was the scientific advice he received spared criticism. The Advisory Council on Scientific Policy, as the report acidly remarked, was hampered by inadequate powers, limited membership and a tiny secretariat. Thus the report concluded:

The various agencies concerned with the promotion of civil science do not, in the aggregate, constitute a coherent and articulated pattern of organization . . . the arrangements for coordinating the government's scientific effort, and for apportioning the available resources between the agencies on a rational basis, are insufficiently clear and precise . . . precision and flexibility presuppose a rational structure, organically articulated.

Unfortunately the report was worse at cure than at diagnosis. Without seriously studying radical alternatives, it merely proposed a tidying up of the current mess. The D.S.I.R. was to be dismembered and replaced by two new councils, one for pure science and one for industrial research and development, which was also to absorb the old N.R.D.C. But in basic structure and autonomy, the new research councils were to resemble the old: no change was deemed necessary in the – by now time-honoured – principles under which the councils operate. The Minister for Science was to be strengthened by being made responsible for research council budgets, and by linking his activities with those of the Department of Education. The A.C.S.P. was to be made more powerful, manned by professional administrators but including several people of 'wide experience of public affairs'. The key questions, of how to formulate scientific advice and planning, and how to strengthen parliamentary control over scientific decision-making, were scarcely raised.

Nonetheless, the government rapidly accepted the bulk of the Trend proposals, and announced their intention of dismembering the D.S.I.R., creating an Industrial Research and Development Authority and expanding the activities of N.R.D.C., and for the remainder of the Conservative administration linked the Ministry for Science and the Department of Education into a new combined Ministry, in which both Sir Edward Boyle (previously Minister of Education) and Lord Hailsham served. The division of labour within the new Ministry, though, remained much as before; Hailsham was still in command of civil science, and now the University Grants Committee as well, whilst education was left with Boyle. But time was running out on the Conservatives, and it was already clear that the 1964 election would be fought over science in addition to the standard bread-and-butter political issues.

Socialism and the White Heat of Science

The history of the conversion of the Labour Party to the cause of science also spans the years 1961 to 1964, beginning with the setting up of the committee which produced the policy documents already referred to in 1961. This committee, under the chairmanship of Alfred Robens, later Chairman of the National Coal Board, but then still a Labour M.P., drew a variety of interested scientists into an intimacy with the Labour Party which had not really existed since the early post-war period. Recognition that the first statement was inadequate led to the proliferation of Labour and Fabian Society science study groups through 1962 and 1963. Several of these groups, more or less overlapping, and representing conflicting streams of advice, and, in part, ideological complexions within the party, seem to have come into existence about the same time. Meanwhile the original group, under Blackett, which had offered advice to the Party in opposition through the 'dead years' of the late 1950s, continued. A study group on higher education, under the physician Lord Taylor, was set up by Hugh Gaitskell in 1962, whilst Wilson had created a science and industry group in 1960–61. After Gaitskell's death and Wilson's succession to the leadership, the running of the science and industry group was taken over by R. H. S. Crossman, the Party's new spokesman on science and education. Crossman formed his own, more free-ranging group of science advisers a year later, in 1963. The Fabian Society had had its own – rather divided – group in more-or-less continuous existence from 1962 onwards,[15] whilst a quite independent set of proposals was being formulated by yet another group, convened by the wealthy maverick publisher and Labour candidate Robert Maxwell (now M.P. for Buckingham). Maxwell's group was apparently initially called together at the private instigation of Gaitskell, just prior to his death. The deliberations of all these groups culminated in two full-day conferences held at the Bonnington Hotel in Bloomsbury in 1963.[16]

The diagnosis agreed upon at these conferences was clear. Britain was facing an industrial, educational and scientific crisis. Industrially many of our firms were uncompetitive, technologically backward, and inferior not only to the U.S. but also to some European countries. The need was to force industry to rationalize and innovate, increase its research effort and above all to apply the results of research already done. The existing structures of the D.S.I.R. and N.R.D.C. had failed to achieve this end, for a variety of structural and financial reasons. Educationally and scientifically Britain was suffering from a chronic shortage of science teachers, and a maldistributed and ill-planned scientific effort, which resulted in massive spending on aircraft and atomic energy, little on computers and advanced electronics, and a lack of effective permeation of government by scientists and scientific techniques.

Although the advice proffered by the several groups was conflicting on several points they did achieve a broad consensus. At least in part, this was because at no point did the advisers attempt a radical and structural critique of the problems of harnessing science in a post-imperial capitalist society. Nor did they look for what might be regarded as conspicuously socialist answers to the problems presented by a technological and scientific explosion which had become largely removed from democratic control. One attempt to do this, from within the Fabian science group, was rapidly ruled out of court. Instead, the problems were seen as an integral part of Labour's political and economic interests; that is, of how to modify the existing capitalist order so as to enable it to work more effectively. Thus the major problem was seen as one of 'Ministry-building'. Granted the appropriate structure in Whitehall, and the appropriate choice of financial sticks and carrots for inefficient management, capitalism would see the error of its ways, would begin to, or be forced to, innovate and rationalize, science would be harnessed to technology and economic growth, and the British economic miracle would begin. Today, the enormity of this naïveté is manifest.

At the time, though, the Labour prescription which emerged from this critique, whose tone will not be unfamiliar to the reader in the light of the series of such debates from 1830 onwards, appeared fairly incisive. Industry was to be rescued from itself by the application of new planning techniques. 'Technical Progress Teams' would investigate, diagnose and provide recommended cures for whole areas of derelict British industry, which a thrusting, dynamic government would then turn into reality. Government itself would invest massively in new technologies, by a greatly expanded National Research Development Corporation, by the principle of development contracts let to particular firms, and in some cases, particularly of new technologies, by setting up state factories. 'New Public Enterprise' was the key phrase. Above all, this effort would be presided over by a new Ministry, a Ministry of Industry or Technology, which would spearhead the advance towards economic growth and an adequate rate of exports – though this principle was not accepted without some heartsearching.

As far as science and education were concerned the Robbins target was to be accepted or improved upon – 280,000 university places would be provided by the mid-1970s, more funds would transform the universities, and science planning was to be ensured by an effective Minister advised by a board of full-time experts. The principle of the expert was one which the Labour Party felt very strongly about. There were enough Labour politicians still bearing the brandmarks of 1945 to 1951 to demand that the new government should bring with it into Whitehall its own expert advisers to reform and transcend the Civil Service.[17]

The criticisms that could be levelled at A.C.S.P. hinged on two factors. They were only, and inadequately, advisory, and they were oligarchic. About the second it was felt that little could be done. About the first one could do a lot. All that was necessary was to delete the advisory A from the A.C.S.P.'s title. The committee should be made full-time, adequately backed by researching staff. Similarly, scientists would be drafted into all other departments of government as a matter of urgent policy, to provide the expertise sadly lacking in most areas of Whitehall. Many of these points were made forcibly by P. M. S. Blackett, one of the architects of the old A.C.S.P. and the N.R.D.C., in a *New Statesman* article just before the 1964 election which called for a 'Wand over Whitehall'.

The culmination of all this activity came when the key-note speech of the last Labour Party Conference prior to the election, at Scarborough, was made by Harold Wilson introducing the new plan for science. It was here that the equation of science and socialism was so forcibly made, when Mr Wilson referred to the New Britain, 'that is going to be forged in the white heat of this [scientific] revolution'. 'If there is one word,' said Harold Wilson in an interview, 'I would use to identify modern socialism it is "science".' Meanwhile, the Bonnington conferences were to be the forerunners of a group of Labour scientists, more-or-less formally organized into a permanent 'standing conference on science', with Tam Dalyell, the young Labour M.P. for West Lothian, as its secretary.

The Labour scientists never did in fact meet again *en masse* after the second of the Bonnington conferences, although Dalyell and Crossman spent some time in late 1963 and early 1964 touring the country attending a series of meetings held at universities and technical colleges. But the Labour election manifesto of 1964 maintained the tempo with as many as twelve separate mentions of science and technology within the twenty-four pages of 'The New Britain'. And when the Labour Party won the 1964 election, there can be little doubt that one contributory factor to the victory was the feeling amongst many of the 280,000-odd scientists and engineers, that the new Britain would help herald a substantial reform of scientific administration. That technical and scientific class which once before, in 1945, had voted so overwhelmingly for change, had spoken again in favour of the harnessing of science and – what? Socialism? The succeeding years were to tell.

CHAPTER SIX

The New Britain?

Why 1964?

The deliberate placing of science and technology at the centre of a political platform during the 1964 election demonstrated clearly the extent to which the interaction of science and society had, nineteen years after the end of the first truly science-based war in history, emerged into public consciousness. Certainly, this had been a steadily increasing post-war phenomenon;* indeed, although it is easy to argue that it is primarily a post-Hiroshima rather than just a post-war event, nonetheless the implications of the history we have traced make this simple equation less than the whole truth. The newspaper headlines of the 1950s and 1960s were increasingly peppered with technological references, and by the end of the 1950s British success and failure in the technology race was being anxiously examined in many quarters as yet another symptom of economic, political and imperial decline. What is more, the recognition that *how* one conducted one's science and *what* science one did were matters in which politics had a role to play, had become accepted by members of all parties except perhaps the highest of Conservative theoreticians. One interesting measure of this growth of interest, calculated by Norman Vig, is the increase in the number of parliamentary questions asked on scientific and industrial research topics since the war. Thus while in the five years 1945–50

* Though we are not trying to claim that the emergence of science as a public issue meant that it replaced the basic political divide of class and its expression in, for instance, housing.

there were a total of fifty-three such questions, and the number had only risen to seventy-seven in the years 1950–55, it increased dramatically to 445 in the period 1955–9. In the period 1959–64 there were more Commons debates on science policy than in all the preceding fifteen years combined, with six full-day debates on general policy and twenty shorter ones on more specific issues.

Throughout the 1950s, it was believed fairly generally that Britain could successfully compete technologically and scientifically right across the board with any other nation. Even for those fields of research in which the need was accepted for international co-operation, such as high-energy physics, where the European co-operative effort of C.E.R.N. in Geneva was founded in 1953 (see Chapter 7), Britain nonetheless took care to retain her own independent activities at the Rutherford Laboratory, at Daresbury, at Culham, and elsewhere. The possibility that the country might have specifically to opt out of certain technologies was still unacceptable. In part, indeed, the entire debate triggered in 1957 by the emergence of the Campaign for Nuclear Disarmament, which called for Britain to abandon nuclear weapons, represented, if stripped of its moral overtones, one of the first attempts to argue that certain areas of technology were inappropriate to Britain's present status and role in the world. Much C.N.D. propaganda was devoted to arguing that the excessive cost of nuclear weapons (and subsequently of the delivery systems, such as Polaris) distorted the economy and that the money could and should be put to other uses such as building hospitals and schools.

Yet for the bulk of the community, it still seemed in 1957, as it had appeared to the Attlee Cabinet in 1945 when it made the secret decision to go ahead with the development of an independent British-made A-bomb, almost unthinkable to propose that Britain had no future in this type of technology, that the inevitable and continuous escalation in terms of cost, men and material diverted would soon become more than the country could bear. The subsequent debates, from 1957 onwards, about the 'independent deterrent' – and British-designed and -built planes and missiles to carry it – were part of this slow and painful learning process. More than a decade later, the manifest logic of at least the economic arguments advanced by C.N.D. have at last begun to permeate what Galbraith has called 'the conventional wisdom'. But even now, it is doubtful if the politicians, at least, *really* believe it. The

Labour leaders who had scornfully rejected Lord Home's meanderings with the firm statement that the independent deterrent was *neither* independent *nor* a deterrent were, on translation to office, to be found launching Polaris submarines with all the accoutrements of Church, champagne and sub-Churchillian rhetoric that, out of power, they had scorned.

It took another issue to bring the financial limitations more crudely into the public eye; the emergence, following the launching of Sputnik I by the U.S.S.R. in October 1957, of what was at once recognized as a space race. Particularly when the U.S. under Kennedy formally took up the challenge to put an American on to the moon by 1970, the British government was under considerable pressure to join the space club as it had once entered the nuclear club. This time, though, it was clear that the entry fee was too high. Despite the forceful campaign among sections of the popular press (such as the *Daily Express*) for British participation, as a symbol of our technological virility, one of the most interesting signs of the times was the extreme reluctance of the government to be drawn into this battle; already the technological limitations were beginning to impinge. Unlike either the French or the Japanese, both of whom subsequently found themselves involved in modest but still increasingly expensive satellite programmes, the British response was initially a model of caution – a glow of pride in the existence of the radio telescope at Jodrell Bank which became an important part of the machinery for tracking both the Russian and U.S. satellites, a mild expansion of the rocket programme under way at the Australian testing range at Woomera, and the setting up of yet another *ad hoc* committee (under Sir Edward Bullard) to consider future developments. However, this cautious passivity could not long survive the débâcle of the British missile programme which crashed ignominiously in 1960 with the cancellation of the Blue Streak project. An ingenious solution to both headaches was found in the establishment of the European Launcher and Satellite Development Organizations (E.L.D.O. and E.S.R.O.) into which Blue Streak could be fitted as the first stage of a European satellite launcher (see p. 194).

But non-participation in the space race was still the first publicly admitted opting-out, and it made apparent to the public at large what years of publicity hand-outs about Calder Hall, Windscale and Dungeness B had obscured – the fact that the nation was now for the first time genuinely face-to-face with its technological and financial limitations. And the implications of this were not far to seek. If expansion into space research was not possible the limitation of adjacent fields, such as aeronautics became inevitable. As the big airframe and engine manufacturers began to feel the pinch, and were unable to save themselves by a dynamic sales policy, so the already existing attraction of the U.S. for young engineers and scientists began to magnify, until, at least in the popular imagination, the brain drain of talent from these shores to America began to reach alarming proportions.

The troubles of the aero industry were, to some extent, only the troubles of the other research-based industries writ large, and a chorus of complaints of financial deprivation arose, first from industry, and then, increasingly vociferous after the Robbins Committee was set up, from the universities as well. Various distinguished scientists, such as Sir Bernard Lovell of radio-telescope fame and Sir Neville Mott, the Cambridge physicist, began to paint increasingly gloomy pictures of financial shortage within the universities. The demands were still naïve; money was seen as the major limitation, and if more money were to be provided all would be well, and the universities would become once again homes of sweetness and light. It was on to this band-wagon that the then Opposition spokesman Richard Crossman firmly jumped when he promised the universities an immediate increase in funding of some thirty-five million pounds. The complexity of a situation in which limited funds, limited manpower, uncertain and only primitive techniques of technological forecasting were available was still only apparent to a few. All that was sure was that something drastic had to be done. And this diagnosis was, of course, of a piece with that other part of the Labour analysis of the problems of Britain prior to 1964 – the need to 'modernize' British industry, to rid it of its more outmoded and inefficient practices, both in management, production and technological innovation, which were seen as one of the major obstacles to the unshackling of economic growth. Technology, and a new policy for its fostering, would be the key here, too.

This, we would argue, is the objective reality behind the scientific orientation of the 1964 election. The more crudely electioneering reasons why the Labour leadership chose so flamboyantly to re-invest science and technology with the progressive, socialist aura which they had worn in the minds of Engels or Lenin, but which had perhaps since the development of atomic weapons seemed less glowing to many, are not so much our concern here.

It has been argued, for instance, that the issue of 'modernizing Britain' and the reassertion of the importance of science, was little more than a deliberately planned campaign strategy, part of an attempt to divert the Labour Party's attention from its self-destroying ideological debates over Clause IV, nationalization and unilateralism, which threatened its stability in the early 1960s. This interpretation is at least implicitly argued by Norman Vig, when he quotes Wilson as having said after the Clause IV debate:

> What was needed . . . was not to drop Clause IV but to redefine our socialism in terms of the modern scientific age. Instead of nationalizing old, ailing sectors of the economy, we should apply public ownership to the growing points of industry and in the manufacture, for example, of products created by Government-sponsored research and development.

Another, less ideological, function was suspected, especially when disillusionment with the Labour government began to set in after 1966: that the whole exercise was little more than an electoral ploy, Wilson having recognized, as he said at Scarborough at 1960, that:

> it is a terrible reflection on us that in 1945 four out of five scientists voted Labour, whereas I do not think that last October [i.e. 1959] one out of five voted Labour. That is why we emphasize the need for a socialist policy for science . . .

It would be idle to maintain that such electoral considerations did not enter into Labour Party strategy. But it would be wrong to go on from there to a belief that the whole episode was a mere epiphenomenon, only mildly disturbing the broad consensus pattern of British political life, as Vig seems to imply. There was, and is, as we have shown, an objective infrastructure to the debate, and to the fact that the debate came into the open at this particular historical point. The relative inability of the Labour administration to cope subsequently with the problems they correctly perceived in opposition equally reflects a much more serious state of affairs regarding the inability of a social democratic government to reform society whilst leaving the base of that society intact, than a simple analysis of rival plans for 'Ministry-building' and incentive devices would suggest.

What is more, the fact that the underlying links between science policy, technological growth and economic development, and the general problem of the development of democratic control over scientific activities were becoming urgent issues began to achieve recognition in this period from groups other than those principally concerned with the day-to-day formulation of political strategy. It is from this period that one must date the rapid growth of serious science policy studies in Britain. An early exploration of the links between science and economic growth was made by C.F. Carter and Bruce Williams[1] (*Industry and Technical Progress*, 1957), and later by the economist Christopher Freeman,[2] concentrating on the electronics industry. A journal of science policy studies, *Minerva*, edited by the sociologist Edward Shils, was established in 1962, with a small but international readership. A 'Science of Science' foundation, which functioned primarily as a discussion group, was set up in 1965 under the directorship of the science writer, Maurice Goldsmith, inspired by the approach established twenty-five years earlier by Bernal. This was shortly followed by the development of a number of science studies in the universities and colleges of technology.*

What we must try to identify are those major issues which, in 1964, the new Labour government found itself challenged with, and to which, in a sense, it has been responding ever since. From the late 1950s, as we have seen, there was an increasing need to re-define the government's attitudes towards science and technology, so as to establish a series of guides to issues which were becoming increasingly complex. Given the definitions of science and technology which had begun to emerge from the examination of the relationships between science, education and economic growth, the problem was to devise new structures and processes of government to administer them.

Two problems above all others presented themselves for resolution within any proposed new framework:

(i) How to speed up industrial innovation, given that economic growth was perceived to depend on it?

(ii) How to choose between different research and development projects, always a serious problem for a middling rich society, but now critical in the context of the economic decline of the 1960s

* University units or departments researching and teaching science policy and the sociology of science include those in the universities of Bath, Edinburgh, Loughborough, Manchester and Sussex.

which culminated in an £800 million balance-of-payments deficit in 1964?

The following years were to test Labour's diagnosis of the problem, and the proposed cures.

The Labour Government

Indeed, the reconstruction began almost as soon as the Labour Party took power, well within its self-allotted timespan of 'a hundred days' of dynamic government. In fact, so quickly as to irritate the Institution of Professional Civil Servants, whose members staffed the government laboratories, and who felt they had not been properly consulted about the changes.[3,4]

The great debate about where to divide administrative function in the continuum which stretched from primary schools on the one hand, through universities and pure science, to technology and industry on the other, was resolved, to no one's complete satisfaction, by drawing a dividing line between science and technology. The Department of Education and Science – the D.E.S. – was initially under the charge of Michael Stewart and Lord Bowden (Principal of Manchester College of Science and Technology), as Senior and Junior Ministers. It took under its control all of education, including the U.G.C., in rejection of the Robbins proposals, and all of what could be claimed to represent pure science – that is, the Medical and Agricultural Research Councils, and the old Nature Conservancy expanded to form the new Natural Environment Research Council for geology, hydrology, ecology and oceanography. The major newcomer, though, was the new Science Research Council (S.R.C.), which was assembled by the dismemberment of D.S.I.R., taking responsibility mainly for D.S.I.R.'s university functions in the funding of student grants and basic science research projects. At the same time, several of D.S.I.R.'s research establishments were transferred to the S.R.C., including the Rutherford High Energy Laboratory. But the residue of D.S.I.R., including its industrial affiliations, was awarded, as we shall see, to the Ministry of Technology.

This reconstruction of the Research Councils* and the transfer

* In 1965 the long overdue Social Science Research Council was set up simiarly constituted to the older councils.

Figure 3

THE ORGANIZATION OF SCIENCE AND TECHNOLOGY TODAY

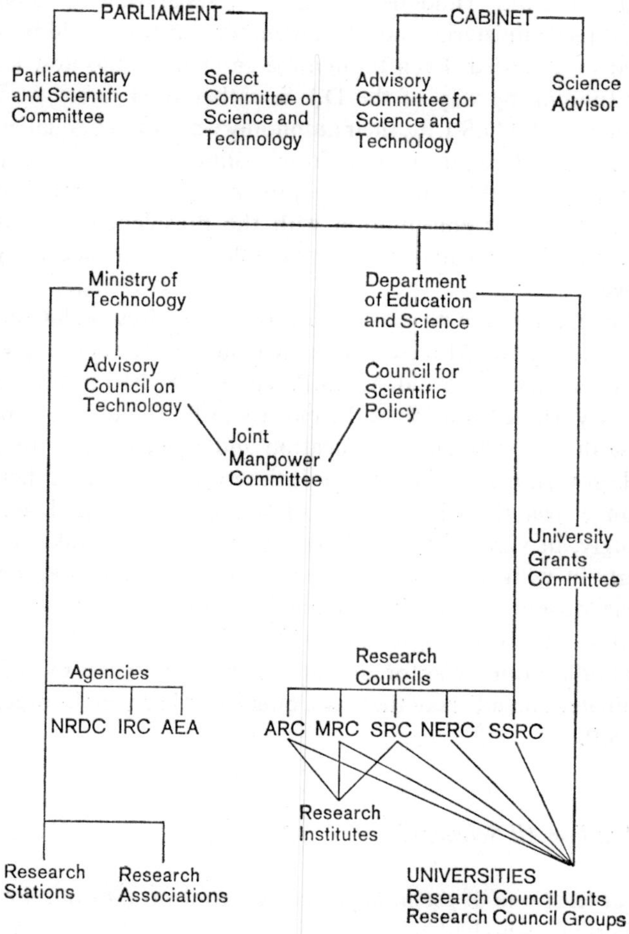

to the D.E.S. involved certain constitutional changes, notably the disbanding of the old Privy Council Committees which had formally run them, but in the administrative reshuffle, considerable care was taken to ensure that the Councils, like U.G.C., would retain their autonomy of action. The pre-election arguments about whether the old 'Haldane principle' of separating the Councils from direct ministerial and parliamentary control should be abandoned were settled. Even though the councils would now receive their funding by way of the D.E.S. rather than direct from the Treasury as did D.S.I.R., their autonomy was not to be challenged; they remained relatively free from political – or democratic – constraint, and their members continued to be appointed by co-option or, 'after consultation with the President of the Royal Society'. Thus no major new principle was introduced by the change.

Above, though in no sense in control of, the Research Councils, and to advise the Minister, the new Council for Scientific Policy (C.S.P.) replaced the old A.C.S.P. The C.S.P. had a much more narrowly defined brief than the old A.C.S.P. The new task was to advise the Department of Education and Science rather than the whole government and to confine its interests to science ather than to range over the whole gamut of science and technology. Surprisingly, in view of Labour's belief that it should take its own experts in with it, the first chairman of the new C.S.P. was Sir Harrie Massey, previously concerned with planning space research, and not notably amongst those who had advised the Party whilst out of office. But it was for all that a fairly clean sweep. Only five of the nineteen members of the new Council had been on the preceding A.C.S.P.

A Man For All Sciences?

For at least one of them, however, it meant promotion. Sir Solly Zuckerman, who had held high scientific office virtually since 1945, was translated into a new post, that of Scientific Adviser to the Cabinet Office, whilst still retaining his special responsibility for defence, disarmament and foreign affairs. Such a translation was the highest point yet reached in the lengthy career of one who was, in the words of a fellow-scientist quoted in the *Guardian* 'a firm believer in survival'. Zuckerman's career as a government adviser had started in the desperate days of the early 1940s when, as we have seen, practically every available scientist was pressed into the service of defence. Whilst most of the biologists were slower off the mark than the physicists, it was as an anatomist that Zuckerman began, with studies of the effect of blast from bombs both on animals (he had worked originally on the social and sexual life of apes) and, as a more acceptable substitute, on flat, man-sized wooden boards which were promptly christened 'zuckermen'.

His interest in anatomy had survived more than twenty-five years of subsequent government service, and he retained both the Chair of Anatomy at Birmingham until 1968 and the Secretaryship of the Zoological Society (which runs the London Zoo), as well as being a member of the B.B.C.'s General Advisory Council and a frequent academic lecturer, author and reviewer. Throughout the war, as we have seen, he was scientific adviser to Combined Operations and afterwards rode out six Prime Ministers, starting on the A.C.S.P. under Tizard and ending as Deputy Chairman under Lord Todd, and encompassing *en route* the chairmanship of the Manpower Committee, the Defence Research Policy Committee, and the Natural Resources (Technical) Committee and the post of Chief Scientific Adviser to the Minister of Defence. What is less clear, certainly, is the role Zuckerman has played in these various posts. Until recently he has been a relatively retiring figure, at least so far as the general public are concerned, but the new tendency to permit more public comment from civil servants has perhaps made him feel freer to publish (his latest book is called *Scientists at War*, from which we quoted in Chapter 3) and lecture on science policy as well as his academic specialities. Yet not too much emerges from these new statements, except, perhaps, a generalized scepticism about the value or utility of scientific advice at all.[25] Clearly an able committee man, nonetheless his previous committees have not been conspicuously successful in their reporting; the Manpower Committee, for instance, operated throughout the later 1950s with statistics that seriously under-estimated the total of scientists and technologists in Britain, and which were remedied only with the arrival of the 1961 census data, whilst the report of his Committee on the Management and Control of Research and Development in 1961 painted a fairly anodyne picture of the health of current

British governmental research establishments only two years before the Trend Committee advocated the radical re-organization which we have already discussed.

What was to be the role of Zuckerman's new office? Was he to become a second Cherwell, in all but the political commitment which made Cherwell acceptable to a Conservative but not to a Labour administration? Such speculations are still far from resolved, but as the shape of the Labour administration developed, Zuckerman's position, as we shall see, has apparently steadily strengthened. In Harold Wilson's view, there was no doubt that the appointment of such a Cabinet adviser on science policy was another step forward in the move to endow the British Prime Ministership with quasi-Presidential authority, and the role of Sir Solly Zuckerman was to be seen as that of an incipient Jerome Wiesner or Donald Hornig[3]— (see p. 155).

Friends and Cousins

Just as the decision to combine science and education into the D.E.S., and to drop the idea of a Minister of Science, ran into criticism, so did the much more controversial division of technology from science in the establishment of the new Ministry of Technology. In Parliament and press, the functions of this new Ministry were immediately under attack, for no better reason apparently, than that the new Minister was the Secretary of the Transport and General Workers Union, Mr Frank Cousins, with the author Lord (C.P.) Snow as Minister of State. Less publicly known was Cousins's service on the Council of D.S.I.R., and Snow's work as Chairman of the Civil Service Appointments Board. The new Ministry was set up, as we have already seen, as a means of spearheading the drive for technological efficiency. It received as christening presents the National Physical Laboratory, the Atomic Energy Authority, most of the research stations which had once been the possessions of the old D.S.I.R. (other than those which were allotted to S.R.C.) and of the Research Associations, and rescued from the Board of Trade the National Research Development Corporation (see p.75). Scientifically it was headed by a new Advisory Council on Technology with P.M.S. Blackett as vice-chairman (he resigned in 1969), and the Minister himself as chairman and containing a substantial proportion of not-too-old technologists and industrialists (at least six actually drawn from technologically-based industries) and two ex-government defence scientists (the press were quick to seize on the incongruity of the one-time Head of the Atomic Weapons Research Establishment at Aldermaston as an adviser for Frank Cousins).

The rationale of the Ministry of Technology was clear;[5] despite tentative steps towards the recognition of industrial scientists, such as that by which the Royal Society had deliberately set aside certain of its fellowships for deserving engineers, a more comprehensive approach was needed. The Ministry was initially given responsibility for four industries: computers, electronics, telecommunications and machine tools. Before long it had also taken over mechanical and electrical engineering and motor vehicles from the Board of Trade, and it was widely assumed (although in reality the transfer only came two years later) that it would get the aeronautical industry, too, when the Ministry of Aviation was wound up. Furthermore, the Ministry got virtually a blank cheque as to the method it used to improve the industries of which it was sponsor – at least an organizational cheque, if not a financial one. Solutions could range from the use of the N.R.D.C., through development contracts to new public enterprise. And before long, we shall see, a new government creation, that of the Industrial Reorganization Commission (I.R.C.), was to emerge.

The shape of the new administrative structure that emerged from the turmoil of the previous four years was not necessarily the best. In particular there remained the ever-present danger of consolidating the split between science and technology. There was no shortage of people to argue that whilst universities and science remained so indissolubly linked the prestige of technology would remain low. But as a short-term measure, directed with sufficient resolution, it was probably true that the Ministry of Technology would have succeeded. What it needed above all was a certain charismatic quality of leadership. Whilst it could not subsist indefinitely on the white heat of revolution, a little applied in appropriate quarters might have been sufficient to see it off the ground. In fact, it stumbled.

Five Wasted Years?

As we have seen, the first steps were substantial ones, at least at the level of Ministerial reorganization. Whether the pace could have been kept up beyond the first hundred days is now a matter of historical speculation only, for, of course, a financial crisis intervened. As a result, far from the massive financial expansion which had been the pre-election hope, scientists found themselves having to struggle hard against proposals for extensive cuts which were being pressed more and more audibly by the Treasury, even though it was 1967–8 before the cuts became operative. The promised extra money for the universities became an ironic vision of the past when colleges found themselves faced with a moratorium on new building. A determined attempt to persuade the Research Councils to re-assess their future commitments led to the somewhat surprised recognition that commitments already entered into, without any new projects being embarked upon at all, would still demand a rate of growth of the science budget substantially more rapid than that of G.N.P., whilst the extent to which apparently prestige technological products, like the cancelled TSR–2 plane, bit deep into the infrastructure of the economy was only realized when the powerful air lobby[6] swung into action, and the pained cries of the aircraft workers, that they hadn't voted Labour for this, became heard.

Other attempts to slash major commitments, such as the Anglo-French Concorde, were hastily abandoned in the face of French threats to take the case to the International Court of Justice at The Hague. In some areas (Polaris, the withdrawal from E.S.R.O.), the attempt was confined merely to a cautious testing of the water temperature; the commitment was already so deep, and the political repercussions potentially so great, that when a series of detailed press leaks made the government's apparent intentions clear, it was forced rapidly to deny them. On the other hand, where the commitment did not yet exist – for instance, with respect to Britain's share in the proposed European 300 GEV accelerator, it was possible to postpone making a decision for more than three years. Indeed it was not until the report of the Council for Scientific Policy in October of 1967[7] finally came down in favour of the proposed accelerator, that the government was forced to commit itself at all, though it took another nine months before it finally summoned enough courage to defy the Council's advice, and refuse to participate.

Thus the financial room for manoeuvre which the government found itself with was comparatively limited. Nonetheless it seemed determined to provide itself with some theoretical backing for any proposed slackening in the rate of growth of scientific spending and to do this jumped eagerly at the theory of scientific growth which had been advanced some years earlier by the historian of science de Solla Price, and which was accepted by the C.S.P. Indeed, this must be one of the few cases in which an historian's ideas have been called into service by the Treasury quite so eagerly. Price, it will be recalled from Chapter 1, had argued that scientific growth proceeded exponentially, and it was now at such a point in the growth curve that continued expansion at the current rate (ten to fifteen per cent per annum) would soon eat up an insupportable amount of the G.N.P. It followed, ran Price's argument, that over the course of this current scientific doubling period, some levelling-off could be expected to occur.

Even though it was the scientists themselves who applied the theory to British science policy, the Treasury seized upon it with an almost audible sigh of relief. Thus the theory was set out in two remarkable articles analysing the growth and future development of science, by Lord Bowden, published in the *New Scientist* in September 1965. The articles constituted a swansong as they practically coincided with Bowden's resignation from his Ministerial post at the D.E.S. He plotted some exponential growth rates for a variety of activities, such as employment in the electrical manufacturing industry, showed that extrapolation would lead to the usual absurdities, and Bowden concluded that we were approaching a crisis in history.

> Processes which have been going on quite steadily for centuries may have to stop quite suddenly and quite soon . . . policies . . . may have to be scrapped at great cost in spiritual anguish and perhaps at the price of great economic upheaval. . . . We know (and no one has ever known this before) that science has grown steadily for two hundred years or more, but *we* have to decide not *whether* but *when* this steady exponential expansion must be stopped. . . . I know of very few people who expect that we shall be able to double our present rate of expenditure (on pure science) more than three times in the foreseeable future. . . . in future we shall be able to begin a new project only if we can first find the money by stopping an old one . . . all that the Government can do about scientific

fashions is to deny some of its scientists the funds they want, and if it does this some of these distinguished and important men will fold up their tents like Arabs and as silently steal away.

In fact, amid the sense of rising hysteria implied by this type of statement, Bowden went on to make a number of quite sensible policy suggestions on the need for scientific administration. The point of listing the above extracts, from someone who was at that time a Minister, is to indicate the feeling of blank despair that the projection of trend curves of growth-rates apparently produced. Some of the criticism of this type of approach has already been made in Chapter 1; the real significance of Bowden's foreboding about the future we will discuss only towards the end of this book.[8] For now, we may merely note it as an indication of the way in which, within a year of being elected, Labour's euphoria about the inexorable march of technology had vanished – the white heat of revolution was now little more than a few glowing embers.

A similar depressed caution was expressed in the first report of the new Council for Scientific Policy, dated May 1966.[9] The C.S.P., officially only concerned with those specific aspects of science which were the responsibility of the D.E.S., nonetheless utilized its report to survey the whole scientific scene, at least in a broad – and perhaps superficial – manner.

It has been represented to us that the capacity of the national economy will not permit the growth of Research Councils' expenditure at present rates . . . this situation . . . is not yet faced by other countries in the van of scientific advance* . . . the question at issue is when and at what rate and on what criteria the levelling off of the growth rate should take place.

The report went on to stress the need for understanding the mechanisms of scientific growth and to make policy decisions in advance to avoid subsequent catastrophic perturbations, but the key paragraph indicated the limitations within which such studies were to be framed.

We have accordingly invited the Research Councils to consider their long term programmes in order to assess the effect of tapering off of growth rates, particularly in relation to new and scientifically desirable projects which might be excluded. We have invited them to develop the justification for their policies, both in terms of intrinsic scientific criteria

* However, within the next couple of years several other countries, including the U.S., realized that they were in the same uncomfortable position.

and in relation to the educational, social and economic benefits. To assess this process we have held a number of full day informal discussions of specific fields . . . to clarify the criteria relevant to each programme. . .

Such an approach has perhaps typified the Labour government's attempt to plan for science. After all the pre-election talk of 'Wand over Whitehall', when it came down to it the best that could be achieved was 'a number of full day informal discussions' – with the administrators who had been in office long before Labour came to power. Thus the extent of the hoped for scientific 'permeation' has certainly been minimal. In fact how such decisions on priorities are really made is quite another matter and it is one that we will discuss in more detail in Chapter 12; the point for the moment is merely to note the gulf between the hope and the attainment. The concluding paragraph of the final report of the old Advisory Council on Scientific Policy spelt out the key issue it bequeathed to its successors thus:

The problem of priorities in science and technology lies at the heart of national science policy, and therefore of our national destiny . . . it will be up to the government itself to decide, on the best advice that can be tendered, what our national priorities should be.[10]

And in a sense Sir Harrie Massey, Chairman of the new C.S.P., replied to this statement when he said as he launched the first C.S.P. report that there was still 'nothing in the way of real direction involved'. In fact, when the C.S.P. came to consider how much levelling-off could be achieved it found itself stuck with the embarrassing fact that the forward commitments of the Research Council alone, without any further expenditure, would ensure an increase of twelve per cent in real terms in 1966–7 over 1965–6, and that it would be several years before any present cut-backs would seriously begin to affect the growth rate. Nonetheless the principle was laid down, to the distress of more than one academic scientist. Thus Sir Bernard Lovell of Jodrell Bank and Professor C. F. Powell, the physicist president of the A.Sc.W., for instance, claimed that it would be catastrophic if the growth rate were to be cut back to five or six per cent – the magic figure that the C.S.P. had decided was the long-term aim.

By its second annual report, in October 1967, the C.S.P.[11] had further refined the figures for their projected cut-backs; whereas from 1964 to 1968 the annual growth rate of the Research Councils was eleven per cent (A.R.C. thirteen per cent, M.R.C. fifteen per cent, N.E.R.C. twenty per cent, and S.R.C. seven per cent) by 1969–70 the rate would be reduced to nine per cent (A.R.C. five per cent, M.R.C. nine per cent, N.E.R.C. fifteen per cent, and S.R.C. eight per cent). It may be noticed that the cut-back in growth-rate as projected fell hardest on the Agricultural and Medical Research Councils, whereas the Science Research Council was projected to suffer the least, if at all. The reasons for this relate at least in part to the changing role of the Research Councils that we consider in more detail in the next section. These trends were confirmed in succeeding years. By 1969 growth rates had in fact dropped below the C.S.P.'s projections. For the S.R.C. growth was down to an annual four per cent, for M.R.C. seven per cent, for A.R.C. under one per cent; only N.E.R.C. held its own, with a growth of twenty per cent.[23]

No doubt a more determined battle might have been fought with the Treasury were it not for the fact that the major interests of the new Minister, Mr Anthony Crosland,* undoubtedly lay elsewhere. Even with technology hived off, the D.E.S. was an unwieldy empire, stretching from primary schools to high-energy physics, and faced with the challenges of the Plowden Report, the battle for comprehensivization, the public schools, the binary system of higher education (whereby the Minister ultimately has responsibility for teacher-training colleges and colleges of advanced technology but not directly for the universities), the university revolt against the moratorium on capital expenditure and the proposal to raise the fees for foreign students at British universities, it is perhaps not surprising that the problems of science took a relatively subsidiary place in Mr Crosland's words and deeds. Another Minister might have arranged his priorities differently, nor was he helped by the inadequacies of his junior ministers, but ultimately this overloading of the D.E.S. was part of the price that had to be paid for the structural rearrangements that Labour brought in.

Nonetheless, Mr Crosland slowly built up for himself a certain reputation, as was shown when, in the autumn of 1967, he was replaced as Secretary of State for Education and Science by Mr Gordon Walker. In commemoration *Nature* produced the following slightly backhanded obituary, saying of Mr Crosland, that he had:

* Michael Stewart had by this time been translated to the Foreign Office.

won for himself a reputation which engendered something akin to security . . . [he] seems to have put up a stalwart fight in the past few months to prevent too great an erosion of the education budget . . . he has been an able Minister. . .

Mr Gordon Walker, on the other hand was:

by comparison an unknown quantity. He is scholarly (which should help) donnish (which is if anything a disadvantage) and has such a reputation for loyalty to the government as a whole that people will naturally fear. . .

However, said *Nature*,

the loss occasioned by the departure of Mr Crosland will to some extent be cancelled out by the simultaneous departure of Mr Goronwy Roberts, who has for several months been concerned with the administration of the Research Councils. He has not always inspired confidence on scientific matters . . .[12]

Gordon Walker's term of office itself was brief; in the next Cabinet re-shuffle, in the spring of 1968, he was in turn replaced by the ex-schoolteacher Mr Edward Short, a man more known for his antiquated views on the need for religious education and discipline in the schools than his interest in the fate of civil science.

The Research Councils

The Research Councils themselves had more to worry about than merely who replaced Mr Goronwy Roberts. The new-format,which had split the old D.S.I.R. in two, and linked the new-formed S.R.C. with M.R.C., A.R.C., and the equally new N.E.R.C. under the Department of Education and Science, had certainly rationalized things, but had left the Councils plenty to think over. Their thinking was dominated by three issues, the increasing emphasis on forward planning, the severe budgetary restrictions being imposed upon them from above, and their relationship with the outside world, which included for each of them not only the new colossus of the Ministry of Technology and industry and the universities, but one another as well. Such problems are most clearly indicated in the development of the S.R.C. and of M.R.C.

S.R.C. lost little time in learning the new ropes. Although its chairman until 1967 remained Sir Harry Melville, of the old

D.S.I.R., the first report of the new Council[13] already sounded many of the notes we have previously heard from the overlord Council for Scientific Policy, on growth rates, forward planning and the importance of the links between science and technology. Even basic research, the Council implied, somewhat self-defensively, had a technological pay-off somewhere down the line, and could hence be justified; under no circumstances could a slackening of the growth rate below the magic minimum of five to six per cent be accepted, for this irreducible figure represented, the S.R.C. claimed, a 'sophistication factor',* an increase inevitable in sheer nature of the increasing complexity of science itself, quite independent of any real advance in the subject. Such a 'sophistication factor' takes into consideration, for instance, the development of newer and cleverer machines, and recognizes also the changing nature of the actual problems the scientist is called upon to solve. Nonetheless the S.R.C. budget, £28·2 million in 1965–6, rose to £45·8 million in 1969–70, and most importantly, was secured with the promise of a steady increase of some eight per cent per annum (at constant prices) into the early 1970s. This assurance represented something of a success for the S.R.C.'s demands for some security in forward planning. But this figure, large as it was, was spread thin. It included astronomy and space research (twenty-five per cent of the total budget), including contributions to E.S.R.O., the support of twenty-five British space research groups in the universities and elsewhere, rocket launching at Woomera, and the development of radio telescopes. It covered nuclear physics (forty-three per cent of the total) including £3·6 million pounds to C.E.R.N. in 1966-7 and support for the indigenous British laboratories (Daresbury and Rutherford).

What was left was spread over the whole of university science and technology, including research grants for students, provision of computers and all aspects of academic science, including an increasing commitment to biology and some of those intermediate regions which had hitherto been the province of M.R.C. To assist in the financial allocation, the S.R.C., following D.S.I.R.'s pattern, set up a number of advisory boards, committees and panels. In

* An explanatory attempt to quantify this sophistication factor by analysing research expenditure in government research stations and two university departments, was reported as 'Science Policy Study Number 1' by the D.E.S. staff.[14]

response to the growing demand for better informed discussions of science policy-making, it commissioned surveys of research needs, assessed priorities as between subject and discipline, and made tentative steps towards the concept of 'centres of excellence' (see Chapter 12 below). Indeed, by the time Sir Harry Melville left in 1968, to become Principal of Queen Mary's College, London, and handed the chairmanship over to the physicist Professor Brian Flowers (who had earlier chaired the committee which produced the report on computer policy for the Ministry of Technology), the S.R.C. had moved substantially forward in its concept of the role of science planning in the new conditions of Britain of the 1960s and 1970s.

By contrast to the S.R.C.'s energy, M.R C. seemed relatively unadventurous. Unaffected by the great shake-up, except for a mere minor expansion of its council, the M.R.C. continued with policy much as before, supporting semi-permanent research units under eminent individuals, more temporary research groups under less eminent ones, and its home units at Mill Hill and Carshalton, and the now nearly completed Clinical Research Centre at Northwick Park, Harrow. But somehow it seemed less in touch than it had been previously; its policies and planning showed little external sign of the revolution that had overtaken the S.R.C.'s thinking; for example, it still saw no reason to embark on elaborate public exercises in 'justification' or 'assessment of priority' in the allocation of its now substantial budget – £11 million in 1965–6, £17·1 million in 1968–9.

The virtual doubling of its research budget between 1962 and 1967 made no difference to what it regarded as its tried and true method of judiciously selecting individual scientists of promise – a process described by *Nature* as 'growth like Topsy's . . . a kleptomaniac baseball promoter anxious to see that every player of distinction is properly signed up . . .'. For all the serious doubts about its advantages, the policy of setting up research units and groups almost feudally bound to individual directors apparently remained unquestioned. 'Nothing,' as *Nature* concluded, '. . . could be mistaken for a proof that the Council [was] possessed of a coherent strategy for medical research.'[15] But indeed, other signs that the outside world, at least, was questioning the M.R.C.'s role and achievement as the self-chosen backer of excellence, could be read. Thus the expansion of the S.R.C.'s interest into the fields of biology and biochemistry, long regarded by M.R.C. as its own province, is known to have led to a certain strain in the relationship between the Councils. Another sign of the times might well be that the forward growth projection set by the C.S.P. in 1967 for the Research Councils, whilst maintaining S.R.C.'s steady growth, cut the M.R.C. back severely from an expansion rate which had been running at fifteen to twenty per cent per annum – in one year even 24·5 per cent – to a proposed nine per cent by 1970.

Reform by financial starvation? Perhaps, but the M.R.C., gentlemanly as ever, refrained from comment in its own Annual Report. But we will return later to a discussion of the changing role of the M.R.C., and of the other Research Councils. For the moment, it is time to leave the dilemmas of basic science for those of the industrial empire of the Ministry of Technology.

Technology for Whom?

Mintech – as Anthony Wedgwood Benn persists in calling it – was set up with only the sketchiest of outlines of how to proceed. It was as if Mr Cousins had been presented with a sheet of paper empty except for the magic words 'computer' and 'electronics' and the guiding ethos that 'technology is a good thing'. Failing the decisiveness of a really determined leadership, it is not really surprising that the Ministry at first seemed to stumble unhappily from event to event. By 1965 the House of Commons Estimates Committee criticized quite sharply the new Ministry's surveys of selected industries, and an editorial in *Nature* commented that the Estimates Committee was

> not satisfied that the terms set up for these initial studies had the appropriate membership or that they were being set up with sufficient speed; the Minutes of evidence suggest that on both points the Estimates Committee's comments were very mild. That some at least of the investigators should have had up-to-date experience of the industry in question seems a prerequisite; that they should have been drawn mainly from within the Government service seems as indefensible as the dilatoriness with which the teams [were] appointed.[16]

Doubtless some of these comments were inspired by the political malice that the then Minister of Technology attracted; nonetheless there was enough truth in the matter to be disturbing.[4] It should be noted that, by 1967, of the original quartet of Ministers running D.E.S. and technology not one remained, and three (Lords Snow and Bowden and Frank Cousins) had in fact left the government entirely. Similarly, the Permanent Secretary and the Controller (responsible for the overall planning of the Ministry's technological strategy) both left the Ministry of Technology after a couple of years. The Ministry was certainly unhurried in the pursuit of its objectives. Many of the 'studies in depth' it commissioned were taken over lock, stock and barrel from amongst what have been described as the 'timeless projects' of the old D.S.I.R.

Machine tools is one such; before the Ministry of Technology, D.S.I.R. was doing its own survey of the machine-tool industry, a survey continued, with similar personnel and similar leisure, in the new Ministry. If the results were ever concluded, action upon them was far from apparent. In another case, a delay of six months occurred between the setting up of the working group to consider a certain class of technological development, and its first meeting. Of course, there were reasons . . . first the summer holidays . . . then Christmas . . . and the problems of inter-departmental cooperation. The officials of other Ministries were not always cooperative; for example, the Board of Trade apparently regarded some of its information as virtually classified or only to be revealed to other departments as the result of immense pressure, and in just the same way there is a certain degree of suspicion of motives and jealousy of personnel and unwillingness to share information between one Research Council and another and even one section of the Ministry of Technology and another.

In fact, its first eighteen months were probably the Ministry of Technology's unhappiest. Inevitably, its officials argued, many of the things it was trying to do were long-term; it would be wrong to look for an immediate success right the way across the board. At least part of this uncertainty was due to the Ministry's duality of role. Initially these roles were seen as complementary; to act as a flagbearer of industrial efficiency, and to foster radically new technologies; not the technology of a decade ago, but that of a decade ahead. In the event, particularly with the departure of the early group of Ministers, and the arrival of Mr Anthony Wedgwood Benn, it became apparent that, far from this latter role increasing in significance, there were indications that it was being discarded in favour of the first.

A Ministry of Industrial Efficiency

Thus there was an increasing tendency for the role of the Ministry to be seen as that of promoting industrial efficiency, carrying the gospel of operations research into the factories, and reforming elderly industries by the introduction of technologies which were themselves not new. Perhaps symptomatic of this approach was the Ministry's first task – and often cited major success – the encouragement of the application of computers. However, computers are not really a new technology today, though they were in 1954 when the first industrial computer in the world – LEO (Lyons Electronic Office) – was produced in Britain for the catering firm of Lyons to do its accounts. It is very probably true that, as a result of the Ministry's activities, the 'computer gap' between Britain and the U.S. has been cut to only a few years. However, in 1965 a sub-committee of the D.E.S. under Professor Brian Flowers, later chairman of the Science Research Council, produced a report that gloomily concluded that Britain ought probably to buy American computers anyway, at least for many of the more advanced computer applications for which the universities were now pressing.[17]

But in a sense it is typical of many problems that beset British technological development that the Ministry of Technology's major, and most significant success, has been in an industry which has been lacking neither technological expertise nor yet a willingness to listen to the scientist, but merely hard cash and a little economic rationalization. Indeed, in this latest foray of government into industry, there are distinct undertones of the attempts of D.S.I.R. to achieve the same function after the First World War, at that time, as we have described, by means of the Research Associations. The Associations that succeeded were those of the then glamour industries with a high technological component. The same search for glamour industries was perhaps apparent in the choice of the initial fields of activity for Mintech.

In the case of the computer industry economic rationalization was achieved by a series of heavily government-encouraged mergers, culminating first in the £170 million link-up between English Electric and Elliott-Automation, reducing the British computer industry essentially to two firms, the new giant and I.C.T. (International Computers and Tabulators), and then, in rapid and logical progression, the merging of the two into International Computers Limited (I.C.L.) in the spring of 1968. This new giant company was now the largest computer firm outside the United States with a turnover in its first year of £92 million, though still puny when compared to the monumental American I.B.M., with its annual turnover of $3,570 million. The economic rationale of such an approximation towards monopoly was no doubt substantial, even if capitalist managers needed to be shown what was best for them by a Labour government.

Meanwhile, the forcing of the pace on computers and the policy of buying British, led to their own strains, such as sharp shortages of manpower for staffing the new computer centres, and complaints by university scientists that important work was being held up because they had to wait for British computers instead of the more readily available American equipment. Such examples illustrate the difficulty of catching up once a research and development lead, like the one Britain once had in computers, is lost, so that I.B.M. (which had earlier itself gone through its own severe crisis before ever starting to make computers, at the time when LEO first went into service in Britain) has an estimated eighty per cent share of the total world market.

The merger encouraged in the computer industry was lubricated with a £50 million float from one of the Ministry of Technology's most interesting branches, the Industrial Reorganization Corporation (I.R.C.). This body was modelled on a similar organization, I.R.I. (the Industrial Reconstruction Institute), which had been set up in Italy by Mussolini in the 1930s and revitalized after the Second World War, and had been instrumental in creating a whole host of enterprises in which public and private financial interests were inextricably mingled. I.R.C. had been foreshadowed before the 1966 election, but only really got into its stride in 1967, with the computer loan. Intended as a thoroughly commercially-minded exercise, I.R.C. has a board composed of leading industrialists and is advised by a major firm of merchant bankers. Thus its relationship to the 'new public enterprise' of state-owned and publicly run organizations spearheading the new technological drive, is extremely remote.

Indeed, the I.R.C.'s next major ventures, the battle to merge the two electrical giants, General Electric (G.E.C.) and Associated Electrical Industries (A.E.I.), and the successful thwarting of the attempts by Ranks to take over the Cambridge Instrument Company were carried out in the hectic atmosphere of a major take-over bid rather than the supposedly calm environment of research. The take-over bid involved columns of gossip in the press's city pages,[18] a certain amount of hesitation by the Board of Trade as to whether the whole take-over might be barred by the Monopolies Commission, and a general atmosphere of financial jiggery-pokery in which both sides, G.E.C. and A.E.I., took large advertisements in *The Times* in order to explain the relative merits and demerits of the take-over bid to their shareholders, who could be convinced of only one thing – that whoever won, the value of their shares at least would be increased.

The Rank–Cambridge affair was even more complex, with the I.R.C. intervening on behalf of another firm of instrument-makers, George Kent, and itself buying shares on the market so as to ensure the failure of the Rank bid and the success of that by Kent. This activity led to protest by some Conservative back-benchers that this was too enthusiastic a playing of the capitalist game for a government agency. Labour back-benchers, who might have been expected to have been equally critical but for opposite reasons, were conspicuously silent about the merits of this new contribution to the armoury of weapons by which socialism might be expected to capture the commanding heights of the economy. It is indeed hard to see the world of the I.R.C. as one purely concerned with industrial or even research efficiency. It is becoming much more of an instrument of government involvement in industry, to the point of becoming a corporate state.

Thus the Ministry of Technology has inevitably become more and more deeply involved with such industrial imbroglios, turning more and more into a device for the efficient management of contemporary British capitalism. True, in certain cases, it still found itself *directly* backing new technologies by way of the expanded National Research Development Corporation (N.R.D.C.) which had some of its financial limitations lifted from it by the new government (such as the ultimate objective of breaking even 'taking one year with another'), and indeed actually found itself managing one or two projects that looked like being successful, such as the hovercraft, the 'dracone' – an inflatable balloon-like structure of vast size intended for towing oil and other fluids behind a ship – a new drug called cephalosporin, and one or two smaller projects as well. But the inadequacies of N.R.D.C.'s attempts to tear off the tourniquet of established practice which still blocks genuine innovation are probably more deeply structured than can be altered by merely a more generous financial provision, though N.R.D.C.'s budget was markedly increased to £50 million. For in fact, the number of new technological developments successfully pioneered by N.R.D.C. proved far smaller than its godfather, Blackett, had hoped. It simply wasn't that there were that number of inventions dying for lack of support; by 1969 Blackett was to come to argue that the problem was structural to British industry instead.

The major expansion of the Ministry of Technology which occurred when it finally swallowed the old Ministry of Aviation in February 1967, was likened by the press to a gnat swallowing an elephant. Indeed the absorption increased Mintech's staff from 5,000 to 36,500, and its turnover increased to some £800 million a year with a flow of orders to British industry worth £575 million a year. Much of this, though, represented a routine supply function by the Ministry to other government departments, and there were fears that the vastness of the enterprise would lead to either too much power for Mr Benn or too little efficiency.

The Minister himself was at pains to dispel such doubts. Much more acutely conscious of the advantages of good public relations than Mr Cousins ever was, Mr Benn sped to and from Europe, the U.S.A. and U.S.S.R., opening institutes, conferences, laboratories and factories with a demonic energy. Nor was it all entirely a surface phenomenon, for his speeches contained a substantial measure of – often unpalatable – industrial truth. Thus he celebrated his take-over of Aviation and an invitation as guest of honour to a dinner of the Society of British Aerospace Companies by a speech which caused his hosts no little discomfort:

> In the old days, the Minister of Aviation was an aviation man through and through and was seen as such by his Ministerial colleagues. He was the last of the big spenders. He could spot a Minister of Health with a big hospital programme and stop him dead in his tracks with a large, new and expensive aircraft project. Successive Ministers of Aviation secured victory after victory in the battle for the public purse. As a result they became the most hated and feared men in Government. While their colleagues were grateful for anything they could wring from the Chancellor, Ministers of Aviation ran off with sums of money that made the

great train robbers look like schoolboys pinching pennies from a blind man's tin.[19]

Fighting talk, which caused the aerospace men – backed by a powerful press lobby – considerable pain. But in practice, despite the implied threat that the language of the Minister of Technology might indeed become the language of priorities, it is still far from clear who has won this particular battle.

The losers, though, were plain enough. Such battles with unwilling or inefficient magnates left little time for the other fifteen per cent of Mintech's inheritance, the National Physical Laboratory, the ex-D.S.I.R. Research Stations, and the Atomic Energy Authority, and its new acquisitions of the research labs once belonging to Aviation, such as the Radar Establishment at Malvern and the Testing Station at Farnborough. As with science inside the D.E.S., the direct sponsorship of research and development itself seems to become less and less relevant to the shifting perspectives of the Ministry of Technology's new interests.

Recognition of this increased irrelevance came from no less a source than the new President of the Royal Society, Professor Blackett, when he speculated publicly on whether it was not the case that the whole of the British research effort might have taken a wrong turning after the war when the decision was made to concentrate talent in public laboratories rather than scatter it through private industry.[20] This was a surprising statement from one who was once refused an American visa on political grounds and was barred by Churchill from visiting a Russian scientific meeting in 1945 (along with Bernal, Darwin, Mott, Norrish, Rideal, Milne and Dirac) for fear he might 'leak' atomic secrets. But it was an accurate reflection of the embarrassment which several of the big laboratories had now become. The sharpest problem was undoubtedly that erstwhile darling of the press, the Atomic Energy Authority, now the subject of mounting attack.

Such attacks revealed the problems of British technological development more clearly than almost any other single case, for atomic energy was what Britain had invested in most highly ever since the war, and it was generally reckoned that British nuclear research led the world by a margin of several years in many fields. Britain had been the first country to obtain electricity on a routine basis from atomic power stations and it had perhaps the most advanced future plans for the commissioning of further stations.

What was more, a new British reactor design, the advanced gas cooled reactor (A.G.R.), seemed to offer for the first time a possibility that, in terms of cost, the electricity generated from atomic power would be competitive with that from conventional power sources, such as coal and oil. Yet the A.G.R. represented British failure as well as success, for despite its wide-hailed advantages, it was proving stubbornly unexportable, by contrast with the alternative boiling water reactor system (B.W.R.) offered by the U.S., for example. The reasons for this failure are certainly not entirely straightforward, but owe something to the difference between the requirements of the British market – essentially the monolithic Central Electricity Generating Board – and the widely varying conditions of the export market. For Britain's grid system the A.G.R. can provide competitive power stations of 300-Megawatt size, but for most non-grid countries the power stations required are of the 50–200-Megawatt size; here A.G.R.s become uncompetitive but B.W.R.s are still economic. In addition there was the reluctance of the three British consortia, which had been established, under government pressure, from a host of smaller firms, to build atomic power stations, to cooperate with one another even on the simple issue of strengthening the Ministry of Technology's Nuclear Export Executive, which had been created precisely to avoid this particular problem of competition by coordinating the export effort. Recently, Mr Benn, with the help of I.R.C., has forced a reduction in the number of the consortia to two. This was to have been coupled with a partial dismemberment of the A.E.A. and a transfer of some of its functions to the remaining consortia. But because neither of the two companies is willing to take on the commercial development of the A.E.A.'s £16 million heavy water reactor at Winfreth, the final shape that this transformation will take remains to be seen.[21]

Meanwhile, until – if ever – the A.G.R. broke even with conventional power stations, British investment in atomic energy was still to pay off. The chairman of the Coal Board, Lord Robens, estimated that by 1967 the pursuit of atomic energy had already cost the country an irretrievable £800 million, to say nothing of the loss that the failure to make alternative investments of this amount of time, money and manpower might have produced. Certain sections of the A.E.A.'s work seemed more remote from real need than ever before. Thus research in atomic weaponry had been pruned partly as a result of the signing of the Nuclear Test Ban Treaty, but also, perhaps more cynically, as a result of the general recognition on the part of all the nuclear powers that research on atomic warheads had gone about as far as was necessary and that the next phase of this particular arms race would be in missile–anti-missile systems, an aspect of development that, as we have already seen, Britain has tacitly opted out of. This cut-back had left the large A.E.A. Weapons Research Establishment at Aldermaston – one time starting-point for the C.N.D. Easter marches to London – without a real full-time job to do.

Similarly, on the civil research side, another major aspect of the A.E.A.'s activities was research on the alternative to atomic fission as a source of power, that is, atomic fusion, and the long dreamed-of hope of harnessing the hydrogen bomb for peaceful uses. Long ago in the 1950s British scientists had once thought that their project 'Zeta' had achieved a form of controlled fusion that indicated that fusion power was at last at hand. The hope was short-lived, and researchers in Britain, the U.S. and U.S.S.R. had been pursuing what seemed an ever-receding dream of fusion power ever since; the formidable technological problem still remained, whilst the A.E.A. maintained, at some expense, one of the world's foremost fusion laboratories at Culham in Berkshire. How long could the expenditure of substantial sums on establishments like Aldermaston, Culham, or even Harwell, be maintained?

There were two arguments; one, that the laboratories be maintained but their work diversified to other problems – an analysis that had appealed to the Labour Party in opposition, particularly as it seemed to represent something of a traditional beating of swords into ploughshares – the other that they be run down and their talent dispersed over private industry. It was this second proposal that Blackett had now publicly endorsed; whichever solution was adopted was scarcely likely to be popular with the scientists themselves or with the A.E.A., and in fact, both methods were finally tried. Aldermaston, with its staff of 4,000, was to be retained and a variety of new civil research tasks provided for it in the design and development of new equipment and techniques, in the field of radiation and of computers, whilst a massive run-down, by about half, over a period of five years, was embarked upon at Culham in 1967, with the promise that should the experimental work take a dramatic new turn for the better, then the position would be revised. That neither, essentially negative, solution was ideal was generally recognized; that they should be amongst the few clear major management decisions by the Ministry of Technology in respect of its researching wing seemed still further to sharpen the discrepancy between the two roles of Mintech which had emerged. Thus whilst the first years of the Ministry have resolved much of the initial ambiguity as to what its task was, it was by 1969 questionable whether it was doing more than half its job.

'*Time for Decision*'

As the 1966 election approached a balance sheet of the changes of the preceding eighteen months would have been only partly encouraging even by Mr Wilson's own criteria. Not only had D.E.S. and Mintech a somewhat patchy record, but other aspects of the Wilson revolution had also failed to materialize. Thus there was still little sign of that 'scientific permeation' which was to have been one of the hallmarks of the Labour government. Economists and planners had moved into Whitehall in large numbers but there was still a marked reluctance for academic scientists to detach themselves except on the most modest of part-time bases. What is more, it seemed probable that the reluctance was not so much that of the scientists to move as of Whitehall to use them. By 1967, the Civil Service Commissioners reported cheerfully that for the first time applications for Civil Service posts from universities other than Oxford and Cambridge were in the majority, and that it was now only *twice* as likely for a successful candidate to come from Oxbridge as from elsewhere.[25] Nevertheless, they only managed to recruit ten scientists and mathematicians into the administrative class compared with thirty-four historians, thirteen modern linguists and ten classicists.

Long gone indeed were the days when it was felt that membership of the C.S.P. or the Advisory Council on Technology should be full-time, or even nearly full-time. Members seemed to be able to combine it with holding full professorships, and even vice-chancellorships of universities as well. Professor Blackett – Lord Blackett from 1969 – found it possible for a while at least to combine his role on the Advisory Council for Technology with the Presidency of the Royal Society.

Meanwhile, another deficiency in the system had begun to emerge, and one of the more predictable ones at that. The major criticism that had been levelled at the split of the D.E.S. and Mintech was that it would encourage a continued gulf between science and technology at both the intellectual and administrative levels. In the early days of the Labour government this criticism tended to be shrugged off as soluble – at least at the administrative level – by creating a sort of 'interlocking directorship' of administrators and committee members, between, for instance, the C.S.P. and the Advisory Council on Technology, whilst one committee linking the two, a revamped version of the old Manpower Committee of the A.C.S.P., recreated under the chairmanship of Sir Willis (now Lord) Jackson, was early established. Predictably, it did not work.

In a strange way, both new committees had become less powerful than the old A.C.S.P. was, for each was now merely 'departmental', reporting to, and responsible to, their respective Ministers. The resultant 'underlap' and the lack of any clear central coordinating body, drove power further and further into the hands of the Treasury and the Scientific Adviser to the Cabinet, Sir Solly Zuckerman. Whilst Sir Solly's supporting staff was increased, he was still far from being in the position of his American equivalent – the Special Adviser to the President – for his staff was neither numerous enough, nor had it adequate information-gathering services.

It was perhaps the growing awareness of these problems, and the knowledge that, within its own self-imposed terms of reference, there was no easy solution to them, that led to the conspicuous silence about science and technology which contrasted the election of 1966 with that of 1964. The Labour Party Manifesto of the 1964 election, 'The New Britain', had given science and technology no fewer than twelve mentions in its twenty-four pages – as many as three on the first page. By 1966, 'Time for Decision' found room for only three mentions – deep in the small print of industrial reorganization and expanding industrial and cultural contacts with Europe.

It was only after the 1966 election that the immediate underlap problem was tackled, by the open recognition of the need for a new non-departmental committee to sit atop the C.S.P. and A.C.T.; Sir Solly Zuckerman was appointed Chairman of the new Central

Advisory Council on Science and Technology by the autumn of 1966, but it took several months of backstage negotiations before the final shape of the new committee emerged from its chrysalis. Initially, it was to have been manned in part by constituencies, that is, by *representatives* of the Royal Society etc. But the idea was soon dropped and the traditional British device of membership by personal merit was adopted, although this still meant that the membership was derived from the Royal Society, the Ministry of Defence, the Council for Scientific Policy, the Advisory Council on Technology and a powerful group of academic, industrial and government scientists and technologists (including also, to the surprise of some since his departure from the Ministry of Technology, Mr Frank Cousins). But it is interesting to compare this approach to committee-building with, say, that of the French or Germans described in the next chapter.

The terms of reference of the new committee were to advise the government on 'the most effective national strategy for the use and development of our scientific and technical resources'. Just how it will set out to achieve this task, which had earlier been that of the C.S.P. and the Advisory Council on Technology and, before them, of A.C.S.P., all with similarly composed boards, and the best of intentions, and how it will succeed where these earlier bodies failed is difficult to gauge, not least because its proceedings are to be confidential, although its first item of study is known to be more effective distribution of skilled manpower within government and other public laboratories, and the better articulation of civil and defence research – both problems highlighted in the case of the A.E.A. which we discussed above.

Although confidential, the proceedings of the new Council are accessible to at least one other equally new body, the House of Commons Select Committee on Science and Technology. This group, set up early in 1967 concurrently with Sir Solly's council, was the only tangible measure of the extent to which concern for the restructuring of science policy had permeated from Whitehall to Westminster. Few M.P.s – though perhaps more than before 1964 – had scientific backgrounds. Several (notably the ex-computer mathematician Dr Jeremy Bray) had been drafted into the government, and it would be hard to argue that the level of the several Commons debates on scientific and technological issues had advanced at a rate commensurate with scientific growth and the changes in scientific administration which Mr Wilson's arrival at Downing Street had heralded. Until the Select Committee, the old Parliamentary and Scientific Committee had functioned as before – that is, as a platform for the presentation of scientific developments to a largely lay parliamentary audience, with one or two back-benchers on both sides of the house specializing in scientific and technological matters; the air lobby, of course, was still represented in strength.

The new Select Committee, though, one of a few set up at about the same time as part of the (to the outsider, almost imperceptible) programme of modernizing the House of Commons procedure presided over by Crossman, was intended to play a more aggressive role, with public sessions, and the opportunity to call for evidence from a wide range of people, including Ministers. It was an innovation that the Parliamentary and Scientific Committee itself had been calling for for some time. The first Select Committee on Science and Technology had a Labour Chairman, Mr Arthur Palmer (an engineer and fuel technologist), replaced in 1969 by David Ginsburg, a medical doctor, and seven Labour, five Conservative and one Liberal members. Its first topics for study were the British reactor programme[21] and aerospace research, and its meetings soon provided an opportunity for vigorous polemic – Lord Robens's attack on the A.E.A. as having cost the country £800 million, to which we referred above, was made at one such session.

Despite the somewhat tenuous and perhaps superficial conclusions which the Committee has so far been able to draw – its first report, on space research, was widely criticized in this respect – it does seem a modest step forward in improving the grasp that Parliament has over public affairs. Its investigation of Defence Research Establishments[22] was revealing: it led to a breach of privilege complaint concerning a Member – Tam Dalyell – who gave details of some of the evidence to the Committee on the Chemical Defence Experimental Establishment at Porton to the press, in the belief that the proceedings were to be published.* It has also been severely hampered by the continual reluctance of the Treasury to provide the funds for adequate staffing – even down to

* One of the penalties for taking his publicist role too seriously was that Mr Dalyell lost his membership of the Select Committee. One of the benefits was that the public gained a better understanding of Porton.

secretarial assistance. The Treasury's distrust of parliamentary enquiry runs deep, and it has consistently attempted to cut back the powers of such scrutinizing committees. So much so, in this case, that the Clerk to the House of Commons made a public protest in June 1968 about the lack of finance for the adequate servicing of the Committee.[23] It required considerable pressure before a research division specializing in scientific affairs could be established in the House of Commons library – a modest effort only achieved in 1966.

Thus when we come to draw the total balance sheet of the five years that have so far gone into the forging of Socialism in the white heat of the scientific revolution, the total remains obscure. On balance, the problems of managing and controlling research and development at the national level are better understood now than they were a few years ago, even though many of the earlier hopes have sadly faded, and what remains varies from the grey despondency of some sections of academic science, to the bright make-do-and-mend approach of Mintech. But whether the new scientific revolution is to drive Britain towards a new future, or whether we have merely, after all the committee turmoil and Ministerial merry-go-round, settled down very much where we were before is still open. It is this question that the rest of the book is, in part, an attempt to answer. But before we try to examine in more detail the realities of some of the decision-making problems which currently face Britain's scientific and technological policy-makers, it is time to take a look at how countries other than Britain manage their affairs. In the next chapters we try to describe the types of policy and decision-making apparatus that have evolved in other countries over the past few years. In point of fact, many of the aspects of the debate which has racked the British scene will be seen to be reproduced in a similar form in countries as diverse as the United States and the Soviet Union. It is to this comparison that we now turn.

The Pattern of Research and Development Expenditure in Britain

1 Finance for Research and Development, 1961–2, 1964–5, 1966–7

	1961–2 Amount (£ million)	Percentage	1964–5 Amount (£ million)	Percentage	1966–7 Amount (£ million)	Percentage
Sector providing the funds						
Government						
Defence	245·7	*36·7*	255·1	*32·6*	226·3	*25·4*
Civil	110·1	*16·4*	128·2	*16·4*	167·4	*18·8*
Research councils	29·2	*4·4*	43·7	*5·6*	54·0	*6·1*
Total	**385·0**	*57·5*	**427·0**	***54·6***	**447·7**	***50·2***
Universities	1·3	*0·2*	1·8	*0·2*	1·8	*0·2*
Public corporations	22·7	*3·5*	26·8	*3·5*	35·1	*4·0*
Private industry	243·5	*37·0*	284·8	*36·9*	352·0	*39·9*
Overseas } Other	12·0	*1·8*				
Overseas			20·8	*2·7*	27·6	*3·1*
Other			16·0	*2·1*	23·2	*2·6*
Total	**657·7**	***100·0***	**771·4**	***100·0***	**882·9**	***100·0***

Source: Department of Education and Science

2 Central Government Expenditure on Research and Development, 1961–2, 1967–8.

(£ *thousand*)	1961–2	1962–3	1963–4	1964–5	1965–6	1966–7 (Provisional)	1967–8 (Estimates)
	£	£	£	£	£	£	£
Defence	*249,796*	*244,511*	*241,804*	*263,537*	*263,000*	*241,084*	*262,432*
Civil							
Agriculture, fishing and forestry	12,702	13,020	13,797	15,551	18,625	22,801	27,809
Atomic energy	49,000	48,000	45,000	47,600	47,100	49,600	48,700
Industry	43,859	56,113	65,262	79,021	79,986	104,484	125,998
Medical and health	5,832	6,185	7,412	9,535	11,669	13,713	16,526
Overseas research	1,510	1,575	2,275	2,301	2,131	2,227	2,704
Transport	293	346	351	731	3,987	4,716	4,215
Universities and learned societies	20,658	23,967	28,927	34,000	37,525	39,809	44,853
Other	1,538	1,796	2,452	3,099	4,887	5,906	7,010
Total Civil	*135,392*	*151,002*	*165,476*	*191,838*	*205,910*	*243,256*	*277,815*
Total	**385,188**	**395,513**	**407,280**	**455,375**	**468,910**	**484,340**	**540,247**
of which							
Overseas expenditure	*6,100*	*12,900*	*17,500*	*30,313*	*31,200*	*38,400*	*36,000*
Total central government expenditure on research and development in the United Kingdom	**379,088**	**382,613**	**389,780**	**425,062**	**437,710**	**445,940**	**504,247**

Source: Department of Education and Science

3 Stock and Deployment of Qualified Manpower, 1961 to 1966.

(*thousands*)	1961	1962	1963	1964	1965	1966
Engineering and technology						
Chemical engineering	6·0	6·4	6·9	7·3	7·6	8·0
Civil and structural engineering	25·1	26·5	27·5	28·6	30·0	31·4
Electrical engineering	35·1	36·9	38·8	40·5	42·4	44·3
Mechanical engineering	55·6	58·9	61·6	64·4	67·2	69·9
Metallurgy	5·6	6·0	6·5	6·9	7·3	7·8
Mining engineering	3·8	3·9	3·9	3·9	4·0	4·1
Other engineering and technologies	10·7	11·6	12·3	12·9	13·5	14·3
Total	*142·0*	*150·2*	*157·4*	*164·5*	*172·1*	*179·9*
Science						
Agriculture	9·0	9·4	9·7	10·0	10·3	10·6
Biology	13·3	14·2	15·1	16·0	17·0	18·1
Chemistry	36·4	37·7	39·4	41·1	43·0	45·1
Geology	2·9	3·1	3·2	3·3	3·4	3·5
Mathematics	17·6	18·2	18·8	19·5	20·4	21·5
Physics	17·9	19·1	20·1	21·1	22·3	23·7
General and other sciences	20·7	21·6	22·5	23·5	24·7	24·9
Total	*117·7*	*123·2*	*128·8*	*134·5*	*141·1*	*147·4*
Total qualified manpower	**259·7**	**273·4**	**286·2**	**299·0**	**313·2**	**327·4**

Source: Ministry of Technology

CHAPTER SEVEN

Science in Western Europe

For the rest of the world, as well as for Britain, the last ten years have seen the crystallization of something we have learned to call national science policy, that is, the deliberate attempt by government to utilize its scientific resources, its manpower and its laboratories towards the nation's interest. For almost all Western industrial societies this has meant a marked change in the way that government views science. When previously it had been regarded almost entirely – however false this view may, with hindsight, seem to us – in terms of its role as a cultural activity, such as literature or music, and to be an object of patronage in much the same way, as awareness grew of science's more utilitarian implications for economic growth and for war its relations with government were transformed.

This transformation has not been a smooth linear development; as in Britain, government typically wooed science in time of war and then abandoned her in peace. Not really until the Second World War was the scientific underpinning of our society recognized. The Marxists, and communist nations based on Marxist thought, were quicker to perceive the social relations of science, arguing that science has a dual role both as an agent of change, in that new discovery potentially changed technology and hence society, and at the same time as a reflection of the needs of society and its particular productive methods. Inevitably its holders consider science as an integral and essential institution for planning in the classless society. After the 1917 Russian revolution, the deployment of the nation's scientific resources – diminished by war and civil war – was perceived as one of the many urgent tasks. But as the level of scientific activity was generally low, the headstart in planning for science that this gave the Soviet Union was perhaps more theoretical than real. Lenin himself was so impressed with the need to organize science that, as far back as April 1918, he drew up an 'Outline of the Plan of Scientific and Technological Work'.[1] Other countries such as Britain, slowly building research associations for industry, trying to increase the numbers of science graduates, fostering research in the universities, were in a sense moving in the same direction but without the ideology.

International comparison is always difficult, but because during this last decade most nations have felt it necessary to re-examine their policies for science it becomes necessary to attempt such comparisons. The material is uneven, and for Eastern European countries one has to rely on a limited amount of data published in English. One must select in order to systematize and this permits all the usual charges of arbitrariness. However, in order to delineate the distinctive features of a national science policy, and to attempt some assessment of the contemporary variations within this pattern, there is fortunately available some quantitative comparative data on research and development expenditures, provided by a series of studies produced for O.E.C.D. (the Organization for Economic Co-operation and Development), which, along with a growing body of knowledge on the unique historical development of the assortment of institutions, associations and governmental committees which together add up to any particular nation's organization for science, provides the basis for the outline we provide in this chapter.

The Allocation of Resources

The most frequently cited single index of scientific activity of any given country is the percentage of gross national product that is allocated to research and development, figures we have already seen applied to Britain in earlier chapters. While it by no means has to follow that the frontiers of knowledge are automatically pushed out by money, the expenditure pattern remains a useful guideline to the relative level of resources employed. Even this, however, has certain difficulties since what is counted in or excluded from the research and development budget varies slightly from country to country, even though by setting up a Statistical Year for the collection of research and development data in 1964 the O.E.C.D. made substantial inroads into achieving a standardized measure.[2] The major problemof comparison is how to treat the Soviet bloc figures, where the problem is twofold. While the Russians have data stretching over a longer time period, reflecting their longer interest in science planning, the definitions used do not precisely tie in with those of Western Europe, either for research and development or for gross national product. But a comparison made by O.E.C.D. in 1962[3] showed that the U.S.S.R. was spending some 2·5 per cent of gross national product on research and development – although recent evidence gathered by Professor Robert Davies[4] at Birmingham suggests that this figure may have been an underestimate. At the same period U.S. was spending some 3·1 per cent, the U.K. 2·2 per cent and the average for Western Europe – including the U.K. – was some 1·6 per cent (Table 4, *overleaf*).

On the whole there seems to be a correlation between the wealth of the country and the size of its research budget, not only in cash terms – such as the $17·5 thousand million spent by the U.S. during 1962 on research and development compared with the $4·2 thousand million spent by the whole of Western Europe – but also in terms of the actual proportion of G.N.P. spent on research and development, which seems to increase with the overall wealth of the country. Thus in developing countries it is rare to find more than 0·2 per cent of gross national product committed to research and development. The countries deviating from this pattern, such as Australia and Canada, which are both wealthy and yet not heavy researchers, have substantial sections of their economies devoted to traditional industries, agriculture and mining, which are not research-prone. Canadian industry also enjoys a special relationship with the United States in that many Canadian firms are subsidiaries of American parent companies. Thus research and development tend to be carried out by the parent and applied to the subsidiary. To the extent that American companies, such as the pharmaceutical firms, are finding Europe cheaper to conduct research in, there is also currently a general displacement of research and development funds from the U.S. towards Europe, which produces conflicting trends.

The second most generally applied measurement of overall research activity is the percentage of manpower employed in the research and development sector of the economy. In the United

4 The Overall Level and Structure of Research and Development in Selected Countries.

*	Population (millions)	G.N.P. percentage	$ *per capita* spent on research and development	qualified scientists, engineers, and technicians per 10,000 population
U.S.A.	193	3·4	110·5	35·8
France	49	1·6	27·1	17·9
Germany	59	1·4	24·6	18·0
Italy	52	0·6	5·7	6·0
Japan	98	1·4	9·3	19·5
U.K.	55	2·3	39·8	29·4
Austria	9	0·3	3·8	4·5
Belgium	17	1·0	14·7	16·8
Canada	48	1·1	22·5	12·6
Netherlands	19	1·9	27·2	25·8
Norway	7	0·7	11·5	10·4
Sweden	19	1·5	33·5	21·6

Data from different countries has been given for differing times between 1963–5.

Source: O.E.C.D.

States in 1962, some 6·2 per thousand of the total population were employed on research and development compared with only 2·9 per thousand in Western Europe, including Britain. Taking a generous interpretation of the Russian research and development estimates (which probably include rather a lot of routine testing which is not really research and development) they also employ 6·2 per thousand of the total population. Or looked at another way, for every one researcher in Germany, France or Belgium there are two in Britain, and four in Russia and the United States. This manpower index, plus the research ratio, are probably the two most useful indicators of the overall level of research commitment. The gross science budget of America – some $19 thousand million in 1967, or about four times the whole European budget – is not an entirely satisfactory measure of research activity since the cost of living and research are so much greater in the United States. For example, a preliminary exercise by the economist Christopher Freeman,[5] in making a research exchange rate, suggested that to buy the same research resources in the United States as in Britain one needed slightly over $6 to every £1, while the official rate of exchange was then $2·8 to the £1. In the same way, even within any one country, there is uneven economic development, which makes research dearer or cheaper to conduct in different parts of the country. Thus in France, most research is carried out in and around Paris or Lyons, where costs are higher than in other parts of the country.

The Research Goals

While the overall level of research and development expenditure provides a base line for considering the way in which governments view science, what is even more telling is the allocation of these funds between alternative goals within science, and in particular the split between defence and civil science. Thus Japan, which since the war has rejected defence research entirely, commits all her research and development activity to civil research, both contributing to and reflecting her commitment to rapid economic expansion. By contrast, in 1963 America spent as much as sixty-two per cent of her total science budget on defence-related items. As Table 5 shows, both France and Britain are similarly heavily committed to defence

5 The Percentage Allocation of Research and Development Budgets to Research Goals for Selected Countries

	Atomic	Space	Defence	Atomic Space and Defence	Economic Motivated	Welfare and Miscellaneous
U.S.A.	7	21	34	62	28	10
France	22	1	22	45	41	14
Germany	8	1	8	17	62	21
Italy	15	1	5	21	63	16
Japan	—	—	—	—	73	27
U.K.	7	—	33	40	51	9
Austria	11	—	1	12	62	26
Belgium	—	—	—	4	82	14
Canada	10	1	15	26	51	23
Norway	7	—	7	14	56	30
Netherlands	—	—	—	5	70	25
Sweden	27	—	7	34	50	16

Source: O.E.C.D.

research, spending forty-five and forty per cent of their total science budgets respectively, followed by Sweden with thirty-four per cent. The item which pushes up the American defence programme beyond all others is space research which, since October 1957 and the first sputnik, has received massive political and economic support. Both the United States and Britain have long-standing atomic programmes, and spend some seven per cent of their budgets on atomic research, while France and Sweden with research programmes which have been expanded only relatively recently, spend as much as twenty-two and twenty-seven per cent of their budgets on the same item.

The research goals described in the Table as 'mainly welfare' and 'economically motivated' are correspondingly depressed by these high defence expenditures. America spent $110 on research per head of population per year. Even when only ten per cent is allocated to welfare objectives this still means some $11 per head – more than any other country, although again one should note that European money buys more research per 'dollar' than American. However, for Britain, which spends $39 a head on research, nine per cent on welfare means only $3·8 a head. France, spending forty-five per cent of her research budget on defence, reduces her welfare expenditure to slightly over $3 a head. The Netherlands, by contrast, with a lesser overall research and development expenditure *per capita* than the U.K. ($27·2), spends less on defence and can thus allocate $6·8 to welfare. Similarly Germany, with a modest defence research budget (seventeen per cent) is able to spend almost $5 a head on welfare, with a population very similar to Britain's.

The distribution of the research budget, for anything less than the richest society, is therefore of key importance in determining the real inputs into constructive aspects of science as against the defence and destructive side. The overall level of research and development alone can therefore be very misleading, particularly for the medium-sized country. A high research expenditure which might not unreasonably be expected to be associated with rapid economic growth is, when pared down by excluding defence expenditure, very much more modest in character, with a correspondingly modest economic growth performance – *pace* Britain.

It is against this general background that we can view the growth of research policy-making institutions as they have developed in several countries over the past few years. The choice of countries for examination, and the treatment of the problems that we present, is necessarily both arbitrary and somewhat cursory. The point of making it is to demonstrate that neither the problems that beset Britain, nor the solutions she has found to them, are unique. Both can be seen as part of a general pattern of accommodation to the demands of science in advanced industrial societies that have been felt throughout the world. To illustrate the universality of these problems we have chosen to describe the scientific institutions of two major nations in Western Europe, Germany and France, with whom, as middle-rank industrial powers, Britain has a great deal in common. No survey of this sort would be complete without at least a brief look at the policies of the U.S.A. and U.S.S.R., and we must also consider the problems of those countries which are attempting to build a contemporary science policy on the basis of only very recent or partial industrialization, in particular such developing nations as India and China, and one recently industrialized country, Japan, which now rivals the nations of Western Europe.

France

France has a long tradition of science, a population about the same size as that of Britain, and like Britain, too, is an ex-imperial power, though one in which the transition from empire has scarcely been as smooth. For our present purposes, we are concerned with the development of French scientific policy since the advent of de Gaulle in 1958, though any consideration of France today will also demand the assimilation of the significance of the May days of revolution of 1968 as well. The one easily recognizable characteristic of the Gaullist political strategy has been to make France independent of the U.S.A. Science and technology were early identified as being one of the important keys to this separation. This political aim of France for independence was thrown into sharp relief when the French, in pursuit of the nuclear weaponry that they deemed essential for national status, sought the necessary advanced computers for development from America. The Americans, because of their political aims of limiting the possession of nuclear weapons to the then members of the 'nuclear club', refused to sell the computers. The choice for France became abundantly clear; she had to develop her own. The need for an advanced technological base for national independence was clearly understood. Thus the Minister of State for Science published an article in 1960, called 'Science and National Independence', which in its title alone stands as a manifesto of the current French aims.

The Present System[6]– Research in France is carried out by a variety of bodies which reflect the rich scientific tradition laid down from the days of the academy through the French revolution and the construction of French universities and schools on the Napoleonic system. Today, the split is broadly between basic research, essentially confined to universities and government institutes, and applied research which is carried out in special establishments in both the public and private sectors of the economy.

The prime policy-making body in French science is the 'Interministerial Committee for Scientific and Technological Research' (C.I.M.R.S.T.) which was set up in 1958. This body consists of eight Ministers; those for the Forces, Finance, National Education, Industry, Agriculture, Public Health and Communications, chaired by the Prime Minister. Thus it includes all the main departments which conduct research. But the Committee only meets once a year. More important are the 'twelve wise men' who form the Advisory Committee attached to the C.I.M.R.S.T. which meets twice a month and also includes a delegate nominated by the Prime Minister for scientific, atomic and space research. The C.I.M.R.S.T. is charged with proposing all measures favouring the development of scientific and technological research, equipment programmes and allocating resources to the various ministries. The Inter-Ministerial Committee and the Advisory Committee share a common secretariat under the Prime Minister's delegate.The General Delegation itself has a staff of about a hundred fairly senior professional men.

Initially the job of the government science machinery was to administer state-controlled research establishments such as the universities, the National Scientific Research Centre (C.N.R.S.) – which both allocates funds for basic research and runs institutes – and the applied establishments of the Ministries. This task has now been broadened and the Inter-Ministerial Committee, Advisory Committee, General Delegation and the board of the C.N.R.S. jointly produce a National Plan for scientific development. To do this the government bodies enlist and occasionally enforce the cooperation of private industry in deciding the direction of research policy.*

In addition to direct state finance, some industrial research establishments are financed by compulsory levies from firms in the trade served. These establishments work on a cooperative basis in the trade in question, rather like the British research associations. Such establishments are submitted to state supervision through a government commissioner.

Private research is performed by many large industrial firms. In addition non-profit research institutes exist in many universities and in 1963 there were forty-one non-profit researching trade associations.

Finally, private foundations exist, and though not numerically strong, one in particular, the Pasteur Institute, is of great importance. The Pasteur, named after Louis Pasteur, the great nineteenth-century founder of modern microbiology, is classed as an 'establishment of public benefit'. Its work covers the whole field of microbiology, both basic and applied, and its purpose is the 'protection of public health'. The Institute is administered by a Board of Trustees which had over the years become increasingly close to government and remote from scientists. Rising discontent amongst the scientists, highlighted by the public rows in which the two most recent French Nobel prize-winners, Jacob and Monod became involved, resulted in efforts to reverse the trend by partially democratizing the structure of its Board.[7] The Pasteur is financed partly by the sale of its products (vaccines and antisera) and partly

* Research which is directly financed by the state is budgeted by a system introduced in 1958. Each Ministry and department extracts from its annual budget the proposed expenditures on research and development and these are combined into a budget known as the 'research envelope', which is essentially a block grant. This is surveyed by the General Delegation and presented to the C.I.M.R.S.T. and Advisory Committee and, after settling the details between these bodies, it is presented to the Legislative Assembly for voting. The C.I.M.R.S.T. then allocates the resources voted under the 'envelope' to the various ministries, for specific project allocation. This system is said to have the advantage of ensuring continuity of decisions and also of preventing the sacrifice of essential research and development resources to short-term political considerations during budget debates. The establishments financed under the 'envelope' include the universities, the C.N.R.S. institutes, the Ministries represented on C.I.M.R.S.T., and the Atomic and Aerospace Commissions which are treated separately from the Ministries.

by public subsidies, a recent development which partly explains how an increasingly non-scientist administration had developed over the years.

Science and the 'Plan' – In setting up the 'Plan', the French operate by a series of 'vertical commissions' – that is, on a sector-by-sector approach. The implications of scientific research for planning for economic growth were only systematically spelt out in 1960, as the first four National Plans gave little specific emphasis to research and development, the Fourth only going so far as to include government and university research. The Fifth Plan, however, places great stress on the importance of scientific and technical research and coordinates all sectors of the economy. The plans drawn up by the Vertical Commissions are then brought together by the Horizontal Commissions which integrate them as between the various sectors and then submit them to the General Planning Commissariat which produces the draft National Plan.

The Fifth Plan (1966–70) sets out in the research and development field to increase the percentage of gross national product spent on research (in both private and public sectors) from 2·06 per cent in 1965 to 2·5 per cent by 1970. By comparison Britain spent 2·3 per cent in 1964 and the United States three per cent. Under the previous French plans this figure rose from 0·97 per cent in 1958 to 1·63 per cent in 1963 and 2·06 per cent in 1965. By including for the first time the private research sector in the Fifth Plan it was hoped to achieve a more rational and systematic use of research and development by industry. France, however, was still far from solving the dilemma posed by her pursuit of national independence. Thus computers and nuclear power were specified in the Plan as two particularly high priority projects, within a general commitment to modernize and close the transatlantic research and development gap.

Cooperation in the Plan is supposedly voluntary for private bodies; although industry has been willing to inform the government of its planned research and development expenditures, it refuses in the main to forecast new products or process technologies or strategic plans and technical information. But the government has weapons, such as tax concessions and penalties, the granting or withholding of licences and permits, and the lure of investment in industry, by which it can pressure industry into following the main objectives of its Plan.

Fundamental research is almost entirely financed by the C.N.R.S., which allocates funds to universities, and the '*grands etablissements*' of the Collège de France and the academies. Since the C.N.R.S. reports directly to the Minister of Education, co-ordination of fundamental research within the Plan is, at least in principle relatively straightforward. But, unlike the situation in the U.S.A. for example, university-based research in France is not closely linked with industry, industrial sponsorship and consulting being discouraged. Firms wishing to support research in a university must go through the C.N.R.S. to do it.*

Science and the French Revolution – It is this singleness of political goal combined with the elaborate machinery of planning which makes French science policy appear, on the surface at least, one of the most highly articulated and organized. But such a unitary goal may well bring disadvantages. It is certainly questionable whether basic research is quite so nationalistic in character as the French planners imply, whilst the pressure on distinguished French scientists to give papers at international meetings in French rather than English, recognized as the major conference language, or to publish their research in French rather than in international journals, has been much resented. The pursuit of national independence in science and technology in both computers and nuclear weapons, not to mention aircraft, has generated an enormous waste of resources. But the clarity of purpose has served to streamline the structures for science policy-making in a virtually unique manner and explains why we have set out the French organization at length. Perhaps the only other country with an equally well developed national policy is Belgium, but the problem there may be that the actual quality of the science carried out does not really live up to the elegance of the machinery.

But if this political clarity had been an unqualified success, one might ask why there was the explosion of wrath which so dramati-

* To achieve more flexibility in directing research and development efforts Development Funds exist which can be used to channel extra resources into areas which suddenly require more assistance between formal budget periods. These are allocated by 'round tables', called by the General Delegation with representatives of the field in question. The Development Funds are of limited size – only $58 million altogether for the period 1962–5 compared with a total research and development 'envelope' of $200 million in 1965, but add to the flexibility of the Plan.

cally developed, first at the universities, then subsequently in the rest of the country, during May 1968? One cannot here add substantially to the comment which those few weeks produced, but only note their implications for science policy. Scientists appeared to be prominent amongst the academics who supported the student and worker protests. University departments and laboratories were 'occupied' by the staff, senior professors not infrequently excluded, and criticisms of the prevailing scientific system were sharply voiced. Many of these complaints had been presaged by the earlier row at the Pasteur Institute, many of whose distinguished researchers were amongst the new dissenters. The main complaints were of bureaucratized administration, a decision-making apparatus out of reach and beyond the influence of the individual scientist, rigidly hierarchical control of the universities and research institutes, imposed from above and ensuring the teaching of out-of-date and irrelevant material, and, by implication, out-of-date research as well. The attack on the system was for its internal structural malaise, not its failure to emulate the U.S.A. or achieve national independence.

The many solutions and alternative structures proposed in the confused days that followed, where each laboratory appears almost endlessly to have discussed its own role and structure, crystallized in a three-day conference held at Orsay in July 1968, attended by some 700 scientists. Whilst partly concerned with reform of the pay and promotion structures, the conference also argued for the debureaucratizing of the policy structure, proposing, for instance, a central coordinating office of scientific and technological research with a budget to be independent of ministerial control but administered by scientists – a majority of them elected from amongst all laboratory workers. Such elective committees should also run the individual institutes. Although France, still under de Gaulle and his disciple Pompidou, then returned to the expertocratic style of government which existed prior to the May revolution, these proposals – and the analysis that underlies them – come close to the core of many problems relevant to Britain which we raise at greater length in the final chapter of this book. But for now we must turn from France to a consideration of the experience of post-war Germany.

West Germany

The struggles of the Federal Republic (West Germany) to achieve a science policy form an interesting counterpoint to those of Britain and France.[8] Germany's past history of integrating science and technology into the order of society has often been held up as an example to Britain, yet the ideological and physical ravages suffered under the Nazis and the war meant that to some extent West Germany emerged into the 1950s with a set of rather special problems. Perhaps the central problem of science policy formation in the G.F.R. is a constitutional one, in that West Germany is a federation of eleven states, or *Länder*, each with full cultural autonomy. The phrase 'full cultural autonomy' must be seen in its broadest sense; it has meant for example that each separate *Land* has its own educational system, its own universities, and therefore its own science, whilst the *Bund*, or Federal Government, has only residual national cultural functions. Each of these systems has its own minister, so that early on in the life of the Republic, educational policies of different *Länder* were coordinated through a standing conference of *Länder* ministers (*Ständige Konferenz der Kulturminister der Länder* – K.M.K.). The measure of the importance of the *Länder* is reflected in the high percentage – seven per cent – of *Länder* budget committed to science, which in 1962 was equivalent to sixty per cent of all public money spent on science. The development of science policy in the G.F.R. is therefore a history of attempts to coordinate *Länder* and *Bund*, to overcome the built-in fragmentation that the system provided.

Against this decentralizing structure should be set the concept of *Wissenschaft*, embodied in the title of the West German Scientific Council, the '*Wissenschaftsrat*' (W.R.). The concept implies more than just 'science' or 'science and technology' but embraces something more nearly like 'all systematic human knowledge' or 'all scholarship'. In that the *Wissenschaftsrat*, the offspring of the K.M.K. and the *Bund*, was created in the early years of reconstruction, following the period of Nazi depredation – in terms of both people and their culture – this reassertion of the traditional German concept of the unity of knowledge becomes both meaningful and necessary. In practice, the *Wissenschaftsrat* has been rather less encyclopedic in scope, and has concerned itself with problems of the reform, expansion and the establishment of new universities. Progress has been extremely slow in securing reform, as the *Länder* are the chief financial supports of the universities (in 1962 they contributed some seventy-three per cent of university costs), and will respond only sluggishly to pressure from the centre.

This impulse towards integration in science is shared by the two non-industrial scientific associations, the *Deutches Forschungs Gemeinschaft*, the German Research Association (D.F.G.), and the *Max Planck Gesellschaft*, the Max Planck Society for the Promotion of Science (M.P.G.) which between them combine most of the functions covered by their five British Research Council counterparts (agriculture, medicine, science, environmental and social science). The two associations are primarily concerned with non-industrial research, with a third, the *Arbeitsgemeinschaft Industrieller Forschungsvereinigungen* (Federation of Industrial Research Associations) (A.I.F.), whose function is specifically industrial and, which is relatively speaking, self-contained and independent of government.

The prime sources of financial support for both the D.F.G. and M.P.G. are the *Bund* and *Länder* authorities, yet despite this governmental support the two organizations are autonomous in a way that the British parallel organizations are not. The British Research Councils are statutory bodies; their members are government-appointed, albeit on the advice of the members of the existing Councils and the Royal Society. (It has been argued that for practical purposes this matters very little, but this is a point to which we will return.)

The two organizations serve different roles, the D.F.G.'s function being to scan the state of the field ranging from the humanities, through the social sciences to the natural sciences, identifying gaps and supporting projects varying from funds for individuals to major support for university and institute research. Again, like the West German science council (the W.R.), the D.F.G. covers knowledge across the board. In recent years there has been a tendency for the bulk of their support to go to science and technology, partly because costs are rising faster in these research fields, and partly because in the social sciences the universities are better able to provide for their own individual researchers. The *Max Planck Gesellschaft* have quite a different function, that of actually establishing and financing research institutes. There are upwards of fifty institutes in West Germany today, with a substantial research record varying from education – with a new institute recently established in Berlin – through law and history to their major interests of medicine and the natural sciences. Initially established as the *Kaiser Wilhelm Gesellschaft* in 1911 with the explicit aims of filling the gaps left by the shortcomings of university research, they were deliberately fostered by the British and Americans after the war, and renamed after Max Planck, the distinguished physicist and founder of quantum theory. Originally the M.P.G. institutes were conceived as one-man institutes, centred round distinguished directors, in what has generally become known as the 'German-style' of research, which places enormous research power in the hands of the professors, with an autocratic tradition of control, but this tradition has more recently been developing towards the less centralized institute.

The changing pattern of support for these two organizations, the D.F.G. and M.P.G., in Germany, reflects and parallels the emergence of something like a national science policy from the conscious fragmentation of 1949 to the centralization of policy in the later 1960s. Thus in 1949 both organizations were financed exclusively by the *Länder*, whilst by 1964 a new agreement had been reached whereby *Bund* and *Länder* paid half each.

What has happened is that as the need for rather more than mere inter-*Länder* cooperation has been felt, the *Bund* has expanded its role rather faster than the *Länder*. The clause in the constitution regulating the relationship between the two, of 'competitive legislative competence', has proved to be the thin end of the wedge to achieve centralization. The German nuclear programme was always a federal responsibility, and the *Bund* ministry for nuclear science subsequently became the *Bund* ministry for science when 'general science promotion', space and defence research, and student grants became identified as the five special fields requiring specific *Bund* intervention.

In 1965 the new Minister for Scientific Research, Dr Stoltenberg,[9] felt sufficiently strong to attack the almost total independence of the universities – an immensely deep-rooted tradition, for the German universities are amongst the oldest in Europe – pointing to the deficiencies in basic science which, twenty years after the war, should have been made good. He argued for a greater rationalization of the division of research labour and the establishment of a coordinated system of priorities. In assuming this position the Minister was publicizing a theme already vigorously expressed by the scientific community, which argued that, despite the loss of the Jewish scientists, the attack on knowledge and the collapse and partition of Germany, the state of science should have recovered. In fact the state of basic science, and of the unreformed universities, gave rise to concern. Rigidity of organizational structures and the lack of coordination were hampering creativity in science.

Two years later, in October 1967, the Minister issued a statement which crowned the efforts of the previous years, enunciating federal commitment to five fields of scientific and technological research. This commitment, especially when it is considered that at that time the Germans had their own economic crisis, showed that at last the Federal Government took science seriously. It maintained the percentage of G.N.P. allocated to science at a level, in cash terms, of the equivalent of £350 million a year, in a situation of generalized government cut-back. Space research, marine research, nuclear fuel technology, radio astronomy and energy conversion were identified as the key fields for expansion. Thus the government made a clear set of choices as to those technologies it was prepared to 'opt into' in a systematic way. Simultaneously Stoltenberg announced a policy of building up 'centres of excellence' in the universities where the quality of research was promising. These two steps, regardless of whether the five chosen fields are really the best priorities, must be seen as the beginning of a national policy for science.

Thus, even this briefly summarized account shows the G.F.R. facing some of the same class of problems that have troubled Britain[10] – the reforms of outmoded structures, the move towards a more centralized and coordinated policy system and the recognition of priority areas for expansion and resource allocation. That there has been relatively little debate in Germany about the one further issue that is of such significance to the British, the link between science and technology and industrial efficiency, must be seen in part as a tribute to the durability of the traditional research intensiveness of German industry, so noticeable a hundred years ago in the case of the aniline dye industry, and strongly continued in the present research activities of many major German firms, despite the disruption of the period 1933–45. West Germany may have been particularly fortunate in that, at partition, most of the advanced industrial regions fell to her and not to the German Democratic Republic in the East, whose inheritance was mainly rather poor farmland, with the exception of the glass and optics works of Zeiss at Jena. She may have been equally fortunate in that foreign capital flowed into the country in large quantities for re construction, especially in the decade 1947–56. But an equally striking factor is that of her science budget. West Germany spends only eight per cent on defence research compared to Britain's thirty-three per cent; sixty-two per cent of Germany's science budget is economic-motivated, compared with only fifty-one per cent of Britain's. There is thus a major difference not only in tradition but also in current orientation which must be taken into account as we search the German experience for meaningful parallels.

Thus we see for two countries not so different from Britain in terms of their wealth and their population, in terms of both size and skill, with comparable histories of scientific development, rather different attempts to formulate a solution to the problems of organizing science. Both France and Germany have had to increase their financial allocation to science dramatically, more so than Britain, which was less damaged by war; but the former two countries have been faced with different tasks: Germany to integrate a fragmented culture, France to close a technological gap. And both countries have been steadily increasing their military research and development budgets over recent years, at a time when British and American expenditure in these areas has been stagnating or even declining.

Despite the slightly different time-scale, the parallels in the broad outlines of the policy-making bodies are interesting. If we look at other countries in Western Europe we can see this pattern of institutions repeated. Typical of this rationalized approach is the attempt to locate specific areas within both pure and applied research and to achieve the cultural threshold of effort in these. Other smaller countries such as Holland, or poorer, such as Portugal, had already faced this problem before it hit the middle-rank powers. Thus Holland has concentrated on the expansion of her electrical and electronics research, centred industrially on the Philips firm, fourth largest in the world, with the gigantic complex comprising technical schools, universities and industrial labs at Eindhoven.

If the small countries of Europe have become increasingly

sensitive to their need for choice in research, and it has become pressing too for the middle-power European nations; hitherto this has not been such a problem for the Americans, who as the richest nation in the world, were seen to be able to spend their way out of any research and development dilemma. But how far is this still true?

CHAPTER EIGHT

America, Russia and the Third World

The U.S.A.

Because American science contributes to the technological underpinning of the richest society ever known, it is necessary to say something about the historical development of the American Federal government's role in supporting science. But in trying to write even a pared-down account, it is uncomfortable to be quite so conscious of the weight of scholarship which has been seeking to define American science policy over the last fourteen years. The precursor to these formal studies was the *Bulletin of the Atomic Scientists*, which, in the crisis of conscience for the physicists posed in 1945 by their bomb, intensely illuminated some of the relationships between science and society. The more formal studies themselves began with the publication of Don K. Price's book, *Science and Government*, in 1954. The flow of books has since continued increasingly.*[1]

Attempting to pull together the salient aspects of a science policy which has been described as not one but many science policies, is a dangerous exercise. Inevitably we can do no more than produce a thematic essay, attempting to sketch in some of the development

* Since then several major research units and academic departments have added to the area, such, for example, as the Harvard Program on The Impact of Technology on Society, directed by Emanuel Mesthene or the work of de Solla Price at Yale, or the Department of Politics at M.I.T., to say nothing of the researches of the National Science Foundation. Most recently, in 1968, O.E.C.D., substantially drawing on the work generated by these researches, has published its national science policy review of the U.S.A.

and current stresses of a system, which, viewed in its own terms at least, has doubtless been remarkably successful, even though it now seems to stand at a sort of crossroads, so that the developments of the next few years have become more unpredictable than in almost any other major nation.

The organization of science and science policy-making in the United States has to be seen against the traditional Jeffersonian distrust of Federal control, which leads to the paradoxical situation that despite the magnitude of the overall American scientific effort, it is not unified and centralized but is a mosaic of competing and sometimes overlapping efforts. Thus, while it remains true that ninety per cent of history's scientists and engineers are alive today and of them approximately half are American, it is also true that there is no coordinating body in the United States equivalent to the French, British or German central advisory bodies. The earliest move to circumvent this almost pathological anti-centralist feeling was the passing by Congress in 1862 of the Morell Act which established the agriculturally-based Land Grant Colleges. This represented the first major step towards national support of science and technology. The following year the National Academy of Science was established, one of whose tasks was to advise the federal government, in a style substantially following the pattern of European academies, or the Royal Society in Britain.

But apart from research attached to government agencies, such as Agriculture and the Bureau of Standards, Federal support remained slight. The *élite* universities remained financially independent of government, an independence which forced them to search for funds from private – and later, industrial – patrons. In turn, the necessity to be thoroughly commercially minded, and to maintain close industrial links, always prevented, in America, that division between pure and applied science, between research and development, that we have seen as characterizing British, and to a lesser extent, West European science. The interlocking of university and industry, so that there is a ready flow of personnel between them at all levels, has become one of the characteristics of the American scene. To those concerned with the relative failure of Britain to achieve economic pay-off from her science, it is a lesson to be learned; for those hopeful of securing 'academic freedom' against the encroachment of the external world, it remains a dreadful example.

The transformation which occurred has to be explained not only in terms of the development of the internal structure of science within the country, but also of America's emergence from isolation as a dominant world power. Two events stand above all others as watersheds marking the dramatic intervention by government in science. The first was the Einstein letter to President Roosevelt of 2 August 1939, the second was the launching of the Russian Sputnik in October 1957.

To quote Einstein's letter:

> Some recent work . . . leads me to expect that the element uranium may be turned into a new and important source of energy in the immediate future . . . possible to set up a nuclear chain reaction in a large mass of uranium . . . also lead to the construction of bombs . . . extremely powerful bomb of a new type may thus be constructed. . . . The U.S. has only very poor ores of uranium in moderate quantities; there is some good ore in Canada and in former Czechoslovakia . . .

As a measure of the need for immediate action, Einstein added warningly:

> I understand that Germany has actually stopped the sale of uranium from the Czech mines which she has taken over. That she should have taken such early action might perhaps be understood on the grounds that the son of the German under-Secretary of State, von Weizsäcker, is attached to the Kaiser Wilhelm Institute in Berlin where some of the American work on uranium is now being repeated.

That this letter should have led to the gigantic ManhattanProject,[2] which itself culminated in the dropping of the atomic bombs on Hiroshima and Nagasaki on 6 and 9 August 1945, and that this in turn led to a crisis of conscience for the physicists, not least Einstein himself, together with others such as Born and Szilard, all three of whom became critical of the further development of the bomb, is not here our concern. What is important is that essentially the involvement of government in science was in response to a military and power challenge. (It has been suggested that U.S. science policy owes most to three foreigners – Hitler, Stalin and Khrushchev.) Alongside the wedge driven by this recognition of physics as an instrument of war, came another in the chemical and biological sciences, operating at the junction of government, academic and industrial science, typified by the fact that when Florey and his co-workers pioneered penicillin at Oxford in 1942, the only allied laboratories which were sufficiently large-scale to convert the research laboratory techniques to mass production belonged to the American pharmaceutical industry.

This example also points to one characteristic of American science which was, and is, strikingly different from that of Britain: the practice of locating research financed by government in the private sector rather than in public research institutes. Currently, for example, the federal government pays for sixty-four per cent of all research and development, but only carries out fifteen per cent of the research. The private sector finances thirty-six per cent of research and does eighty-five per cent of the work. Thus, in the United States, while industrial research is far greater in scale than any in Europe, it is also much more heavily supported by government, a strange anomaly in a supposedly free-enterprise society. But where in Britain much industrial research has been located in the government-sponsored Research Associations, in America this is carried out by industry itself, and when the work is not suitable for industry, the governmental response has been to support private non-profit-making institutes such as the J. Arthur Little Company or the Rand Corporation, particularly for defence research, thus again avoiding the setting up of public research institutes. When, however, only fundamental research is considered, the traditional pattern, familiar to Europe, holds, and, with the exception of a few major firms such as Bell Telephone and General Electric, the research is carried out in the university.

In a country the size of America, there are of course many exceptions. There are great federal laboratories, such as those belonging to the Navy, the Public Health Service and, more recently, those concerned with environmental pollution. Nonetheless, the emphasis remains on research conducted in the private sector. (It is perhaps ironic that, as we have seen (see p. 120) in Britain some opinion is turning towards this approach as, after fifty years, the Research Associations cannot even charitably be regarded as outstandingly successful. It is doubly ironic that it is a Labour government and Professor Patrick Blackett who have expressed this view most forcibly.) Because of the mission-oriented nature of much American research, fundamental research often feels itself to be threatened. The classic report to President Roosevelt, 'Science, the Endless Frontier', was written by Vannevar Bush, the earliest of U.S. Presidential advisers on science, in 1945. The subsequent

Steelman Report supported basic research even more vigorously, claiming for example, that the U.S. ought to spend one per cent of G.N.P. on research and development. However, it was five years after the war before the necessary new agency, the National Science Foundation (N.S.F.), whose terms of reference were to protect and support both fundamental research and higher education, was established, although it should be pointed out that the big private foundations, like Ford and Rockefeller, had been in existence for some time, and play a much more substantial role in financing research in the U.S. than their equivalents elsewhere.

In the summer of 1967, President Johnson implicitly attacked fundamental research once again as not being sufficiently relevant to social need and national goals, and again disturbed the confidence of the scientific community.[3] This quest for relevance to social need has had certain even more pronounced effects as science has moved into Big Science, that is, as it has become intrinsically highly expensive. When a need has become identified by a political process, funds are made available and the response of research is to move immediately into the centre of the field, industry, the private non-profit institutions and academic departments alike. This 'New Federalism', as this has been called, or Federalism by contract, circumvents the traditional problem of the relationship of Federal and state government by establishing an individual agency which can negotiate directly with the firm or institution involved.

Thus it was possible, from the initial trauma imposed by Sputnik in 1957, for the space programme to develop in ten years from spending two per cent of the country's total research budget, to thirty-five per cent. But Sputnik I, as well as producing the standard, highly specific, governmental response, of setting up a new federal agency – in this case the National Aeronautic and Space Agency (N.A.S.A.) – to deal with the immediate problem of matching and beating the Russians, thereby changing the conflict from the arms race to the conflict of prestige in space, had one non-standard response of great significance. It is because of this that it may be singled out as representing a second major watershed in U.S. science policy. This was in the soul-searching days that followed Sputnik, when Eisenhower appointed a special adviser on Science and Technology who was supposed to provide some sort of coordinating overview of the whole of science – essentially so that the Americans would not be caught again with their pants down. This key role of special adviser only became fully articulated when Jerome Wiesner held the position during the Kennedy administration. Subsequently, when Johnson became President, Wiesner was replaced by Don Hornig. Under the Republican administration of Nixon, Lee DuBridge, President of the Californian Institute of Technology, was appointed.

Rapidly the special adviser became involved in helping set up three other bodies. To start with, a pre-existing Defence Advisory Committee was resuscitated and reconvened as the President's Scientific Advisory Committee (P.S.A.C.). P.S.A.C. is composed of some eighteen eminent non-government scientists and engineers and by convention is chaired by the special adviser. Within two years P.S.A.C. was able to recommend and obtain the setting up of a Federal Council on Science and Technology. Where P.S.A.C.'s role had been to initiate ideas, the Federal Council's was to negotiate them through the specialized agencies, particularly where two or more shared an interest. Thus all the big researching agencies were represented, such as the Department of Defense (D.O.D.), N.A.S.A., Agriculture and Health (under whose aegis comes the giant National Institutes of Health (N.I.H.), approximately the equivalent of the British M.R.C., supporting a similar range of work in its own institutes and by way of research grants), as well as the Bureau of the Budget, etc., with all the difficulties that inter-agency committees entail. Once again the Science Adviser was Chairman. The third sector of his empire came in 1962 with the setting up of the Office of Science and Technology (O.S.T.) which had the responsibility for aiding in the formulation of national science policies, an office under the directorship of the Science Adviser. Thus the coordination of science is a curious affair of a Science Adviser who wears three separate hats.

This has not been uncritically accepted as adequate. Alternative proposals have ranged from the setting up of a Department of Science to the proposal and congressional bill put forward by the Daddario Committee for strengthening the role of the National Science Foundation (N.S.F.) so that it could share in the formulation of national science policy. The House of Representatives Sub-Committee for Science, Research and Development, chaired by Representative Daddario,[4] was set up when the previous congressional science and astronautics committee found itself overwhelmed by the latter half of its brief in 1965. The new committee, outstanding for the drive of its chairman and members, has cordial relations with the basic scientific community and has established itself as its political champion. One might point out in parentheses the illustration this provides of the role the congressional committee, with its powers to call for evidence, plays in U.S. politics; even given the size and complexity of the U.S., the fact that Senators and Representatives are allocated twenty and six private staff members, respectively, facilitates this type of highly informed congressional committee. The roughly equivalent British Select Committee on Science and Technology has to manage with one shared paid assistant, a single post not gained without opposition from the Treasury as being unconstitutional.

The framework in which this plurality of agencies, industries, research institutes and academic departments compete is further complicated by America's relations with the outside world, with her conception of her role as world protector of the capitalist system, and the existence, ever since the Second World War, of a Department of Defense ever-increasing in scope and range of activities. It is not merely that Defense and Space between them absorb such a high proportion of the total science budget of the U.S., for neither N.A.S.A. nor the D.O.D. is a discrete self-contained agency; their funding and researching activities spread out across the entire scientific scene; N.A.S.A. and D.O.D. research contracts are let to many universities and institutes,[5] (D.O.D.'s to the tune of $380 million in 1967), manyof them for research projects apparently remote from the agencies' prime interests. D.O.D. supports research on linguistics and basic biochemistry, N.A.S.A. on psychology and biology. Indeed these agencies have also developed substantial interests, and finance research, in universities and institutes outside the U.S., as does N.I.H. Sometimes, as with the Office of Naval Research, they have even maintained separate offices in Europe for the purpose of handling such overseas contracts.

That many facets of U.S. academic life are supported by agencies whose fundamental goals are alien to the universities is something which has recently caused much heart-searching amongst the American scientific community. D.O.D.'s impressively financed research into chemical and biological warfare, for example, now running at something over $300 million annually, is carried out not only 'in house' at such establishments as Fort Detrick and

Edgewood Arsenal in Maryland, but has also recently been shown to involve a network of contracts, both secret and open, with many of the most distinguished universities in the country. Indeed, the U.S. army's highest civilian award was given in 1967 to a woman scientist from Detrick for her work in developing a more efficient form of rice-blast fungus.[6] A similar scandal rocked the sociological community in 1965–6 when it was revealed that D.O.D. was financing a major study of the best methods of avoiding revolution in Latin America involving many university sociologists – the so-called Project Camelot.[7] Under such conditions scientific validity often seems a less important criterion in evaluating a research area than its bearing on the war in Vietnam. The scientific and university communities have become inextricably part of what Eisenhower once described as the 'industrial–military complex'.

When funds were unlimited, or effectively seemed to be unlimited, abundant money solved the problem of choice and it was virtually true to say that all science, good, bad or indifferent, could find a sponsor. All that was required was a steady hand in filling in grant applications appropriately slanted to the particular orientation of the relevant agency. However, this abundance, even before the war in Vietnam, could no longer be taken completely for granted. Choices were being made and it is not necessarily clear that they were or are the wisest. A Matthew principle, of 'to him that hath much, more shall be given' operates in science, which it is extremely hard to offset. Thus Hornig has described the intransigence of the situation in higher education:

Out of 2,200 colleges and universities, only about 200 award the degree of Doctor [i.e. Ph.D.]. Out of these 200, only 20, spread all over the country can be regarded as in the front line. To these twenty can be added another forty which are excellent though to a level definitely below that of the first twenty. These sixty universities produce 80 per cent of all doctorates and receive 80 per cent of all federal research funds.[8]

But not only is it difficult to redress the balance so as to create new centres of excellence. Such a heavy concentration of talent, chiefly in the north-east from Boston down to Philadelphia and on the west coast from San Francisco to Los Angeles, has social consequences far beyond the imbalance of higher education.

This wider effect has become particularly obvious in the intensive inter-State lobbying for the siting of such plums as the new high-energy accelerator, which brings with it a highly skilled, high-income group, immediately attractive to any local politician, who can see the cash value for his community. Although the economists maintain that there is no simple relationship between investment in science and economic growth, it is sufficiently plain at grass-roots level that new big science can often transform a depressed area.

Currently, however, the crisis in U.S. science funding has become sharper than just deciding where and when to create centres of excellence. While under Eisenhower Federal research and development had an annual growth rate of 15·1 per cent, and under Kennedy of 16·6 per cent, in the years since 1964 the growth rate has declined to a mere three per cent, with an actual 1·2 per cent decline in 1968–9; the total Federal budget is now some $17·3 thousand million. These overall figures conceal other changes, a sharp cutback in the research and development funds of D.O.D. and N.A.S.A. (N.A.S.A.'s budget declined from a peak of $5,423 million in 1967 to $4,573 million in 1969, its basic science spending from $624 million to $498 million), whilst the basic research agencies themselves have been in danger of quite substantial cutbacks; thus the House of Representatives Appropriation Committee has recently cut $100 million from N.S.F.'s request for $500 million in 1969.[9]

Simultaneously, there has been an increased emphasis on applied rather than basic research and a sharp increase in the proportion spent on the social sciences (up to $278 million in 1969). The result has been a tendency for the applied agencies to cut back on their basic research funding.

The immediate cause of such cutbacks is, of course, the Vietnam war, with its increasing drain on money and manpower – and indeed, one other effect of the U.S. involvement in Vietnam has been the virtual abandonment of the policy of giving draft-deferment to graduates who wish to go on to do doctoral degrees. Such young men are now liable to be called up, and the output of Ph.Ds. from American universities stands in danger of falling dramatically should the war extend much longer.

But many observers of the U.S. scene argue that the cause of the decline is more deep-rooted. They profess to see signs of a disenchantment by the U.S. public with a science and technology which seem inevitably involved with the priorities of war and international prestige, and too little with the solutions to America's internal problems. Such observers would see the decline – comparable to the falling off in the British growth rate to which we have already referred, and to the decline observed in all major Western countries in the proportion of students wishing to read science degrees at university – as symptomatic of a general turning from the tarnished promise of the natural sciences to the still unfulfilled one of the social sciences. In this light, the increase in the funding of the social sciences may be seen as a significant – if perhaps not fully articulated – attempt by the U.S. government to come to grips with the problem.

Hornig[8] has argued that the diffuseness of American science policy-making institutions is deliberate because research is meant to be a function attached to an agency not, as it were, a separate institution in its own right. Thus Johnson[10] attacked the miserable amount of money spent on urban research compared with the massive national expenditure on the urban areas themselves. The difficulty with this sector-by-sector approach is that although it may be correct in terms of the sector, it does not necessarily help the whole society. Indeed, given that each project operates on its own merits, established research in a politically identified area tends to pre-empt new research regardless of its nature. Together with this cumulative piling up of scientific goodies, goes that sort of institutional and scientific deformation, pounced upon in different ways by such different commentators as Alvin Weinberg,[11] Director of Oak Ridge Natural Laboratory, C.H. Waddington,[8] Edinburgh geneticist and an O.E.C.D. examiner, and by the students criticizing the involvement of universities in D.O.D.-sponsored projects, such as that at the University of Pennsylvania. Weinberg noted that Big Science led to self-advertising and a continuous vulgarization of scientific findings in order to maintain the necessary financial support. Waddington made similar comments on Federal support, and added that the rather rigid policy line laid down by the private foundations tended to confirm this imbalance. The students, in a sense, picked on the same point, although specifically they were objecting to the chemical and biological war research project at Pennsylvania, known as Operation Spicerack.[12]

Both in the university and elsewhere research is to no little extent performed as a result of massive funds being readily made available in given areas, until research threatens the balance of the university, becomes almost the most important function of the institution. The function of a university is dual, both to teach and to research, but the attachment of huge grants to individuals and their teams has decreased their interest in teaching and diminished their involvement in their place of work. The university has become merely a roof rather than a vital social institution. Partly these are problems generated by Big Science itself, which the U.S. reveals most clearly; partly, however, they are confirmed by America's pluralistic system, which serves to conceal the subservience of science to short-term political pressures.

The U.S.S.R.

How can we come to terms with Soviet science? For many reasons this presents a harder task of summary and evaluation even than the diffuse structure of the U.S.A. If the travails of American policy are over-documented, analysed and discussed, those of Russian science policy for a Western observer have suffered from the opposite failing.* There exist sufficient hagiographic accounts of the wonders of a scientific organization that can produce sputniks within forty years of October 1917, and of ideological attacks against many of the supposed theoretical underpinnings of Soviet society, with appropriate asides about Lysenko and the mutilation of Russian genetics, for it to be difficult to assemble a balanced account. Does the Soviet experience represent a truly different approach to the organization of science from that of Europe or the U.S.A. and, if so, is it a workable or desirable alternative? A few years ago it might have been possible to claim, as an – albeit oversimplified – hypothesis that, where the American response was to buy their way out of any policy problems, that of the Russians was to plan their way out. But it is far from clear that this even begins to resemble the situation today, so rapid has been the rate of policy evolution in both countries over the last decade or so.

Whilst we will not discuss here the experience of Eastern European countries other than the U.S.S.R., it may be pointed out that, with certain characteristic differences reflecting differences in scientific and cultural traditions and economic development, the science policy institutions that they have built are in many

* The publication of the O.E.C.D. review of Soviet Science Policy[13] has gone some way to offset this lack.

respects comparable to those of the Soviet Union, particularly in terms of the central role of the various national Academies of Science.

Three factors above all have helped to set the direction that Soviet science policy has taken. The first is that until relatively recently Russia was an underdeveloped country; the development of science and of industry has gone hand-in-hand since 1917 and the growth of both has been telescoped over a much shorter time-scale than that of the Western European countries or the U.S.A., though not that of Japan. This state of initial technological backwardness, coupled with the vast damage and disruption of the Second World War, help account for much of the curiously patchy way in which science has developed. Indeed, many of the powerful contradictions that afflicted Soviet science, particularly in the 1930s, are more reminiscent of those of a developing country such as India, where science has to be grafted on to a basically non-scientific culture, than of any problems consequent upon a dialectical approach to science.

But despite this, the second crucial factor in the development of Soviet science policy is undoubtedly the influence of ideology. Not only has Marxism always been committed to a belief in the intimate interrelationships of science and society, the continuous interpenetration of basic scientific developments, the technology of production and the political and social superstructure, but it was unequivocally clear to those who made the Bolshevik Revolution in 1917 that their ultimate goal – socialism – could only be achieved on the basis of a scientific revolution that transformed the technological base of a largely peasant society.[14] Lenin's dictum that socialism followed electrification was not mere rhetoric. From the beginning, the revolutionary leaders in Russia were committed to the development of science and to the establishment of a science policy. They had an enthusiasm – often misguided – for the results of science which was conspicuously lacking until much later – indeed until the Second World War – in either Britain or the U.S. One should perhaps point out that the Russian conception of science, like that of the Germans and French, has always embraced economics, sociology, the other social sciences, philosophy and history. It is truly *Wissenschaft*. Thus the concept of what a science policy ought to be has inevitably become entangled with the more obviously political overtones of some of these other disciplines in a way rather confusing to someone brought up within the narrow Anglo-Saxon concept of what is, and what is not, science.

The third factor which is central to an understanding of the Russian approach to science policy is that one of the few central scientific institutions that they started with in 1917 was an Academy founded by Peter the Great in 1724 on the model of the French and German academies (see p. 10) as part of his Westernization campaign. Prior to the revolution, the Academy had been largely honorific in function, but had attempted to integrate the work of those few Russian scientists of the nineteenth century who had been of international significance. It was the Academy, a self-electing body of eminent scientists (by 1966 some 200 strong with about 400 corresponding members), that became the chosen instrument by which science, and hence socialism, were to be achieved after the revolution.[15]

Thus the U.S.S.R. has had something identifiable as a science policy, with all that this entails in terms of the collection of statistics, the analysis of progress, and the attempt to plan scientific advance consciously, for longer than any other country in the world. A not always well-conceived policy, true, but a policy nonetheless. It is not our intention here to follow in detail the vicissitudes of this policy through the turbulent Russian politics before the death of Stalin in 1953. This history is one of a slow recovery from the trauma of the civil war, followed by a period of rapid expansion in both scientific spending and the production of trained manpower. The early years, till 1929 – the period of the New Economic Policy – were a time when the Communist Party treated the scientists with caution, expanding resources and manpower, but without an explicitly ideological commitment.

1929 saw the beginning of collectivization and of five-year plans under Stalin's drive towards socialism.[16] It also saw pressure for the replacement of bourgeois science and scientists with those who were politically more sympathetic to the aims of the Party, and a period where considerable efforts were made to define a 'correct' Marxist and dialectical approach to a 'Socialist Physics', 'Socialist Biology', and so forth. Emphasis was not only on a rapid expansion of science – by 1934, according to figures given by Bernal,[17] the science budget apparently amounted to one per cent of G.N.P. (this figure includes testing and is therefore overgenerous), whereas Britain's at the time was 0·1 per cent and the U.S.A.'s 0·3 per cent – but also on the role of the Academy in helping to draw up five-year plans for science, stressing the need for the development of what is now called mission-oriented research.

To achieve this, various combinations of research institutes run by the academy and by individual industries were attempted; the role of the universities in research was and always has been much more limited. A very conscious attempt was also made – and has formed another consistent theme of Soviet science policy, as we shall see – to foster the growth of science in the various autonomous republics of the U.S.S.R. so as to counter the otherwise overwhelming dominance of the Moscow–Leningrad axis.

The same period saw the development of the worst excesses of the attempts to impose a rigid and bureaucratized party orthodoxy, nowhere seen more strikingly than in the long dominance of Lysenkoism in genetics.*

Apart from its human tragedy, this episode stands as the record of an over-hopeful belief in the ease with which direct links between basic science and economic development could be achieved – a belief at least partially shared even today by some Soviet apostles of technology for example. A recent calculation by Academician Trapeznikov,[18] the Vice-Chairman of the State Committee for Science and Technology, claimed that each rouble invested in scientific research increased national income by 1·45 roubles. The basis for such a calculation was not given, but in view of the massively non-productive investment in defence research, it may certainly be questioned. Thus the O.E.C.D. review of Soviet Science policy suggests that profitability varies from 0·89 to 1·35 roubles. It may be noted that the extent to which Soviet defence science

* This episode typified in many respects the uncritical embracing by politicians of the potential of science for economic development. Lysenko's genetics promised a quick agricultural breakthrough by way of the inheritance of acquired favourable characteristics in particular crop species, as well as being theoretically satisfying to a crude version of Marxism. Theoretical and applied science were made to march hand-in-hand, and basic research which ran counter to the Lysenko theories, such as that of the outstanding geneticist, Vavilov, was suppressed and its protagonists purged. In retrospect, whilst Lysenko's ideas today seem naïve, he was certainly dogmatically and uncritically accepted. Current developments in Western 'orthodox' genetics no longer make Lysenkoism appear quite so much the heresy it once seemed to outraged Western scientists. J. B. S. Haldane's position as a British Marxist geneticist is particularly interesting on this topic.

is even now included in science statistics is difficult to estimate.

By the early 1950s the annual expenditure on science (using Soviet figures, which differ, as explained above, in their definition of what is included as science from those generally adopted in the West) stood at 900 million roubles annually.[19] Scattered across the country there were some 3,000 scientific institutes, 1,100 of these defined as 'research institutes' under the control either of the U.S.S.R. Academy or those of the various autonomous republics. In principle, the research tasks for all these separate institutes were coordinated and planned through the Academy, but several factors seem to have combined to bring this policy under criticism. One was the sheer scale of the scientific enterprise, the second an increasing complaint, which rings oddly familiar to English ears, that much of the research activity was divorced from production as such. Although special fields such as aerospace and atomic power were certainly being exploited with impressive efficiency, it was clear by the Twentieth Party Congress (1956) that in many areas the links between research and development were not being adequately made, and the direct result of this seemed to be a steady decline of the economic growth rate and return on capital.

The third element in the change was the general policy principle, enunciated by Khrushchev, of 'decentralization'. This policy, which affected all areas of ministerial activity, was part of a deliberate programme of regionalizing governmental activity. The result was that more planning powers were vested in the academies of the various autonomous republics and only the most important problems remained to be planned and coordinated from the centre. At the same time, some of the secondary research institutes, originally under central scientific control, were subordinated to the new regional economic councils – some 100 of these across the country – where their orientation was supposed to be such as to enable them to concentrate on critical problems of applied research. These policy changes began to come into effect in 1958, by which time scientific spending was already twice the 1950 rate (1,700 million roubles) and the number of full-time research workers 284,000.

One of the most impressive fruits of the regionalizing approach was undoubtedly the decision in 1957 to convert a fifteen-square-kilometre stretch of Siberian forest into a massive 'Science City' in which scientists and their families would live and work at twenty-two new research institutes. The City, Academigorodok, near

Novosibirsk, the capital of the Siberian Republic, now contains about 40,000 inhabitants, and is practically complete. It is in its turn being joined by an equivalent technological centre. New recruits to the centre are selected from an open – primarily mathematical – examination for ten-year-old Siberian schoolchildren, who are then educated as an *élite*, quite separately from other less talented schoolchildren. Novosibirsk thus not only expresses the deliberate shifting of major institutions from the Moscow–Leningrad complex to the poorer regions, but also expresses the deliberate creation of a sponsored scientific *élite* in Russian society. The significance of this scientific *élitism* of contemporary Russian communism is apparent when contrasted with the Chinese variant. Although it is difficult to assess the reality beneath the ideology of the cultural revolution, Mao argues that this technocratic *élitism* is incorrect and that science is better, even if more slowly developed, if shared by all the members of the society. In some ways these contrasting views of science education as an *élitist* or popular activity are reflected in miniature by the British debate on comprehensive education.

A wider debate began in Russia in the nineteen-sixties on what the proper role of the Academy should be; whether it should function as a 'Ministry of Science' as such, and whether its responsibilities should stretch into technology as well.* (Again, themes which strike echoes in Britain.) These doubts of the ability of the Academy to cope with the new shape of research led to an attempt in 1961 to replace it as the central science policy-making body by a new State Committee for the Coordination of Research, intended to have a general overlordship over the drafting of a single state research and development plan, both short- and long-range. In general, though, the concept of planning for particular calendar

* Academician Semyenov,[15] for instance, saw the role of the Academy as covering both some basic and mission-oriented research; very precise project-oriented activities should be the field of the 'Branch-Specialized' (Ministerial) Institutes, whilst some general basic research should come under the aegis of the universities; at the same time the role of the two other central academies, those of Medicine and Agriculture (established in 1944 and 1929, respectively), should be enhanced. The supreme coordinating body should remain the Academy. These proposals were coupled with pressure from the then President of the Academy, A. N. Nesmeyanov, to hive off a substantial amount of technology to the various Ministries, leaving the responsibility of the Academy primarily to be that of basic science.

periods of one to five years was rejected in favour of a plan for the full duration of any given research project. Also, the state coordinating body would have responsibility for the coordination of departmental research, approval of the establishment of new institutes and so forth. This new committee, under K. N. Rudnev, a Deputy Chairman of the Council of Ministers, contained amongst its members all the Ministers interested in technology and education as well as the President of the Academy (by now the missile and space technologist, M. V. Keldysh), but it was clearly one in which the scientists had lost out in their planning role to the politicians and technologists *per se*. The committee was obviously more powerful and broad-ranging than the Academy had ever been; the Academy itself, freed of its more technological institutions, was now to concentrate on Semyenov's 'basic problems' and also to be responsible for the training of research workers.

But the new policy was not to outlast the failure of Khrushchev's regional policy, which seems to have resulted in even more overlapping of research functions, and to the proliferation of numbers of tiny sub-threshold institutes which merely seemed to duplicate the work being done elsewhere. Thus at one point, according to Richard Gill,[20] the oil and gas industry of the North Caucasus seems to have been served by no fewer than ten separate research institutes under five different state committees. Similarly the various bureaucratic diseconomies which the system multiplied seem to have caused much concern, and grumbles of discontent at the inadequacies of the system were reflected in articles by various scientists in *Pravda* and elsewhere, stressing the deficiencies of Soviet science. The difficulty of getting adequate secretarial assistance, or delays in the purchase of research equipment, for example, became a frequent source of complaint. At the national level, the technological problems which were still not overcome, are exemplified by the frequent trade deals by which entire factories for motor-car production or chemical plant have to be purchased abroad. This is despite the continuous growth of scientific investment, which by 1967 was almost double that of 1958 with 612,000 full-time research staff, a budget of 5·5 thousand million roubles and a rate of growth of about fifteen per cent a year which has only recently shown signs of slackening.

The solutions to these problems in general were sought in a reversal of the regionalization policy, symbolized by Khrushchev's replacement by Kosygin in 1964 and in 1965 by the abolition of the State Coordinating Committee and its substitution by a new State Committee for Science and Technology under Academician V. A. Kirillin. This new committee appears much less grandiose in conception than the earlier one and more directly concerned with technology. However, the basic economic decisions which affect science and technology increasingly rest with Gosplan, the main planning agency. Most of the organization of basic research has thus reverted once more to the Academy.

So the current resolution of national policy-making for science in the Soviet Union has been the adoption of separate answers for science and for technology, as a result of several years of tension – perhaps inevitable, and not necessarily non-creative tension – between the two. But it is not the case – even assuming this arrangement to be a final one – that the administrative division of the two need lead to the same problems that we have already suggested might occur with the establishment of a Ministry of Technology in Britain, because the British split was based on a history which has led to a quite explicit linking of science with the universities, and consequently with high prestige, whilst the engineer has relatively low esteem. The Soviet engineer and scientist have always held high status in the Russian community, and their scale of pay is commensurate with such a status – above, for example, that of industrial managers. This is, of course, quite a different situation from that which exists in Britain, nor is the institution of the university itself of such great importance in Russia; the research function of a university and its independence have always been much smaller than in West Europe, and the role of the Academy and its research institutes in training young scientists for their doctorate degrees is considerable. In 1964 only two per cent of university-attached scientists were engaged in full-time scientific research, as opposed to full-time teaching.

It is probably fair to say that despite the bureaucratized structure of Soviet institutions (although one American study by Norman Kaplan[21] suggests that there is less administration attached to the running of a Russian than an American scientific institution), the Soviet scientist on paper at least, is more directly involved in helping draw up the plans for his institute than is his Western equivalent. Throughout the changing forms of the overall co-ordinating body for science policy, the mechanisms for drawing up the research plans have remained broadly similar, a process whereby Directors of Institutes and their Academic Councils – bodies on which all the post-doctoral scientists of the Institute sit – are involved in the drawing up of programmatic proposals for research. These proposals are considered, in combination and in competition with one another, by the Academy and its scientific Advisory Councils before the overall general plans are formulated.

But against this must be balanced both the limitations imposed by the actual practice of democratic centralism which has tended to leave room for little real discussion at the periphery, as the Czech experience has recently shown,[22] and also the years of tutelage that the Russian educational system, in common with that of Germany, seems to demand before a scientist is considered as qualified. Typically a Ph.D. degree in Russia is likely to be obtained in a researcher's thirties – sometimes even late thirties – five to ten years after his British equivalent – and the road to scientific promotion is hierarchically maintained on a substantially gerontocratic basis. Thus a scientist may well be into his late thirties or early forties before he ever begins to find himself participating in the scientific community, as, so to speak, a consenting adult. In addition, as there is no retirement age 'the professors and senior academicians tend to die at their desks'.[23] Thus despite the formally democratic structure of Russian science, the overall impression is that it is not so very different from the highly articulated – even monolithic – structure of France and Belgium.

Problems of the Third World

While the research and development budgets of industrialized nations are looking towards achieving three per cent of gross national product, the countries of the third world are frequently struggling to achieve 0·3 per cent of their far more slender G.N.P. But not only are the resources allocated to science slender; the task of developing the institutional forms in which science can be practised within an essentially pre-scientific culture is immense. Even in societies such as India, with a long tradition of mathematics and astronomy, or the Arabian tradition of empirical medicine, the technology of the society is not science-based in the way that in the industrialized West, contemporary experimental science continuously informs and transforms technology.

In Britain or Western Europe, today's technology rests on a base of 300 years of development, the transition of feudal to advanced capitalist industrial societies. Such a background makes it possible to take for granted certain types of scientific and technological interactions which were not possible, for instance, even for many years after the revolution in Russia, because of its essentially underdeveloped nature, and are equally not possible today in India or most parts of Africa and Latin America. In this poor and culturally unsympathetic environment the problem of being any sort of a scientist is great; the problem of being a good scientist in communication with the international community of scientists is virtually insuperable. Where in fact the impossible has been achieved and surpassed, it has typically involved a field which represents a translation of a past strength such as the Indian mathematical tradition re-expressed in theoretical physics. An archetypal exponent of this is Abdus Salam, who, as a distinguished theoretical physicist, holds a chair at Imperial College, London, is science adviser to the President of Pakistan and also runs an international centre for theoretical physics at Trieste. Another was Homi Bhaba, tragically killed in a plane crash in 1967, who founded the atomic research institute at Bombay.

The common experience of the more experimental sciences is less happy, as Polanyi has elegantly written:

> Those who have visited parts of the world where scientific life is just beginning, know the backbreaking struggle that the lack of scientific tradition imposes on the pioneers. Here research work stagnates for lack of stimulus, there it runs wild in the absence of any proper directive influence. Unsound reputations grow like mushrooms based on nothing but commonplace achievements, or even more on empty boasts. . . . However rich the fund of local genius may be, such environments will fail to bring it to fruition.[24]

If the traditional culture was unsympathetic to science, the inheritance of colonialism was equally damaging, in that governments learned to turn to the Western developed nations for advice rather than to indigenous scientists, establishing a negative feedback system which weakened the already struggling scientific community. Both scientists and commentators discussing the problems of science in developing countries have documented this double cultural handicap. Mukerjee,[25] writing in *Minerva,* gave as an example, the Rourkela fertilizer plant in India. Built at a cost of 260 million rupees, it can operate at only low efficiency because the administrators rejected out of hand the advice of Indian experts and preferred to rely on what a foreign firm of consultants told them. Nor is Mukerjee alone in these views. Abdus Salam spoke similarly at the United Nations Conference on Science and Technology in Developing Nations. Or, as the third major Indian commission on education noted more recently, nearly all student textbooks in science and technology are imported; more could and should be produced at home. However, even this commission goes on subsequently to recommend acquiring American mathematical programmed learning courses – themselves only a short step from a textbook.

In this hostile environment, the relatively small numbers of scientists physically scattered over a geographically immense country, find it hard to establish themselves as a scientific community. Instead, all too often, they remain as individual scientists working in highly bureaucratized institutions. Indeed most Indian research is carried out in government-sponsored institutes, little is done in the universities and very little in industry.

What research does take place is carried out almost despite the bureaucracy, leading one distinguished scientist to write to the 1964–6 Indian Commission on Education:

> Presently the head of a large science department is largely a glorified clerk, an accountant and form-filler. He is appointed to do teaching and research, but the general set-up around him is such as to lay a dead hand on both. Those who now manage to do something do it at the expense of their personal affairs and the neglect of their families.[25]

Or, for a blow-by-blow account of the problems of processing an application for a very small piece of equipment which has to be imported, one should read Professor Meheshwari's Presidential Address to the National Academy of Science in 1964. With Ministerial correspondence, import clearance, and so forth, obtaining equipment may take up to two years, by which time, as he says 'the scientist may have given up all plans for research and may have taken another job or left for a foreign country'.[25]

But bureaucracy in the departments of the university is reaffirmed by bureaucracy at the centre. The Scientific Advisory Committee to the Cabinet was thus criticized by the Education Commission for being 'mainly constituted of representatives of the important research organizations in the country', and therefore being unable to review objectively current national policy or to formulate adequate policy changes. The severity of this criticism was underlined by an interesting memorandum offered by the Indian Institute of Political and Social Studies to the Government Review Commission on the National Research Laboratories. This drew attention to the ossified selection procedures for research which emphasized caste, language, and formal possession of relevant qualifications, and all too often precluded consideration of actual research potential or research performance. This rigid structure, as we have seen, precipitates trivial administration on to the shoulders of the director who all too commonly becomes authoritarian. Frequently, because each laboratory represents a power empire, overlapping institutes exist or new institutes, such as the Dehra Dam Petroleum Institute, are established when it is almost certain that a petroleum division could have been much more cheaply and more effectively attached to the already existing Central Field Research Institute.

There are twenty-seven national laboratories attached to the Indian Council of Scientific and Industrial Research. Their directors are described as 'rather suppliant' to the Director-General of the Council, who, because he is on tour for three weeks in every month, tends in practice to be represented by non-scientist administrators. Consequently, an emphasis has developed whereby physical facilities and organizational structures have been stressed instead of the true function of a laboratory, which is support for the researcher. 'We have,' the memorandum concludes, 'to attack this all-pervading and authoritarian climate itself.'

In summary, the problem of Indian science policy can be seen as follows. First, it is inextricably entwined with the fate of higher education in India. This itself is caught up in the problem of the New India which has to create some kind of unified culture from what is essentially a federal structure of many states, each with its own powerful language and powerful culture. English, as a solution, has advantages for science, but has grave political disadvantages as it is the language of India's ex-colonial masters. Failing to tackle the problem of the universities, the Indian government has for decades turned to the solution of conducting research in independent research establishments. Thus resources are spread thinly over a multiplicity of institutions which tend to be more bureaucratic than creative.

In many ways the example of India represents but a particular model of the general problems of countries of the third world as they attempt to industrialize and increase their wealth. Significant contributions to science are, in a general sense, likely to succeed rather than precede economic growth, unless the research is either geared into specifically Indian problems or is concentrated on specific fields and centres. The 0·2 per cent of her gross national product which India currently allocates to science is otherwise likely to keep research everywhere at a sub-threshold level, spread too thinly over too many fields and too many institutions. The solution is to concentrate research effort and manpower into a smaller number of institutions and research fields. But this is hard to achieve in a non-revolutionary society. labouring under the dead hand of tradition, precedent and power groups.

Thus this task of developing science in a society which is committed to evolutionary rather than revolutionary change is immensely complex. Where, on the other hand, a breakdown in the traditional non-scientific culture occurs, as for example in China, it is possible for science to grow extremely quickly. Certainly the delegation of Fellows of the British Royal Society which visited China in 1962 was impressed by much of the scientific work they were shown. More recently the chemical synthesis of insulin and the development of an indigenous nuclear weapon have represented major achievements of Chinese experimental science – even if the chief author of most Chinese scientific papers, according to the deferential phraseology of their introductions, seems to be the polymath Chairman Mao.

But the gains initially made by the revolutionary transformation can potentially be lost in the massive bureaucratization of both Communist party and science which has tended generally to follow the setting up of socialist states typified by the atrophied and rather formalistic nature of the establishment of 'the plan' in any Soviet scientific institute. In this highly bureaucratized phase the normal rules of science and scientific conflict are themselves perverted, as when anti-Lysenkoism can be equated with anti-Communism. The heightened awareness of the dangers of bureaucratization which accompanied the Maoist variation of communism, and the breach between Russia and China, which, above all, is the message of the cultural revolution, have led to attempts to prevent this danger in two ways, particularly after the opening of the cultural revolution in 1966.

The first has been through the adoption of Mao's maxim, 'Do not be overawed by what authorities in science say: be willing to challenge their beliefs',[26] which has been applied so as to reinforce that type of questioning and scepticism central to science in general. To most scientists in industrial nations, though not to those of the third world, where the power of authority is immense, the maxim would seem wholly proper. The second, which is unique to China, has been the deliberate attempt to teach science to the masses, socialist man being substantially equated with scientific man. It is difficult to assess the gap between prescription and performance in China, particularly since the conflict accompanying the cultural revolution has led to an increased isolation, so that even the exchange system operating between the Royal Society and the Chinese Academy ceased in 1966. There are also problems in accepting Mao's thought quite at face value. Joseph Stalin made similar statements, including his essay on Marxism in Linguistics, which provides first-hand justification for freedom of expression and freedom of criticism in science. However, before information about China was reduced from the sketchy to the virtually non-existent, Japanese commentators, such as Uchida,[27] had noted the similarity of problems and developmental patterns between Japan and China. His view was that in most fields China would catch up with the level of Japan in some ten to fifteen years. How accurate this estimate remains today is difficult to estimate, for the cultural revolution claims to have set China new goals, other than those of overtaking Japan, or yet Russia.

As Geoffrey Oldham, the British specialist in Chinese science policy, has stressed, the distinctive character of Maoist science, reasserted since the cultural revolution, has been the emphasis on popular scientific man as against the development of an *élite* scientist.[28] This is bound up with the country's changed political and economic goals. When economic goals were alone seen as important, the policy was adopted of importing know-how, from, for example, the Russians, but also from West Germany and Japan, particularly as it left Chinese academic scientists free to concentrate on pure scientific questions. But when the new political goals are considered, the task of creating a mass scientific culture inevitably leads to a slower development, and one which is more closely focused on China's own problems. Nonetheless the unremitting nuclear test programme bears witness to the large military research and development expenditure which continues despite the cultural revolution.

Thus Maoist thought approves of 'self-reliance' in factories and production, rather than dependence on foreign experts. Such a strategy is not without economic benefit, as the Australian economist Bruce McFarlane[29] has pointed out; thus many of the lathes in the factories producing finished goods were made out of scrap iron in the unpaid time of the workers. Such lathes, less efficient than the product of a specialized machine-tool industry might be, are also of course much cheaper. Again, economically, this approach permits various levels of production within the same industry, with mechanized mills and small producers, in, say, textiles, working in harmony rather than competition. It is this approach which, for a developing society, may well offer the greatest gains, but is almost certainly unfeasible except in a post-revolutionary situation.

For non-revolutionary societies which cannot count on the popular enthusiasm which a successful revolution brings, the most favourable development is likely to be through the selection of specific applied goals and the application of science to these, or to the pursuit of a limited number of purely scientific goals. Portugal has shown some success in the latter, and while in no sense could today's Japan be regarded as a third world country, her success in achieving rapid economic growth and in harnessing industrial science and technology to this main goal is outstanding. Paradoxically, the very forces of Japanese feudalism which had been so successful in excluding Western influence before the Mejii restoration in 1867, were those which were so successful in redirecting the society to the goals of strength through wealth, once the decision to move in this direction had been made. While the period of the Second World War represented a flowering of militarism which temporarily deflected these goals, the post-war scientific effort reasserted them once again, and the political alliances which have kept Japan simultaneously Western-oriented yet not militarily mobilized have spared the need to divert great resources to non-economically oriented research.[30]

This unremitting goal has produced a scientific and technological establishment located predominantly in government research institutes and in industry, and only modestly in the university. The latter was the home of pure science, with university teachers constitutionally debarred from becoming associated with industry. Its representative body, the Science Council of Japan, which included all the sciences, is a democratically elected body and, until the past few years was politically weak, unable to achieve reform in the status of the university scientist, or sufficient money for him to work with. Instead the resources have been allocated to research in industry itself. The powerful coordinating science and technology agency attached to the Prime Minister's office has been dominated by the consciousness of the economic benefits to be derived from science. The earlier, centralizing tradition of government conducting the research for industry has, since 1962, been replaced by industry conducting its own research, with the government institutes instead being focused on social welfare problems which were less likely to be served by industry.

The financial success of these goals is illustrated by the tables in the previous chapter, and by the fact that the proportion of Japan's research and development budget spent by industry, now runs at sixty-three per cent of the total, as against fifty-three per cent some ten years earlier, whilst the university proportion of the budget has slipped by a third, from twenty-nine to nineteen per cent. Another result of this emphasis, though, was that by the mid-1960s the Science Council was generating sharp criticism of the neglect of basic science, which the Japanese goals of, first wealth, then welfare, had excluded. The government response took the shape of a new 'Fundamental Law on Science and Technology' which defined the relationship between scientists and the state and hopefully aimed to improve the scientist's situation. But there are rigid divisions which exist between the university and industry. Within the university itself, there are similar conflicts between departments and generations which derive from the powerful professorial system, as strong as that which dominated Germany before the Second World War, and which spring from some of the more feudal attributes of Japanese society. This will continue to strait-jacket the growth of basic science unless the law works.

The traditional scepticism which has dominated the British stereotype of Japanese research until recent years, attributing its success to the efficiency with which designs and advances developed abroad were copied, has enabled easy misconceptions of the nature of the Japanese success in technological exploitation. Thus, frequently commentators note the Japanese skill at buying foreign patent rights and licences (currently running at 3,000 agreements a year) and suggest that Japan's economic success means that this is an alternative to conducting one's own research; a pattern, by implication, which low-income countries would do well to model themselves on. What is often forgotten is the considerable investment in their own industrial research which makes the Japanese sensitive and effective purchasers of relevant know-how. To be an effective consumer, as the middle-class housewife who reads a consumer guidance magazine such as *Which?* knows, means having access to research laboratories.

A Synthesis of Policies?

Is Japan's success, then, a pattern for third world countries? Certainly, there can be many points of resemblance, because the latter today have the task of shifting a *per capita* annual income from under $100 to over $500, crossing the barrier which divides the industrially advanced nations from the developing ones, a task which Japan has achieved over the last twenty years. Those concerned purely with economic growth might argue, therefore, the success of the Japanese model. Thus for pre-1966 China, under the influence of Liu Shao-chi, or today's India, the emphasis was to be similar to Japan's, of buying technology abroad, although because pure scientists dominated the Chinese academy and the Indian cultural tradition of pure science had been fostered by the British, the economic goal was perhaps less sharp.

The abandonment of Japanese-style policies by the Chinese is thus important, because it raises explicitly the question of the goals of science policy. Are there to be found, amongst the several structures, in developed and developing countries alike, any differences more fundamental than the number of Ministers responsible or the name given to the central advisory body?

The sociologist Raymond Aron[31] concluded at a recent conference that, despite ostensible differences, the bureaucratic structures in different societies were very similar. Insofar as this convergent view is correct, it is an indication of the similarity of role which the different societies see for science. For most of the nations we have considered, their goals have become similar; a combination of economic growth and preservation of national independence. Economic growth means a more or less narrowly technologically oriented science; preservation of national independence means both the fostering of *national* scientific enterprise, more or less conspicuously identified, and, of course, spending on military science. Preservation of national independence in science may take many forms; the Stars and Stripes painted on the side of the first manned spacecraft to the moon, the paper at an international meeting given in French, the insistence that the originators of cybernetics and the television were Russian, the national specialization in electronics or the argument over whether the Anglo-French supersonic passenger plane should be Concord or Concorde.

It is our argument, expanded in the final chapter of this book, that, since the war, as science policies have become crystallized, these goals for science have become predominant in many nations, including both Britain and the U.S.S.R. In this sense, the convergence of science policies in these several countries, makes possible the fact that scientific 'competition' between the U.S.A. and U.S.S.R. is an accepted part of international relations.*

Convergence of goals has affected British policy too, insofar as the difference between Labour and Conservative policies has been between an orientation tending towards the pure economism of Labour on the one hand, and the economism plus military-cum-national independence of the Conservatives on the other. It shows how far these internationally perceived goals have become received

* An example of an absurd comparison is that by the physicist Peter Kapitsa,[32] who pointed out that there were 800,000 scientists and engineers in the U.S., and 700,000 in the U.S.S.R., but that the production of papers by U.S. scientists was one-third of the world's scientific output, whilst that of the Russian scientists was one-sixth. Hence Kapitsa argues that the 'productivity' of Russian scientists is only half that of the Americans. Such calculations are made on the basis of figures interpreted without apparent sociological insight nor in the light of any basic questioning of just what productivity means or ought to mean under these circumstances. And in case this should be seen as a recent preoccupation, it may be mentioned that in 1872 Frankland published a calculation that German scientists then produced 1·75 papers per annum, French 1·44 and British only 1·21. Thus, due to the ill-organization of British research, productivity in this country was lower.

wisdom that their partial abandonment by the Chinese has seemed to most commentators – Western and Russian alike – so perverse. It is this reaction which enables us to look more closely at the nature of our goals for science, a point to which we will return only in the last chapter of the book. Before it is considered in greater detail, it is necessary to examine another aspect of the international transition from Little Science to Big Science, the attempt to find a way out of the impasse of developments in national science policies by the development of international and supranational institutions.

CHAPTER NINE

International Science

It is the belief of many scientists that science is international, that research knows no frontiers. The scientific enterprise, they claim, is pushed forward by many workers, in all parts of the world, each adding their individual contribution to the sum total of the published and freely available knowledge. A statement of this sort can be found in most books about science – provided they are written by academic scientists. One must here suffice:

> The internationalism of science is one of its most specific characteristics. Science has been from the start international in the sense that men of scientific temper even in most primitive times were willing to learn from others in different tribes or races. . . . In later times . . . the scientist vied with the trader in breaking down those [national] barriers . . .[1]

Such a statement carries the implication that, where some aspects of contemporary science are not truly international, or have overtones of secrecy or nationalistic characteristics, they depart from the 'true' norm of science – present or past. Consider, for example, either the statute in its Charter of 1662 opening the Royal Society to 'all inquisitive strangers of all countries', or the title of Gavin de Beer's book, published in 1960, *The Sciences Were Never at War*.

And indeed it is quite true that the history of science is studded with examples of science as an international endeavour. From the days of the early scientific letter-writers onwards, scientific journals have circulated freely across the world, penetrating national and ideological frontiers with little difficulty, translated, as the need arises, into English, Russian, Japanese, Chinese, censorship free.

In this sense, that part of science which is published is still and always has been international. From the birth of science in Renaissance Europe, and the correspondence of Kepler and Tycho Brahe and the visit of the poet Milton to Galileo in Italy onwards, there is continuous evidence of an intellectual and specifically scientific international community. The invisible college of scientists, tied by their letters, their visits and their publications, was committed almost by sheer scarcity of numbers, to be international in character in the early days, and the personal visit or private letter remained an important mode of contact.

Even at this time, the easy assumption of universalism – perhaps no more than the product of a European culture still tied to its Latin roots – was not really to survive the rise of nationalism unscathed. Admittedly, the claim that the scientific community was in a sense above material disputes was still maintained; the visit of the British chemist, Sir Humphry Davy, to speak at the Institut Français under safe-conduct from Napoleon during the Anglo–French War had its counterpart when the French scientist and sailor, Chevalier de Rossel, a prisoner-of-war in England, was able to dine with the Royal Society in London on the invitation of Alexander Dalrymple, hydrographer to the Admiralty.

One of the clearest expressions of this concept may perhaps be the instructions provided by the British Admiralty for the captain of H.M.S. *Rattlesnake*, the ship in which the biologist T. H. Huxley sailed in 1846:

> You are to refrain from any act of aggression towards a vessel or settlement of any nation with which we may be at war, as expeditions employed on behalf of discovery and science have always been considered by all civilized communities as acting under a general safeguard.[2]

Even up to the First World War, the charade was maintained; thus when the war broke out in 1914 a party of German astronomers in the Crimea to observe an eclipse of the sun were taken by surprise by the onset of hostilities, but received the Tsar's personal permission to complete their observations before returning to Germany.[3]

But the sense in which the scientist was above national boundaries in this way, could not survive the growing integration of science into the total structure of individual societies that we have catalogued in the earlier chapters of this book. Whilst the individual scientist might maintain his universalistic ethic, it has increasingly become a reality for only an *élite* amongst scientists. Safe conducts across national boundaries are not easily given to atomic physicists, or researchers on chemical and biological warfare, and for industrial scientists the bonds of secrecy and loyalty are tied even more narrowly to the individual company for which they work. None of these could find Bernal's internationalism readily applicable to his own activities today. Freedom to publish to the international academic community is a privilege restricted to only a relatively small proportion of those who regard themselves as – and are regarded as – scientists. Perhaps universalism remains a predominant myth just because it is precisely this group who tend to write about the philosophy and ethics of science as an institution and an activity.

Even in the universities, the traditional home of the universalistic credo in those societies which have inherited the cultural *mores* of Western Europe, the past few years have seen, at least in Britain and the U.S., an increasing involvement in activities which do not satisfy these criteria. Research linked closely with industry, or more significantly, with defence, and supported by 'tied money', with restraints on freedom to publish – and on those selected to carry out the research – exemplify these trends. The existence of large areas of 'secret research' in many U.S. universities financed by the U.S. Department of Defense exemplifies this. In Britain, in 1967 there were 786 research contracts, worth some £1·4 million, placed in universities by the Ministry of Defence and of Technology with restrictions on publishing buried in the small print.

Thus to argue that science is by its very nature universalistic increasingly falls into the fallacy of confusing an *is* with an *ought*. What remains true is that the explicit credo of many – perhaps most – of the outstanding basic scientists has such a universalism about it. There are two consequences of such a universalism. One is an *élitist* belief that scientists *qua* scientists are capable of rescuing the world from the worst abuses of its nationalist divisions. This belief has long historical antecedents, stretching back to the days of the scientific religion founded by St-Simon in the early nineteenth century, and runs through H. G. Wells's *Open Conspiracy* of intellectuals and scientists who would manage the world in its own best interests, to the thesis of John Ryle, Professor of Physics at Cambridge, who argued in 1938 that:

> The medical profession, which is more international than any other, could . . . put a stop to war . . . by withholding service from the armed services before and during war.[4]

It is also apparent in the proposal in 1940 by Einstein that he, Nils Bohr, the Danish atomic physicist, Cherwell and the Russian Peter Kapitsa, should publish the secret of the atomic bomb to the world to avoid its being the monopoly of any one power. The choice of Cherwell as one of these potential conspirators reveals the discrepancy between image and reality embarrassingly sharply.

A contemporary descendant of this type of internationalism is the scientists' Pugwash association, convened originally in 1957 by the millionaire Cyrus Eaton to bring together scientists from East and West to discuss problems of disarmament, arms control and world peace, and named after the Nova Scotia village where the first meeting was held. The organization now has annual meetings attended by eminent, and frequently officially sponsored, scientists from many nations to discuss such topics in depth, and in its early years especially was politically effective at a time when U.S.–Soviet relations were at a low ebb and almost any contact served to improve them.* More recently it has been claimed that the good offices of Pugwash were involved in creating an environment in which the Vietnam peace talks could begin in Paris.

The Non-Governmental Organizations

These are attempts by scientists to act out their universalism on the outside world. Equally, however, there has been a steady growth of international scientific organizations as such, with no avowed external ends other than the improving of efficiency of particular types of research, which have served to propagate and keep alive scientific internationalism. These organizations have derived from the recognition that the nature of scientific advance has often demanded a measure of international collaboration. Both geographical and astronomical surveys demand cooperation across

* The reality of this internationalism amongst a group of 100 scientists at C.E.R.N. has been indicated recently by a survey of their political views, carried out by Daniel Lerner and Albert Teich.[5] It shows the scientists being only slightly more international in outlook than the other professional groups studied in the same survey.

large areas of territory which transcend national borders, and the eighteenth and nineteenth centuries saw the development of joint observations in several areas. Thus from 1829 onwards, under the auspices of the Berlin Academy, a large number of German, Italian and Danish astronomers helped draw up star catalogues, having divided the sky between them.[3] International astronomical and geophysical projects have been a continuous feature of the world ever since, taking the form of 'international years' devoted to specific projects. The International Polar Year (1882–3) involved eleven national expeditions and the observatories of thirty-five countries; it was the earliest forerunner of the ambitious International Geophysical Year (I.G.Y., 1957–8) of which the Sputnik launching was in a sense the highlight, and the International Years of the Quiet Sun (I.Q.S.Y.), which began in 1964.

This type of cooperation was based on the recognition of the advantages of international activity in tasks of observation, not on the whole involving equipment beyond any one country, but where a coordinated effort by many workers can result in significant advance. Characteristically such collaborative ventures are organized and run by the scientists themselves, although they may involve a certain amount of governmental intervention and finance. Frequently, though, the amount of central planning required is relatively slight and the costs of the programme over and above the normal running costs of the participating laboratories are not excessive. I.Q.S.Y., for example, with a working budget of £30,000 annually, had a permanent staff of only three: the secretary, his secretary and a typist. The results, though can certainly advance the selected field substantially, and can produce improved collaboration for many years following the formal 'termination' of the programme. So far as the I.G.Y. was concerned, for example, about sixty countries participated, taking observations over eighteen months at hundreds of stations under plans drawn up by a special committee and with the results collated by a small international secretariat.

The secretariat itself was established by the International Council of Scientific Unions (I.C.S.U.) which is the most embracing of all international scientific organizations. I.C.S.U. is the logical development of the tradition of non-governmental internationalism in science. This development started, as we have seen, in the international circulation of journals and letters. As scientific disciplines became more separate, first national and then international societies of scientists in specific research areas began to develop in the nineteenth century, concerned with the definition of units of measurement, the organization of international conferences and so forth. Amongst the earliest of these was the Universal Society of Ophthalmology (Paris, 1861), the European (later International) Society of Geology (1864) and the International Bureau of Weights and Measures (1875). By 1914 there were fifty-three such bodies. From then on they multiplied rapidly, so that by 1962 there were apparently some 300 international organizations of one sort or another, although many have only a nominal existence.

All these bodies are essentially private societies, neither governmental nor political in nature and, of course, are in no sense themselves researching bodies. Some of them function as little more than international pen-friend clubs on a rather grand scale. Most of the more important, now known as International Unions for the particular discipline (e.g. the International Union for Biology), are linked together in a sort of confederate structure by I.C.S.U., which contains representatives of both the International Union and the most important scientific association of the member-countries, generally their respective academies, or in the case of Britain, the Royal Society. The establishment of I.C.S.U. in 1931, from an earlier, less powerful body, known as the International Research Council, was in some measure the result of pressure from the Royal Society. At the level of I.C.S.U., international governmental and non-governmental organizations merge. I.C.S.U. is financed not only by members' subscriptions, but by an annual grant from U.N.E.S.C.O. (of about £70,000) and in return helps draw up plans for international activities on a governmental level as well – partly by the use of such specialized committees as C.O.S.P.A.R. (Space Research) and S.S.O.R. (Oceanography).

World Federation of Scientific Workers – In some respects a comparable international structure to I.C.S.U., but intended to organize scientists as a community rather than as a hierarchy of disciplines, was also at least in part developed by British initiative. In 1947 the British Association of Scientific Workers (see p. 52), then under the presidency of P. M. S. Blackett, called a meeting in London of representatives of the comparable scientific associations and trade unions in other countries. This resulted in the establishment of a World Federation of Scientific Workers[6] (W.F.S.W.) linking the scientific trade unions of about thirty nations. Frédéric Joliot-Curie, the French nuclear physicist, was its first President and closely associated from Britain were J. D. Bernal, Joseph Needham, the sinologist and biochemist, and Julian Huxley, at that time newly appointed as Executive Secretary to the Commission which was to establish U.N.E.S.C.O. But it would be wrong to say that W.F.S.W. had since grown dramatically. In some respects it has been a victim of cold war politics and the general split in the international trade-union movement, which polarized between the W.F.T.U. (Soviet-dominated) and I.C.F.T.U. (U.S.-dominated) groups. And one of the largest groups of scientific workers in the world is in the United States, which is almost completely non-unionized. Their links with W.F.S.W. are retained by way of the tiny (2,500-strong) Federation of American Scientists. W.F.S.W. as a whole is no more today than about 200,000 strong and its activities mainly lie within the peace movement and international scientific collaboration.

Governmental Organizations

So far we have been primarily discussing those international organizations essentially devised and run by the scientific communities themselves. There exists, however, another class of bodies whose role to some extent overlaps with these non-governmental organizations. These are those whose principal financial support, and hence control, is governmental, ranging from those with highly specific functions – such as the International Atomic Energy Agency (I.A.E.A.), or the World Meteorological Organization (W.M.O.) to the broadest of all – U.N.E.S.C.O. (United Nations Educational, Scientific and Cultural Organization). In some cases a scientific content has developed in an organization in which little scientific cooperation was originally foreseen – such as N.A.T.O. or O.E.C.D. (Organization for Economic Cooperation and Development), or W.H.O. (the World Health Organization). It is not our purpose here to produce a shopping list of the activities and functions of these organizations, for, including those that we shall consider later which have a specific research and development mission, there may be perhaps sixty in all, some linked through the

United Nations, some forming regional and in particular European or N.A.T.O. groupings. We shall merely use some of these to illustrate the general themes.

U.N.E.S.C.O. – U.N.E.S.C.O., successor to a League of Nations International Committee of Intellectual Cooperation, was set up in 1945 with the worthy objective of:

... [contributing] to peace and security by promoting collaboration amongst nations through education, science and culture in order to further universal respect for justice ...

All members of the U.N. are members of U.N.E.S.C.O., which is run from an elegant office in Paris. It is organized along strictly nation-state lines; each member-nation appoints delegates to a biennial general conference, which appoints a thirty-man Executive Board of Members who represent the states of which they are nationals, and a director-general, who is the principal executive officer – currently M. René Maheu. U.N.E.S.C.O. has about 1,300 paid staff, including fifty-eight scientists. Of its budget of about $20 million a year, plus various special funds amounting to a further $34 million, in the region of thirty per cent was spent in 1963–4 on scientific activities which are intended to include the study of international problems beyond the range of any one nation (oceanography, seismology, etc.) often in collaboration with I.C.S.U., the organization of scientific meetings and conferences, and assistance to developing countries which may embrace anything from the sponsoring of scholarships to the building of laboratories. In addition, U.N.E.S.C.O. has its own science policy unit, particularly concerned with studying the problems of science policy in developing countries.

How effectively does U.N.E.S.C.O. operate? It is difficult to draw a very meaningful balance-sheet when so many of the activities of the organization are somewhat intangible, and especially when simple-minded Utopian internationalism might lead one to argue that because U.N E.S.C.O. is an agency of the United Nations, and because it is concerned with what might broadly be described as 'goodness', it must therefore *ipso facto* be satisfactory. Certainly U.N.E.S.C.O.'s staff contains numbers of devoted internationalists and it produces an impressive annual flow of magazines, broadsheets, technical bulletins, published versions of scientific symposia and so on. But the value of many of these documents is limited, and the reasons for their limitations are not hard to find. Because U.N.E.S.C.O. is an organization of representatives of nation states, anything it undertakes is fraught with all the difficulties and delicacies of any politico-diplomatic manoeuvre in a divided world. Written into its constitution is the premise that membership of the U.N.E.S.C.O. committees must have regard to geographical distribution. That is, whether or not any particular nation has a qualified expert in a particular field, it has a right to press for representation even on technical committees (though usually this is tactfully arranged by regions; a particular international conference list may be scanned by the U.N.E.S.C.O. secretariat and word come down that it is 'low on Latin Americans' for example; one may have some justification for assuming that under these circumstances any Latin American with an appropriate degree would be regarded as sufficing).

Extra-scientific geo-political pressures tend to determine, therefore, the selection of scientific personnel, whilst a heavily bureaucratized structure which seems to be characteristic of such international governmental organizations ensures that most activities, however worthy, proceed at an inexorably leisurely pace. It becomes a sort of status for the small developing countries to maintain an ambassador to U.N.E.S.C.O. to look after their national interest, and the ensuing Byzantine complexities which surround any activity must resemble the politicking that is associated with the choice of a U.S. Presidential candidate. One result of such pressures seems to be that U.N.E.S.C.O. finds itself active in fields that ought really to be outside the role of a mission-oriented institution – spending $70,000 a year in 1963–4 in support of brain research, for instance. Another result is that those things that it should be eminently suited to do, such as the production of surveys of the science policy of member-states, it can in fact only do relatively badly, regardless of the skills of the professionals who actually conduct the research. The country-by-country documents on science policy that U.N.E.S.C.O. has issued over the past few years,[7] which could serve a most useful comparative function, are emasculated because no word of criticism or analysis can appear, for the document is compiled by the member government itself, and, before an international audience, nation states are conspicuously lacking in self-criticism. Inevitably such documents are not only anodyne but also virtually unreadable.

O.E.C.D. – Such limitations make a sharp contrast with the functioning of O.E.C.D., essentially a child of Marshall Aid and the whole period of European reconstruction after the Second World War. As its name suggests, it is heavily slanted towards science and technology as factors for economic growth, rather than science as high culture. Initially limited to Europe, as its old title – Organization for European Economic Cooperation – indicated, O.E.C.D. extended its activities in 1961 to embrace a whole range of non-European countries from Japan to Turkey. It has been described as a rich nations' club, and there is some truth in this, as whilst relatively speaking Turkey and, to a lesser extent, Yugoslavia are in the early stages of industrialization and are therefore fairly poor, the range of income per head of population of O.E.C.D. countries is much narrower than that of U.N.E.S.C.O.

O.E.C.D.'s interest in science policy thus stemmed from its interest in productivity and industrial reconstruction. Early in the life of the organization a working committee was established to discuss scientific and technical information. The committee, in fact, was manned by the governmental heads of applied research agencies such as the D.S.I.R. in Britain and chose to interpret its brief fairly widely. Instead of talking about information processes, it set up inquiries and action programmes into the application of scientific method to both the technical and the social problems of industry. Ironically (and reminiscent of the current policy of the Ministry of Technology) rationalization rather than innovation was O.E.C.D.'s theme. The irony lies in the fact that one of the key members of the committee was Alexander King, then also secretary to the British A.C.S.P. King himself, committed to the productivity through rationalization theory, found a readier backing amongst the Europeans than the British. This straightforward utilitarian view of science scarcely coincided with the much more high-faluting attitude of British governmental circles. Evidence that the Federation of British Industries, for example, tended to be very chary of information on new technologies and of new management schemes rather supports this view of British government and industry as conscientiously resistant to rationalization compared with the Europeans.

As it became increasingly clear that not only could operation research methods in industry help the short-term situation, but that in the long-term it was important to know about the state of science and technology, O.E.C.D. began to move away from a major concern with productivity. By 1961 it was ready to set up an *ad hoc* science policy group, under King himself. This has played a pioneering role in gathering research and development statistics and establishing the rules for their collection so that international comparisons are valid. It also organizes a series of national 'country reviews' to discuss the comparative science policies of separate nations (the most recent are those on the United States and the Soviet Union).

Of course, there are fundamental problems in analysing national science policies from the vantage point of an inter-governmental organization, as we have already suggested in the case of U.N.E.S.-C.O., in that the rule of 'he who pays the piper calls the tune', has some relevance to the nature of the final reports produced. O.E.C.D.'s reports tend to be better than those of U.N.E.S.C.O., beginning at least with fairly sharp analyses of the current problems of individual countries, but tending to end with tolerably modest conclusions.

The real truth is probably that the rich nations of O.E.C.D. have a community of interest in the problems of science policy-making which give their attempts to find a common international ground more meaning than is the case for bodies like U.N.E.S.C.O. Indeed, one of the more interesting features of recent O.E.C.D. practice has been the summoning of meetings of Ministers of Science of member-states to a regular series of conferences which has at least succeeded in generating a rapid spread of the parlance, if not the practice, of science policy and its experts across national boundaries.[8] Many of the definitions and terminology we have used in this book, for example, have been developed and become internationally acceptable by virtue of the activities of O.E.C.D.[9]

Project-Oriented Organizations

Thus far we have described the international link-organizations that have been set up either by the scientists to give their internationalism a formally structured framework, or by governments in an attempt to foster collaborative enterprise or to run specific programmes. But none of the bodies we have so far described has a significant natural science research function as such. The international years and programmes might seem exceptions, but on the whole they rely on the coordination of existing institutions rather than the creation of new ones. Both U.N.E.S.C.O. and O.E.C.D., of course, do social and economic research; the existence of science policy study groups within both is an instance. But there are also international organizations which differ in kind, in that their role is the development of a particular science or technology by the actual financing of research. Mostly of course, such groupings are governmental, because, insofar as they involve the committal of relatively large sums of money on an international scale, there is little choice.

There are exceptions to this rule, though, notably the Stazione Zoologica at Naples in Italy, a centre for the study of Mediterranean marine biology which is really a nineteenth-century hangover which has somehow remained, only partially transformed by the passage of time, a pleasant anomaly in the world of governmental science.*

The station illustrates the typical feature of all international project-oriented organizations, that they set out to achieve something which for reasons of cost, geographical location or other factors, cannot be achieved by any individual nation. For Naples

* The Naples station was set up in 1870 by a wealthy German naturalist Anton Dohrn who obtained a concession from Naples of a site on the coast on which he could build a laboratory, largely at his own expense.[3] In the early days it was financed by the income from an aquarium, later by the policy of hiring out research 'tables' to individual scientists who wished to research there; the annual rental today of $3,000 per table is met by private and public institutions and grants to the individual workers who plan to spend time at Naples. It helps pay their expenses and those of the eighty-odd permanent staff. Although the, initially quite private, management of the Institute was opened in 1923, when it became a non-profit institution, something of the old familial control has been retained, for a stipulation of the constitution of the Institute remains that a member of the Dohrn family is on the Administrative Council; Anton Dohrn's grandson is indeed at present the Director of the Institute. In recent years[10] this 'family business' approach to the running of an international laboratory has hit heavy weather financially, whilst the general political crisis which struck Italian science in the mid-1960s, when the directors of several leading Italian government scientific institutions, including health and atomic energy, were impounded following charges of corruption and misappropriation of funds, did not make things easier. Nonetheless, the station has continued in existence and remains a unique site for this type of marine research.

it is the unique biology of the Mediterranean which is the rationale. But for the several other inter-governmental agencies which now exist, cost is generally the critical factor. And as cost has not yet been a limitation to scientific development in the U.S., and as the developing countries, on the whole, have found it necessary to concentrate their resources on building their own indigenous scientific institution (though, for some, contributions to international agencies may represent a substantial proportion of their scientific budget), most examples of this class of collaboration in the last decade or so have been in Europe.

C.E.R.N. – Perhaps the most successful of all has been the European Organization for Nuclear Research, better known for its major laboratory as Le Centre Européen pour Recherche Nucléaire. C.E.R.N. represents all the features most conducive to success in international organizations. When the war-torn nations of Europe began to consider how they could move ahead in the late 1940s it became increasingly clear to the physicists that the scale and cost of the equipment needed for what was plainly to become a most exciting area of physical research – sub-nuclear or particle research – was beyond the reach of any one European state. The equipment required was essentially giant accelerators capable of speeding sub-nuclear particles to speeds of 99·9 per cent (or more) of that of light. Such accelerators, which may be curved tubes a kilometre or more in length, maintained at high vacuum, are pieces of precision engineering. The U.S. was already beginning to press forward vigorously with building one at Brookhaven, and the U.S.S.R. at Dubna. Some sort of collaboration was obviously going to be necessary if Europe was to compete.

At the same time collaboration on an international scientific project of high prestige was seen by national governments as a useful symbol both of European resurgence and potentially of European unity. Nonetheless it is of interest that American scientists figured prominently in the early negotiations for the establishment of C.E.R.N., notably Rabi and Oppenheimer, two of the U.S. scientists who had been closely involved with the bomb project. Europeans included Kowarski and Auger of France and Bohr from Denmark. The British, characteristic of their approach to most international scientific projects, were initially standoffish, being represented at the beginning only as observers. But political reality dawned for the U.K. too, and when the C.E.R.N. project was formalized in 1953, Britain was the first to ratify the convention.

Plans were already under way to build a laboratory on a site near Geneva and the big machine, a proton synchroton, with a power of 28 billion electron volts (GEV),* second in size in the world only to that at Brookhaven in the U.S. (33 GEV), was commissioned in 1959. Since then C.E.R.N. has maintained a steady flow of valuable research and it has proved a powerful magnet for young researchers. Some of the factors in its success are implicit in the nature of the field. With so few machines capable of producing the results, and with the intellectual excitement and rather clear research directions which high-energy physics is currently providing, so that many of the best potential physicists in the world are automatically attracted to it, it is not too hard not to go wrong. Britain and Europe were undoubtedly immensely strong in their pre-war tradition of nuclear physics and this must have helped – even though much of the recent work has been done in a sort of steeplechase competition between C.E.R.N., Brookhaven and the Soviet centres as to who would get the results first. Examples of such chauvinism are reflected in newspaper articles on C.E.R.N.'s activities. Thus in 1966 and 1967 C.E.R.N. scientists were involved in a technical dispute with those of Brookhaven in which C.E.R.N. came off best; the *Guardian* and *Times* headlines were respectively 'European precision defeats U.S. theory' and 'Europe scores a point in physics'.

But wise administration certainly played a part, too, and insistence that with the exception of a relatively small permanent staff most of the scientists using the C.E.R.N. machine came only for a short time, retaining their home university affiliations, and that these scientists should generally be selected on merit rather than on the rigid geographical basis that characterizes other international organizations, all helped, not least in ensuring that a series of directors-general (the chief executive office) of undoubted scientific distinction have been appointed, whilst close relations were built up with the U.S. (partly through the Ford Foundation) and the Soviet Union.

Nonetheless, C.E.R.N.'s future is now seriously in the melting pot. The main problem is that of the next generation of accelerators.

* 1 billion = 1 thousand million or 10^9; the international symbol for this is Giga – hence the abbreviation GEV.

The Russian 70 GEV accelerator at Serpukhov is now established and the Americans have finally decided on a site (at Weston, Illinois) for their proposed 200 GEV machine. If C.E.R.N. is to survive, it is claimed, it must now start building a bigger machine yet, a 300 GEV one. Such a project would cost in the order of £150 million over about ten years. Yet it is hard to argue that this expense would ever really be recovered in terms of a potential technological pay-off on the research, or that the 300 GEV machine would itself be more than a stepping stone on the way to yet bigger machines, perhaps of 1,000 GEV, of which it might well be the case that only one in the world – a truly international rather than a regional venture – would be feasible. Indeed, even before building has started, the Americans have laid plans for doubling the Weston accelerator to a potential 400 GEV. At a time when C.E.R.N. budgets have become relatively tight (in 1966 the annual running budget was some $35 million, twenty-five per cent of which was paid by Britain) and the rate of growth of scientific funding is being sharply cut back in several countries, particularly Britain, which would be one of the major contributors, the arguments in favour of the building of the machine ring a little hollow. The British C.S.P. eventually came down in favour of finding the money with a dissenting minority report (see Chapter 12), and established opinion is undoubtedly in favour. *Nature*, for instance, argued that:

> Europe should not at this stage contract out of what has become the most exacting (and the most expensive) part of physics. . . . The big machine is a good deal more valuable than a full-blooded space programme would be.[11]

whilst *The Times* oratorically thundered:

> If Western Europe has the will, faith and drive to make itself one of the great industrial centres of the world it is right to build this machine. If the future of Britain lies with Europe it is right that Britain should join in the project.

Nonetheless, in June 1968, Professor Brian Flowers, chairman of the British S.R.C., had the duty of telling the meeting of the C.E.R.N. council that the British government had rejected the advice of the C.S.P., and would not support the new machine, a decision from which, as Flowers was at pains to make clear, he personally dissented.[12]

The rational backing for such acts of faith in the machine, however, are less closely argued. They seem to depend mainly on the suggestion that if we do not build the machine physicists who want to work in this field will go elsewhere, thus accelerating the 'brain drain' phenomenon which we discuss later. The extent to which this argument carries weight raises more general problems of decision-making which again we can defer considering for the moment. If the British government's decision was the right one, it was almost certainly made for the wrong reasons.

Meanwhile, one further issue is revealingly illustrated by the C.E.R.N. debate on the big machine. Machines need sites. For any community the establishment of a large and expensive piece of equipment in the vicinity, with its attendant army of scientists, engineers and technicians, probably represents a potential economic boom. Just as the battle for actually building the hardware for a big machine commissioned by the government is intense amongst potentially competing firms, so is that of the choice of site. The choice of Weston in the U.S. for the 200 GEV machine was only arrived at after a series of protracted haggles between the U.S. Atomic Energy Commission[13] and pork-barrel politicians who saw potential gain to their home states. A variety of more or less sophisticated arguments were used on both sides. Although the final site was chosen only after very protracted argument, it promptly ran into difficulties as the area selected is in a rigidly segregated zone, and segregation is, at least theoretically, unacceptable to any U.S. Federal agency. Citizens of Weston are being faced with an uneasy choice between their white conscience and their pockets which so far remains unresolved. In Europe, competition for a site is even fiercer, because national, and not merely state rivalries, are involved and the final decision as between several sites (one of which was in Britain at Mundford in Norfolk) had yet to be taken when the British withdrawal caused the whole project to be reconsidered.

E.L.D.O. and E.S.R.O. – Where C.E.R.N. is an international, or at least an inter-European, success, the European venture into space makes a sorry story. The pressures leading to the creation of the two space organizations were quite different, one primarily political, the other at least substantially scientific.

E.L.D.O. (European Launcher Development Organization) was

conceived to a considerable extent as a means of ridding Britain of an embarrassing technological problem, whilst proving, incidentally, that she was a good 'European'.[13] The problem in 1959–60 was what to do with that Defence white elephant which, prior to TSR-2, stood as the supreme example of bad planning in defence science – the Blue Streak missile–abandoned as a potential weapon after some £100 million had been spent on its research and development, and in the teeth of opposition from the British aerospace lobbies. The proposal was ingenious. It was to use Blue Streak as the first stage of an all-European satellite launcher, and the scheme was itself launched after a round of intensive lobbying by the then Minister of Defence, at the Council of Europe in September, 1960.

It was eagerly embraced by the French, to whom it seemed to offer a fairly cheap way into space, with a French rocket 'Coralie' forming the second stage of the launcher. The third stage would be German, and other participants in the organization, which eventually came fully into effect in 1964, were Belgium, Italy, Holland and Australia, who offered as dowry the Woomera rocket-testing range. A budget of some £70 million was allocated for the first five-year programme, thirty-nine per cent paid by Britain, and the hope was to produce a launcher capable of putting a one-ton satellite into orbit some 500 kilometres above the earth by 1966. Such a launcher would provide the mechanism for putting E.S.R.O. (European Space Research Organization) satellites into orbit, and would incidentally assist the Europeans to move into the potentially profitable satellite telecommunications area, otherwise a U.S.–U.S.S.R. monopoly.[14]

The timetable almost immediately ran into difficulties; there were problems with the French second stage, the launch date of 'Europa I' was put steadily back and the costs began to escalate. By late 1965 they were already twenty-five per cent above the earlier estimates and the Europa I payload was down from one ton to 1,500 pounds. The stretching of the timetable and down-grading of the payload capacity continued; the test flight of Europa I, which finally took place in 1967, was a fiasco as the second stage failed to work adequately. Meanwhile bitter behind-the-scenes international wrangles over costs resulted in repeated rumours throughout 1965, 1966 and 1967 that the British would axe the entire project.

The whole issue came to a head with the publication, early in 1968, of the Causse Report, commissioned the previous summer by the European Space Conference, projected the E.L.D.O. plans forward to 1977, when a two-ton satellite would be launched, firmly pegged at a yearly cost (of £30 million to Britain).[15] The net result of this would be to make Britain's space budget – less than £10 million in 1963–4 and £24 million in 1968–9, rise to £31 million by 1971–2 – and on past experience go on up after that. At this point the Wedgwood Benn axe fell. 'The Government,' he said, 'sees no economic justification for undertaking further financial contributions to E.L.D.O. or for participating in the proposed experimental television satellite under the European Conference on Satellite Communications.' At the end of the present programme in 1972 Britain would opt out, thus effectively terminating the E.L.D.O. project, although, as we shall see, this still left E.S.R.O. intact.

The interesting point about this Ministerial withdrawal was the use of economic criteria to justify participation or non-participation in an international venture. To Mintech experts, money for aerospace was better invested in projects such as the Rolls-Royce RB-211 aero engine, into which £50 million would be sunk, than such doubtful ventures into space. The good sense of this argument was reflected in the favourable press it received – bar some ritual howls from the aerospace lobby, the British Interplanetary Society, and one or two Conservative M.P.s. Even the French were relatively mild in their criticism – perhaps because much of the earlier trouble with Europa I had been in the French second stage.

But simultaneous with this policy reversal it was emphasized that the British commitment to E.S.R.O. would not only remain unimpaired, but actually rise by some six per cent per annum, nearly as much as the ten per cent that the Causse Report had planned for. E.S.R.O., like E.L.D.O., came into force in 1964. More broadly based than E.L.D.O., with ten nations involved, its relative success is in part because it was initially set up on the basis of scientific rather than political initiative, when proposals made by some of the scientists who had participated in C.E.R.N., notably Pierre Auger from France and Amaldi of Italy, were relayed to a conference convened by the French government in Paris in 1960. The objectives of the organization, too, are purely scientific, concerned with the sending up of experimental satellites and the establishment of a space technology centre (at Delft in Holland), a data centre (at Darmstadt in Germany), a tracking system and so forth.

E.S.R.O.'s budget was about £30 million in its first three years and £45 million in its next, twenty-five per cent of which is met by Britain. It is currently headed by the British nuclear physicist and mathematician, Herman Bondi.

Despite the criticism of E.S.R.O.'s activity by the British Parliamentary Select Committee,[16] which advocated a more substantial national programme, and evidence of nationalist tensions in the organization, it has on the whole held together a good deal better than E.L.D.O. Financial escalation has certainly occurred, and there have been repeated criticisms of 'not getting one's money's worth', particularly from Britain, whose aerospace industry has been far less successful than the French in winning E.S.R.O. contracts, despite Britain's greater financial contribution to the organization. Partly because of E.L.D.O.'s failure, E.S.R.O. satellites are now to be launched by U.S. rockets and the first was, in fact, attempted in 1966, only to fail when the rocket's upper stage proved faulty. It was not until the spring of 1968 that E.S.R.O. finally achieved a successful launch, and it is certainly still too early to be sure that it will not go the same way as E.L.D.O. within the next few years; however, for the present, its future looks reasonably assured.

CHAPTER TEN

International Gaps and Drains

The Technology Gap

Amongst many international governmental science organizations, we have concentrated on these few, U.N.E.S.C.O. and O.E.C.D., C.E.R.N., E.S.R.O. and E.L.D.O., because they illustrate particularly clearly the objectives and problems which such organizations are likely to face. It is relatively easy for the scientist to set up international groupings for the exchange of information or even for participation in some joint programme of limited scale. Anything more than this though, involves government; and governmental organizations, even the best intentioned, are fraught with the problems of nationalism and bureaucracy that U.N.E.S.C.O. so sadly illustrates. More permanent and ambitious groupings than these have so far proved possible only on a regional scale and of all the regions which might prove appropriate candidates, only Europe has really begun to test the potential of this form of organization. The reasons are not far to seek. European nations are all relatively highly industrialized with independent scientific traditions. The motive force behind their collaboration is that none by itself can afford the sort of project which is still within the financial compass of a super-power such as the U.S. and the U.S.S.R. Because of the magnitude of its scientific effort, the U.S. acts as a magnet for aspiring young European scientists and creates the phenomenon christened 'brain drain'. In order to remain scientifically and economically competitive with the U.S. – at least in the fields which are already Big Science (and this is an important proviso) – it has been necessary for Europe to attempt such joint projects. There are many others, such as Euratom, the European Molecular Biology Organization (E.M.B.O.) and Computation Centre, which we have not had space to discuss. Yet such collaborative efforts are not *ipso facto* successful. Big Science is not, as we have seen, always successful in the U.S. In a far from united Europe the chances and penalties of failure are greater.

Such an analysis, well within the conventional wisdom, has led in recent years to the conclusion that there exists a widening 'technological gap' between Europe and the U.S. Thus in absolute terms the U.S. still spends three times more on science than the whole of Western Europe put together, while her technological preponderance in certain areas, such as space, computers and microcircuitry is both overwhelming and increasing. It is claimed that this gap represents the gravest threat to the maintenance of European 'independence' from U.S. capital and technological penetration.*

Moreover, although the phrase 'technology gap' is only of recent coinage, and is generally assumed to refer to a relatively new phenomenon, there is some evidence to suggest that the roots of the discrepancy lie much deeper. Thus the lack of concern of Americans with basic science, and their attention to invention and technological innovation, was a phenomenon which had been observed time and time again through the nineteenth century; it had been commented on as long ago as 1835 by de Tocqueville,[2] who attributed it to the nature of American democracy:

> In aristocratic ages, science is more particularly called upon to furnish gratification to the mind; in democracies to the body.

Thus in Europe, according to this analysis, also made by, for instance, Ben-David,[3] science was seen as a cultural activity, in the U.S.A. as an economic investment. According to de Tocqueville, the Americans would produce basic research only if it were not available elsewhere.

> I am convinced that if the Americans had been alone in the world . . . they

* Such an analysis has found its clearest popular expositions in the books *Le défi américain* by the French economist Jean–Jacques Servan-Schreiber and *European Advanced Technology, a programme for integration* by Christopher Layton.[1]

would not have been slow to discover that progress cannot be made in the application of the sciences without cultivating the theory of them . . .

And already, by the late nineteenth century, American economic advance was such that it had begun to be unable to borrow the science it needed from elsewhere. Investment in basic science began to increase rapidly, and by the 1930s the proportion of the world's basic scientific literature accounted for by the U.S.A. already amounted to some thirty per cent – a proportion which has remained more or less static ever since, according to counts of papers published made by de Solla Price (the British proportion has also been more or less constant at fourteen per cent; France and Germany have declined, whilst Russia and Japan have expanded). Similar calculations can be made of the numbers of Nobel prizes awarded to workers in different countries, or the country of origin of specific groups of fundamental scientific discoveries.[4] All such evidence points to the relative vigour of U.S. science from an early stage.

But the key point, for those concerned with the links between scientific investment and economic growth, does not lie here. The contribution of Europe to basic science remains substantial, despite two world wars and the ensuing political and economic divisions. The problem lies in the inability of European scientific institutions to convert basic scientific discoveries into fruitful economic pay-off. All too often, research initiated in Europe has remained to be exploited technologically in the U.S. The reason for this inability to deliver the technological goods was said to relate to the different nature of the European and American university traditions; the American tradition has always been an entrepreneurial one. The universities have not been rigid, hierarchically ordered systems, as in Germany, but have been more flexible, often arising to fill specific economic goals, with fluid departmental structures, which has made it possible to recognize and move into new research fields and new 'subjects' for undergraduate teaching so much more early than in Britain or Europe, and with a tradition of self-help in the raising of finance from industry, rather than of being the passive recipients of governmental funds.

This has both encouraged an entrepreneurial attitude amongst university scientists, and helped forge powerful links between university and industry. Of this long-term trend, the recent developments in 'Route 128'-type activities is but the current manifestation. 'Route 128' is the road outside Cambridge, home of the Massachusetts Institute of Technology, along which the factories of so many technologically-based firms have sprung up in recent years, run and staffed by members or ex-members of M.I.T. They typify that close relationship of industry and academia which some critics of the European system who decry the technology gap, such as Ben-David himself, or Servan-Schreiber (whose book reads like a long love-song in favour of U.S. technology, and lament for the inevitable, fallen grandeur of Europe) so clearly envy.[5]

Despite the economic success of the American system – according to these criteria at least – and its current and past contribution to basic science, there is no need to accept these arguments uncritically. In part, this reflects an analysis which, while recognizing the technologically innovatory quality of certain aspects of American society, also sees it as an inseparable counterpoint to those structural faults in the U.S. which loom so large; a depressed black proletariat, the prevailing urban squalor which makes a visit to almost any American city so depressing an experience, and the concomitant drive to rape and despoil the countryside now generally described as 'environmental pollution'. The technological harnessing of the university to the demands of an industrial–military complex typified by the shocking contrasts of the richest society on earth, with its space programme and its slums, is the price of this sort of economic efficiency. It chooses to provide for particular types of needs but not others. If this represents an inevitable result of this type of appreciation of the function of science it is not an acceptable solution.

Furthermore, many of the arguments against capitalist penetration advanced, for instance, by Servan-Schreiber, when stripped of their economic jargon, tend to sound a bit like crude nationalism. Does it matter to an employee of a firm in Holland or Belgium that his employer is part of a capitalist combine whose central offices are in New York, and not in London, Paris or Frankfurt? Perhaps. But the answer can by no means be taken for granted. It is certain that such interdependence of major capitalist enterprises and their internationalism is now so much part of the international scene that it is unwise, if not impossible, to try to reverse it by simple bans on the movement of capital or of individual scientists across boundaries. The answers to the problems generated by international capital ought themselves to be international in nature.

But the technological gap is important from a different point of view if it points to the possibility of a gradual drying up of the inventive powers of European as opposed to U.S. research. Already the flow of know-how, in terms of the licensing of patents on certain manufacturing processes and products in countries other than those in which the patent was first taken out, is flowing strongly from the U.S. to Britain and Europe, implying that it is becoming increasingly necessary for European firms to buy their science abroad, whilst the flow of scientists is running in the other direction. Thus in 1961 the U.S. paid $63 million for technological know-how from abroad, but received more than $577 million, and in 1965 filed more than 100,000 patent applications in foreign countries, as opposed to 22,000 filed by foreign countries in the U.S. in the same year.[3] We consider some of the implications of this movement in the following section.

For the moment we may note that there is one further proposal to counteract these drifts which is being actively canvassed by Mintech and the British government, that of the establishment of a European Technological Institute.[6] Such a proposal has also found favour with the O.E.C.D. study groups which have called for the setting up of numbers of large, multi-disciplinary research institutes. During its 1965–6 attempts to enter the Common Market, the Wilson government made much play with the technological dowry it would bring with it, which would boost European technological competitiveness to a level more comparable with that of the United States.[7] And it is true that, as the previous chapter has shown, Britain is technologically the biggest spender in Europe. Of course, much of this goes on defence. Nonetheless, some pooling of resources and knowledge would probably make economic sense, Common Market or no, and it may well be that a version of the European Technological Institute will eventually materialize. But proposed as it is now, as another political iron in the fire of Britain's involvement with Europe, it seems hardly likely, despite Mr Benn's persuasiveness, to get off the ground. Meanwhile, the brain drain continues and the technological gap, according to the more lugubrious forecasts, widens.[8]

The Brain Drain

The problem of the loss of numbers of Britain's highly qualified scientists to the U.S.A. began to emerge into popular consciousness from 1959 onwards. At recurrent intervals thereafter, but increasing in frequency, press headlines began to report in ominous terms on the magnitude of the loss. For some time, the scientific community itself remained tolerably indifferent to the inflow and outflow of scientists, but by 1963 the Royal Society was sufficiently disturbed to run a small study, confined to the loss of new Ph.D.s, which was found to be some twelve per cent of the annual Ph.D. output.[9]

Press comment became more vigorous. When Professor Ian Bush left the physiology department at Birmingham for the U.S.A. in 1963, he called a press conference to announce his departure, and that of a substantial proportion of his research team; *The Times* report was headed 'Not enough time for creative work; students' equipment 20 years out of date'. Early in 1964 the *Express* (11 February) reported 'Brain storm grows – socialists pounce on Premier over "lost" scientists'. 'Birmingham to lose 3 more scientists' (*The Times*, 16 February) followed shortly, and on 17 March (*The Times*) 'Oxford losing psychology staff – posts in U.S. preferred'.

The political storm grew when, as described in Chapter 5, Lord Hailsham, then Minister for Science, blandly interpreted the phenomenon as no more than a compliment to the British educational system; he accused the Americans of living 'parasitically' on the brains of other nations, and a partly successful move was made to block the award of an honorary degree to him at Cambridge, spearheaded among others by the biochemist Asher Korner. As each departure was noted, the scientists themselves wrote letters to the press, stressing the reasons for the move, and citing constantly the 'lack of facilities in Britain for creative work', 'the general lassitude and lack of enthusiasm for new ventures which is prevalent in Britain', 'British industry makes no effort to attract the best Ph.D.s'. Several stressed the point that it was the most innovatory scientists, therefore working in new fields without the protection of the established disciplines, who were likely to go. In general the reasons cited were the better facilities for research in the U.S., and the relative ease with which young people could achieve research autonomy. Only marginally were salaries regarded as being of critical importance, even though in real terms U.S. salaries for academics must run at two to three times above their British equivalents.

It was against this background that the Manpower Committee – which reports jointly to the D.E.S. and the Ministry of Technology – decided, following its 1965 survey,[10] to commission a special study, to be chaired by Dr F. E. Jones, Managing Director of Mullards, to study the problem, assess its magnitude and make proposals for reducing the outflow. The committee reported, somewhat gloomily, in October 1967, that the problem was real, getting worse, and that many of the short-term measures which had been proposed for correcting it, such as the imposition of physical or financial obstacles to qualified workers wishing to emigrate, were impracticable.[11] In the long run, they felt, a solution would only lie in a transformation in the attitudes and behaviour of British management and industry.

Thus the problem was seen as one special to Britain and as a reflection on the state of British science. Yet in fact, there is good reason to believe that the issue is a far more universal one than the rather parochial press and political capital made of the migrations would lead one to assume. And it is because of this general significance that we have chosen to consider the issue of brain drain here, as part of international science, rather than as the uniquely British phenomenon which was part of the scientific–political scene of the early 1960s. We should begin by trying to assess the reality behind the headlines.

The current pattern of migration, the continuous movement of people to new countries, has one outstanding characteristic which differentiates it from past patterns. Where in the past, even the recent past of twenty years, most migrants were unskilled, those who travel most easily today are the highly skilled, the scientists, the doctors and engineers. The loss of a section of the population to another country in search of work tended in the past to solve economic problems rather than create them: the great Irish emigration to America meant fewer mouths to feed at home and a better chance abroad. But this new mobility of the educational *élite* is the mobility of educational investment, which means that, unless the movement between countries breaks out evenly in terms of gains and losses, some countries are likely to be economic losers and others winners.

Scientists are fairly migratory birds anyway. It was considered proper, for example, for Cherwell to finish off studying physics with a spell in a German laboratory, and where else can a young East European physicist go at some time, other than to Dubna or Serpukhov, to do certain sorts of work? At what point does this necessary and inevitable type of migration become a brain drain? Within the British context, the Jones report on the brain drain concluded that, in 1966, of our annual production of qualified engineers and scientists we lost nineteen per cent of the engineers and nine per cent of the scientists by emigration. It is ironic that the best source of data on the movement of British scientists and engineers are the National Science Foundation statistics, our own migration figures only being collected for sea, and not air travellers. But the problem is not exclusively that of scientists. Brian Abel-Smith and Kathleen Gales' study of British doctors carried out in 1963 showed that we were losing thirty per cent of the annual production of doctors.[12]

Nor is the problem unique to Britain. In the Philippines, for instance, it was reported that a whole year's output of doctors from one medical school had together chartered a plane to fly them to the States – a total clean-out. New Zealand is similarly affected, losing forty per cent of her first-class honours graduates, but retaining those in the life sciences, such as the zoologists, botanists and agriculturalists, which are more closely linked with the specific problems of New Zealand. It has been calculated by Professor West in the *Journal of Medical Education* that the number of foreign doctors recruited in the United States is approximately twenty per cent of the annual production of American doctors starting work, and saves America from having to build and run twelve new medical schools.[13] The inflow is also, in terms of dollar aid from the poorer to the richer countries, about equal to the value of all American aid abroad.

But it does not behove Britain to resent too vigorously the numbers of British doctors leaving for abroad, partly because about a third of them are going to work in low-income countries, which is scarcely undesirable, as it is if anything counter-brain drain, and anyway these subsequently return home. The real difficulty in criticizing our doctors, engineers or scientists emigrating to the rich

U.S. is that Britain is part of a flow system. Thus, though Britain lost 4,300 scientists and engineers in 1966, we gained 2,400, primarily from countries poorer than ourselves.

In British hospitals at the moment more than half the doctors are foreign-born, mainly from low-income countries, and although at a lesser level of skill, nurses are equally highly recruited from abroad. Indeed many of the National Health Service hospitals would not be able to function without the medical staff from the health services of countries much less able than ourselves to pay for their training.*

The point is that Britain is typical of those countries which both lose and gain in the flow of human capital. Brinley Thomas[14] has set up a useful four-fold category of countries on a loss/gain basis. These are:

(i) Countries with a large net inflow, such as the United States and Australia.

(ii) Intermediate advanced countries with a large two-way traffic such as Britain and Canada.

(iii) Advanced countries with a large net outflow, such as the Netherlands, Norway and Switzerland.

(iv) Underdeveloped countries with a large net outflow, like Greece, Iran, Turkey and some Asian countries.

While these four categories sharpen understanding about the main structures of emigration, the situation is not constant. This is particularly noticeable in the case of Canada and Britain both with considerable migrant traffic. Canada is the most extreme, for example, losing about half her annual production of engineers to the States, but then recruiting the equivalent of seventy-three per cent of her engineering cohort from Britain. Each graduate in engineering is 'worth' about £6,000 of educational investment for Britain, which is transferred with him to Canada. But the Jones report[11] is concerned to show that the British situation is worsening, so that while in 1961 there was a net gain of 400 scientists and engineers to the U.K., some five years later there was a net loss of 1,900. Consequently it is clear that countries can shift from Thomas's category (ii), of two-way traffic, to category (iii), with large net outflow, with transparent ease.

* In Britain in 1965, there was one doctor per 850 population; in low-income countries one doctor per 20,000 population is common, and one per 100,000 not unknown.

Almost certainly the difference between holding the position even or losing, is, for the middle-rank countries, a reflection of the short-term economic situation and the specific policies which impinge on scientific workers, which combine to tilt or hold the balance. But what is perhaps more interesting is the long-term effect, and here almost certainly there is a continuous loss to the United States, and in East Europe probably to Russia, for certain sectors of science at least. As the price of conducting research rises in certain fields, the number of fields must inevitably contract in which, first small countries, such as Norway, and later the middle-rank countries, such as the U.K., can effectively research. Thus the position could conceivably emerge whereby all high-energy physics would be carried out in the United States or Russia, leaving only the cheaper solid state physics to be carried out in the middle-income countries. Many non-physicist scientists would perhaps welcome this, for it was notable that the two dissenters to the British Council for Scientific Policy's recommendation that Britain join the European 300 GEV accelerator were chemists.[15] The difficulty is that this rationalization of research also has the effect of locating more and more of science – and therefore scientists and engineers – in the richest nations.

For basic science, which is open and published, some economists, such as Ed Mishen and Harry Johnson, have questioned whether it really matters if a man does his work in India, Britain or the United States.[16] From the short-term point of view, persuading other countries to pay for basic research seems a sensible enterprise, but in the long term there may be less beneficial results. The British Brain Drain Committee chose to illustrate the problem with the semi-magical concept of the 'seedcorn' which would thus be lost, with its overtones of ritual fertility rites.

The solution almost certainly lies in collaborative international scientific ventures. Again it is high-energy physics which supports the argument. C.E.R.N. was established when high-energy physics became uneconomic to individual countries. When subsequently the discussion of the new 300 GEV machine was opened, there was some serious consideration of whether it was not possible to skip this stage, whereby the U.S.S.R. and U.S. and Europe could afford one 200–400 GEV machine apiece, but instead to consider if the time to build a world-wide 1,000 GEV machine had not arrived. It is probably not yet feasible technically to build the bigger machine;

thus somebody, and therefore everybody (such is the nature of keeping up with technology), has to learn how to build the 300 machine. The political arrangements necessary for such a truly international development would have been (will be?) fascinating. The alternative to this internationalism, though, is to let the United States and Russia do all the high-energy physics.

In a sense, because the British Brain Drain Committee wanted to have their cake and eat it – a fairly common attribute of governmental committees – they both adopted the position of saying we cannot afford everything, and that therefore some scientists will have to go to the United States for their own and our good, and at the same time invoked the 'seedcorn' concept as a reason for not letting them *all* go. However, attacking a committee for its internal contradictions is easier than defining the argument which lay beneath the invocation.

Ultimately the discussion becomes one about culture and the kind of values and society that we want. Essentially the logic of the price mechanism is plain; the goods – that is the best scientists, engineers and doctors and so forth – go to those who can and will pay the highest price. For the West this is clearly America. Those countries which can afford less get rather less in the way of such people, not only quantitatively but also qualitatively. As the Jones report recognizes and as the medical profession equally recognizes, it is not just a high proportion overall who go, but a high proportion of the best workers in the field.

Few would share the sanguinity of the economists, like Johnson and Mishen, at this concentration of human capital in the richest societies. This is not because concentration impedes the advance of science, for it may well accelerate it, but because science has a dynamic role in contemporary society. As Bernal once pointed out, it would be possible to concentrate all the basic science now being done in the world into a series of institutes, on, say, Long Island in the U.S.A. – or the Isle of Wight in Britain.[17] The science might well proceed faster for this intellectual close-packing, but the rest of the world would be impoverished, and not only from the withdrawal of potential university teachers into the world of mere research. This belief is supported not only by faith but also by the studies of innovation, which typically report that firms or whole societies need a reasonably sustained research programme in order to utilize the know-how of others. Without this research activity of their own, they seem to be less able to judge just what science or technology is relevant. If all the high professional human capital were located in the United States, the science conducted there might be impressive, but in the middle-income or low-income countries there would be little or only weak science to be seen, and these societies would be decreasingly able to use the research findings of others.

Thus, in the long run, the internationalization of science must be seen as one of the defence mechanisms against the undesirable consequences of this type of concentration.

CHAPTER ELEVEN

Criteria for Choice

We have set out in this book to map the growth of science as an institution within society, and particularly its relation to the principal scientific fund-giver, government. We have seen how the involvement of government and policy-makers in science, an involvement avoided by the politicians and tenaciously resisted by the academic scientists themselves, came into its own in the period following the Second World War and especially in the latter half of the 1950s, so that most countries, industrial and developing alike, now boast of something recognizable as a 'science policy' with a detailed, if varied, political and policy-making structure.

The development of the theory of how these bodies should work has inevitably fallen behind that of practice. Until a few years ago it was still common enough, at least among academic scientists, to hear the viewpoint expressed that: 'Science is essentially unpredictable and hence unplannable. The best thing to do therefore would be to give the scientist as much money as he wants to do what research he wants. Some of it would be bound to pay off, intellectually or economically, or with luck both.' The most eloquent exponent of this view of science is the conservative philosopher Michael Polanyi.[1] Indeed we have heard this point of view endorsed by several scientists who regard themselves as politically of the left, and, in other spheres than their own, feel committed to an ideal of planning.

In truth, of course, even before the days of massive government intervention and science policy-planners, this argument was always somewhat specious. As with the argument about the internationalism of science we discussed in Chapter 9, it was a theory which at most applied to only a fraction of those actually performing science or technology. Industrial science, mission-oriented research or developmental or defence research, is and must always be, of its nature, fairly closely controlled and planned, and not by the scientist or technologist alone or even at all, but by the managerial structure of the industry, inevitably cost- and profit-conscious. Even in the world of the academic scientist 'free research' has traditionally been the perquisite of only a few. For a substantial portion of his working life, the academic scientist, at least in the European tradition, finds himself, first as a doctoral student, later as a post-doctoral fellow or junior researcher, working on aspects of projects planned and organized by others. In academic laboratories run in the Germanic tradition, of which there are many examples in Britain as well as on the Continent, this period of tutelage under the control of an autocratic head of department, may last well into middle life. Only for a comparatively few scientists, comparatively late in their careers, has the concept of academic freedom ever been anything more than an inspirational myth. As one Oxford academic acidulously remarked 'When I hear the word academic freedom mentioned, I know that someone's vested interest is being protected'. Nonetheless, just as we have seen with internationalism, it has been this important minority which has been the most articulate in propagating beliefs about 'the nature of science' to the public at large.

And even in the larger, societal sense, science has been subject to planning control for as long as it has existed, from the study by the Royal Society of projects suggested by their kingly patron onwards. Ever since research costs rose beyond the means of even wealthy individuals, and money has had to be found from outside the researcher's own income, a form of societal control over science has existed, in terms of whether or not such funds would be granted. The last few years have only confirmed that of all the patrons of science within the community that once existed, the state is by now far the most powerful. Those who attack the concept of planning in science now do so primarily because they resent, not the actual limitation on their freedom, which always existed, but the fact that it is now apparent. Perception alters consciousness.

Thus the question is – as probably it should always have been – not *should* science be controlled, but *how* can science be controlled or planned most effectively? For as far back in the development of science as we can see, and for as far into the future as we can project, there is an excess of scientific projects over those that can actually be supported. The limitations on their support are obvious: primarily money and manpower. Even with the maximum growth rate in scientific spending and the production of scientists themselves, such as the period of 1950 to 1965 which saw the most dramatic period of 'exponential growth' which we discussed in Chapter 1, too many research projects were always chasing too few funds.

We can give some evidence to support this from a study of the proportion of grant applications to funding bodies which has been rejected or reduced in any period, even though the index is not precise, for any scientist wise in the ways of the world may apply for funds to several agencies or inflate his application in the expectation that it will be cut down. Nonetheless, most agencies, at least in Britain and the U.S., seem to have funds to cover only some thirty to sixty per cent of the total grant applications made to them.*

In the past there has always been a surplus of projects over the funds available. In the future, as growth rates for funding of scientific projects are reduced for the reasons discussed in Chapter 1, the problem of choice becomes even more inevitable and acute. If we are to rely on positive, explicit planning for the establishment of research priorities rather than the implicit series of negative decisions, sometimes mistaken for academic freedom, then it becomes increasingly urgent to attempt to formulate some type of criteria by which we can decide how much to spend on what. The last decade of science policy has really been an attempt to grapple with some of these problems.

But the recognition and articulation of the issues is only a partial first step towards their resolution, and even the *de facto* solutions that have been arrived at, such as the U.S. siting of the high-energy

* At one point an interesting exception was the British Medical Research Council, which had claimed to have a near perfect record in allotting funds to 'worthwhile' projects, but here we may note at least two other factors intervening. One is that the structure of the M.R.C. is such that we may suspect that only those informally reasonably assured of obtaining a grant actually put in for one, and the second, the weight to be attached to the definition of 'worthwhile' in this context. But even the M.R.C. has now felt the pinch, and in recent years its proportion of successful applications has also dropped to within the 30–60 per cent range.

accelerator and the Anglo–French building of Concorde may be neither the right nor the best resolutions until we know more about the way they have emerged and the types of factor taken into consideration in reaching the conclusions. We have so far little evidence as to how such decisions are *actually* taken, though we are not lacking in exhortatory proposals as to how they *should* be. The crudest of these theoretical devices is undoubtedly that which seems to have obsessed British science policy-makers in recent years, that of merely projecting the growth curves of funding in particular scientific areas and trying desperately to slow them down.

We documented the growth of this numerology, given some type of scanty theoretical clothing by the naïve extension of the work of de Solla Price, in discussing the activities of the Council for Scientific Policy in Chapter 6. We showed it busy projecting trends of spending for the Research Councils over a five-year period, and deciding that they were unacceptably high since the resultant growth would consume an increasing proportion of an only sluggishly growing G.N.P., and holding therefore a 'series of informal full-day conferences' with representatives of the Research Councils as to how growth could be slowed. This approach essentially likens science to a sort of self-expanding balloon continuously increasing in size. The only question then becomes how fast to blow it up, which is dependent upon extraneous external factors which are assumed to impinge more or less uniformly on all sectors of science; more money for nuclear physics means the removal of a section of the science budget and hence less money for biology, for instance.

The Debate over Choice

But is this crude total planning, which may appear, in some sense, the antithesis of a really rational approach, the best that can be done? Attempts to reassert some of the traditional language of priorities in terms of the problems of planning for science have most recently been associated with the name of Dr Alvin Weinberg, a distinguished nuclear physicist and Director of the Oak Ridge National Laboratory in the U.S.[2] Weinberg eloquently restates some familiar dilemmas when he asks what criteria should be adopted for spending money on science.

Essentially, he argues, there are two types of criteria of choice to be applied, internal and external. Internal criteria are generated within the scientific field itself and answer the question: how well is the science done? External criteria are generated outside the scientific field and answer the question: why pursue this particular science?

Of the internal criteria, Weinberg goes on to argue, two can be easily identified: is the field ready for exploitation, and are the scientists working within it really competent? It is, or should be, the job of scientists working within or adjacent to the particular field, to answer both these questions, and this is usually the question asked by specialist grant-giving committees when grant applications are made – in Britain to the M.R.C. or S.R.C. or A.R.C., for example.

But the external criteria are of ultimate importance if we are not merely to assume that society *a priori* owes the scientist a living, and the three identified by Weinberg are technological merit, social merit and scientific merit. Thus if a given technological end is desirable (for example the development of organ transplants as a medical technique), the scientific research needed to achieve it should be supported (for example the biochemistry of the immune response which causes foreign tissues to be rejected by the body). Of course it is not necessarily the case that the basic research needed for a particular technological goal would spring from the explicit recognition of this goal. Much of the biochemical understanding of the processes of immunology has derived from the pursuit of basic molecular biology, such as the determination of protein structures, which was not initially undertaken with a specifically technological pay-off in view.

But, it seems incontrovertible, despite the reluctance of some scientists to accept the argument, that one is more likely to make a particular scientific breakthrough if one is trying to do so than if one simply hopes for a piece of 'research serendipity' – a bit of accidental good luck as a side-effect of some other activity. There is little evidence to support the argument that scientific advance proceeds by unguided chance. Indeed, the often quoted example of a chance discovery – that of the antibiotic effect of penicillin mould by Fleming – is in fact precisely the reverse. The whole of Fleming's research for twenty or so years before the day on which he left his window open and the appropriate penicillium spore floated on to his bacterial preparation, had been devoted to a long, frustrating and largely fruitless search for precisely such an antibiotic substance. The actual event was chance, but it was only Fleming's prior training and research motivation which made the chance event recognizable for what it really was, the clue to the break-through which would lead to the development of antibiotics.

In the context of this repudiation of the advantages of chance in research and the achievement of technological breakthroughs, it may be noted that it is precisely this argument of research serendipity, or, as it is more commonly known, 'spin-off', that has been used by the protagonists of defence research. They argue that spending a very large amount of money on the technological demands of new forms of defence, or rather of war, of weapons and of weapon technology, may lead to a civilian pay-off in terms of the development of potentially useful techniques, for either basic science or civilian technology. This argument has always seemed dubious. Certainly the space programme in America has produced the new material which has gone into the manufacture of ceramics (and for that matter contemporary brass) which have been of particular value in certain types of industrial process, whilst the fields of microcircuitry, solid state technology and the development of very small-scale and highly sophisticated electronic equipment have been much advanced by the needs for the development of such equipment for rocketry. Equally in its turn the Manhattan project produced spin-off in terms of the rapid development of sophisticated machine tools. It is possible for whole new branches of science to emerge in this way, such as operational research and its progeny, critical path analysis. However, it would seem likely that a direct investment in these fields would have produced the same results. But, more importantly, were these the techniques and advances that society needed in the first place? Would a socially conscious decision have been made for machine tools and microminiaturization, or, with spin-off, is there any real opportunity for decision? Instead, *because* something is technically possible it becomes inevitable. Indeed the examples chosen to justify spin-off are typically associated with war or quasi-war science and technology.

Thus it is reasonable to argue that one legitimate extrinsic criterion against which the value of a given piece of basic science could be set is the potential social and technological merit that might be expected to accrue from it. Notice that if it is this type of criterion that is adopted, one vexed problem, that of *how much* to spend on any given field of research, is offered a new and rather different solution. Instead of seeing all science as part of one large combined enterprise for which £X million are available to be split between, say, solid state physics, the chemistry of transition metals and molecular biology, an alternative would be to regard each basic science field as a research overhead on its own technology – solid state physics on electronics and biology on medical care. The merits and demerits of such an approach will not be argued now. This must wait until the final chapter of the book, but it is worth noting these possibilities here as one logical correlate of this alternative view of science policy-making.

There is a second implication to the suggestion that we take social and technological merit as a criterion for the funding of particular types of basic science. The problem here is really one of definition; that is, how do we decide which particular types of social and technological merit are the most meritorious? For instance, it might be decided that organ transplants were a technological good for which we should aim and that therefore immunology should be funded on a substantial scale. If organ transplants are to be judged as a justification for funding immunology, we must consider whether, of the amount of money to be spent on research into problems of health, organ transplants represent a useful and sensible application of research funds. For example, it is very reasonable to argue that more lives – and more valuable lives – could be saved by devoting the amount of money now spent on organ transplants and their related hospital developments, to a study of such problems in public health as that of the death rate of newborn infants in the Rhondda being three times that of infants in Dorking in Surrey.

If we take this type of criterion into consideration – and this is really judging social and technological merit on the broadest of all possible bases – the terms in which we view what science should be supported may be seen to be generalized out into a broad critique of the nature of the society in which we live and the nature of our objectives concerning society.

The Third Criterion

A third criterion, of the scientific merit of a particular field may be seen in some cases, quite distinct from any potential technological or social benefit which may accrue. Some fields of scientific research may seem so remote from any potential pay-off in the sense in which we have used the word, that the criterion may simply not be applicable. Partly this may be because of the deficiencies of our own imagination. It is true that the famous early twentieth-century mathematician, G. H. Hardy defended the pursuit of his mathematics on the grounds that it was of no conceivable practical use to anyone. Equally, the early nuclear physicists, Rutherford amongst them, regarded the potential practical application of their studies as a very remote possibility. Nearer to the present day, one has seen the study of the mode of action of the plant hormones, once regarded by their discoverer, A. W. Galston, as 'a reasonably harmless way to spend the time', turned into an instrument of the spreading of mass starvation in Vietnam, where they form the basis of the extensive defoliation and crop destruction campaign waged by the U.S. Air Force under the slogan 'Only We Can Prevent Forests'.[3]

Any type of assessment of science planning has got to recognize the force of the argument of the essential unpredictability of certain types of basic science and the need to accept that the intellectual conquest and ordering of nature seems to form an essential part of scientific endeavour for many of those who participate in it, technology and economics apart. To recognize that these forms of science may be justified in their own terms – at least to those who are the scientists themselves – is to accept this, yet it is partly to beg the question. A good – because large and expensive – example of this type of problem is that of the high-energy accelerators. High-energy particle physics, the study of the behaviour of the obscure, complex and currently ill-understood fundamental particles of matter, has become an almost occult science, its mysteries comprehended only by its practitioners, who demand ever-increasing sacrifices of men and of money. On what basis could £150 million for the new C.E.R.N. 300 GEV accelerator be justified? Almost certainly not in terms of potential economic pay-off in any sort of short-run, as its proponents, in the case we discuss below, recognize quite clearly. What can justify it (leaving aside the vested interests of those whose researching lives are bound up in particle physics) are the claims of knowledge for its own sake, that one side of man's humanity is bound up with a passionate attempt to expand those areas of his experience which can be formulated in laws expressable in the language of logic and mathematics. One must accept that this is part of what science is about. But in doing so, one is then seeking a different type of justification for supporting it from that chosen hitherto. After all many would argue that the enlarging of consciousness in music, visual arts and the written word, were equally part of what humanity is about, and deserve equal consideration in resource allocation. Indeed, in some ways, accelerators are the cathedrals of the modern age, magnificent collective sacrifices to an extravagant and unapproachable ideal. Yet to argue that the medievals should not have built their cathedrals is to place oneself on dangerous grounds, and to argue for Weston and Serpukhov, but not C.E.R.N., is like claiming Chartres and King's College Chapel, but not Notre Dame.

Thus the path of the scientific planner is beset, even in theory, with thorny problems. Even the most assiduous reading of the theoretical literature from Weinberg on may prove of little help when the need to actually decide occurs, as Professor Michael Swann, Principal of Edinburgh University and member of the Council for Scientific Policy, has wittily if somewhat ruefully admitted in his opening address to a conference on science policy.[4] The study of scientific policy needs to develop both in the direction of a theory of rational scientific choice and the systematic empirical study of actual decisions in the field of scientific policy. Thus to complement these theoretical discussions, the next chapter examines in some detail the actual emergence of some specific decisions which have set problems in British and international science policy-making over recent years. The rejection of the World Health Organization Research Centre and the case for the C.E.R.N. 300 GEV accelerator were both at the focal point of local, national and international pressures. Both have had powerful scientific voices raised in their favour and against them. Each shows something of the complexities of the issues involved.

CHAPTER TWELVE

Decisions: Megamouse and C.E.R.N.

'*Operation Megamouse*'*

The proposal of the World Health Organization (W.H.O.) to establish an international research centre in Edinburgh combined the criteria of intrinsic scientific interest, welfare, national prestige, with manpower problems and committee politics. This proposal, dubbed by its critics 'Operation Megamouse', was to cover three major and closely-related fields of epidemiology, communication sciences and basic biomedical research related to problems of toxicity. It was finally defeated at the Eighteenth World Health Assembly meeting in Geneva in 1965 after a debate which lasted four years, although a modified version of the rejected scheme was eventually established – namely a small research unit within W.H.O. to work on epidemiology and communications.

In 1961, Dr Martin Kaplan, an American veterinarian and public health expert serving as a research adviser to the office of the World Health Director-General, privately set out the case for an international medical research centre at the Seventh Pugwash Conference in Vermont. In 1963, the proposal was taken up officially by the Director-General of the organization in his report to the Sixteenth Assembly gathered in Geneva. The Director-General, Dr Marcolina Candau, argued that for the W.H.O. to fulfil the intentions of the Eleventh Assembly, which had recognized the growing role of research in problems of world health, it was neces-

* A version of this section was originally published in the journal *Minerva* in 1967.[1]

sary to do 'more than co-ordinate and stimulate'; it was necessary, he said, 'to initiate an international approach to the mathematical analysis of disease'. It is important at this stage to recognize the nature of the departure which this approach meant from traditional W.H.O. activities, which had hitherto been characterized by practical intervention in problems such as malaria or tuberculosis, but by conducting only a very limited amount of research. Thus, where in the past the organization had sought to promote medical research relevant to issues of world health by convening conferences and coordinating research work done in different member-countries, the changes Dr Candau proposed involved the conduct of research by the W.H.O. itself.

By the time the Seventeenth Assembly was held, Dr Candau was in a position to place the first draft before the executive board. The board transmitted the proposal, together with a record of their discussion, to the full assembly meeting in May 1964. After very considerable discussion, the assembly decided both to seek more information (chiefly on the budgetary side) and also to sound out the opinions of members and associate members. Dr Candau rapidly established specialist committees of scientists to make the scientific arguments and at the same time his own office prepared a more fully worked-out statement of the financial and organizational aspects of the proposal. However, despite this revision of the proposal, the Eighteenth Assembly in 1965 decisively rejected the international research centre as an autonomous but integral agency of W.H.O., thus concluding its public history in this form.

The Origins of Resistance – With the wisdom of hindsight, it is possible to discern the earliest resistances to the proposal. Even at the Sixteenth Assembly, the retiring Russian chairman, Kuraşov, hinted at new trends with some disapproval:

> the Organization is moving away from its basic function – the co-ordination and planning of international health work – and is transforming itself into an organ for the provision of technical, operational and material assistance.

More revealingly, he added:

> analysis of the figures shows that the annual increase of the W.H.O. budget exceeds the rate of growth in national income of a number of countries. This [he went on], would lead to contradictions between planned resources and activities.[2]

The original proposal laid before the Seventeenth Assembly was certainly ambitious; it envisaged a capital expenditure of some $43 million on laboratories and equipment and annual running costs of $26 million, making a cumulative total of the order of $300 million over ten years. This, as the Hungarians pointed out, would be the equivalent of the full W.H.O. budget for one year. When the proposal was first put forward, there was a quite widespread sentiment in favour of the internationalization of medical research. President Kennedy, in his address to the United Nations General Assembly, a month prior to his assassination, proposed 'a world centre for health and communications under W.H.O.'. Such a centre could 'warn of epidemics, adverse reactions to drugs and . . . transmit results of experimental discoveries'. He envisaged that an international centre would contribute positively to the reduction of the brain drain, which was already regarded as an acute problem for the underdeveloped countries and for Western Europe. Dr Jerome Wiesner, the President's scientific adviser, was also known to support these views.

This internationalist mood had already benefited the French-inspired Cancer Agency, but whereas the centre had been primarily the brain-child of scientists, the Cancer Agency's parentage was very largely political. President de Gaulle had accepted a suggestion by French scientists to reallocate, or at least match, 0·5 per cent of the defence budget to medical research, and transformed it into a specific proposal for a Cancer Agency. Interestingly, the agency received little support from the scientific community despite its easy passage through the World Health Assembly. The scepticism with which many scientists view the probable results of direct cancer research almost certainly provides the explanation for this reluctance. In contrast the Assembly delegates, as politicians or career health administrators, supported by public concern about the threat of cancer, welcomed the proposal unreservedly, and the richer industrial countries underwrote the scheme.

Yet this does not explain the unenthusiastic reception of the research centre scheme at the Seventeenth Assembly compared with the warmth of the reception accorded to the Cancer Agency. The Australian delegate cast doubts on the centre's financial feasibility. The Indian delegate was anxious lest India should lose its best men to the centre. Holland, with many others, accepted the case for international research into epidemiology and communications sciences but looked askance at the biomedical programme. Turkey felt that the support of individuals was more rewarding than building centres. Russia argued that the relationship of the centre to national institutes was not adequately thought out and Hungary expressed some fear about the effect of an international bureaucracy on the spirit of research. Britain saw the centre as having a 'sterilizing rather than fertilizing effect'. To some extent the Czechs, the Norwegians and, more surprisingly, the French, shared Dr Candau's vision. However, it was clear that there was not much agreement with his:

conviction that the creation of the proposed centre is a logical and unavoidable step in the evolution of W.H.O., and would . . . be hailed by the scientific world as one of the most notable events in the history of international public health.[3]

The Scientific Proposals – Between the two critical assemblies, the scientific case was considered by three specialist committees of scientists; each committee consisted of distinguished scientists, with a common secretariat. The preponderance of American advisers – seventeen including Kaplan – suggests that, at least when the proposal was first mooted during the Kennedy administration, there seemed a very real chance of American support. The next largest group were the British with seven scientists, with most other European countries contributing one or two. Dr Adeniyi-Jones of the Public Health Department in Lagos was the sole representative of science drawn from a developing country. To question this does not mean that one wants an automatic 'one country, one scientist' committee, but it does show the difficulty of securing the effective cooperation of scientists drawn from low-income countries with those from the rich countries.

In its final form, the proposal advocated an autonomous centre, its terms of reference to include epidemiology, communication sciences and biomedical research.*

* Each section would be required (*a*) to do research, (*b*) to serve as an information exchange and (*c*) to provide training for young research workers. The report of the advisers on the communication sciences emphasized the need for the development of mathematical techniques in health and biological research; a fundamental research role in this field, as well as into the more mundane problems of information-processing, was envisaged. Such functions would require a large staff of senior communication scientists and substantial computer facilities. Similarly, in the field of biomedical research, the case for the

While the explicit case made by the scientific committees for the research they proposed was ostensibly based on criteria of social need, it is difficult to escape the conclusion that what they finally recommended was a comprehensive list of research projects which covered most aspects of the currently existing interests in biological research. Thus the committee on the biomedical research section recommended projects which covered mammalian pathology, physiology, pharmacology and toxicology, mammalian and non-mammalian genetics, cell biology, immunology, biochemistry, synthetic organic chemistry and biophysics. Each of these was again sub-divided into several fields, and the separate field in turn would clearly demand several post-doctoral research workers. Few universities anywhere in the world can have life science departments which cover so broad a range, and the direct relevance of several of the research topics (such as, say, enzymology and nucleic acid studies) to the ostensibly mission-oriented function of the centre might well be questioned. In fact, the content of the scientific committee's proposals, which might have been a point of vulnerability, was little discussed in the World Health Assembly debate which finally rejected the centre.

The Organizational Proposals – Organizationally the centre was to be modelled on C.E.R.N. and on the U.S. National Institutes of Health (N.I.H.) and the British National Institute for Medical Research (N.I.M.R.). The centre was to have a core of 400 permanent scientists recruited for their specialist skills. These would in due course be joined by up to 150 visiting fellows, drawn from all parts of the world. These fellows would subsequently return to their home laboratories, carrying their enhanced skills with them. It is not clear from the official W.H.O. documents how these figures were arrived at, though it may be noted that, in a letter to the *New Scientist* defending the proposals, Kaplan drew an analogy with C.E.R.N., which is approximately the same size.

---

centre was made on the basis of the need for international criteria in evaluating therapeutic agents and environmental contaminants, and demanded the development of methods for screening and toxicity studies. Yet the disciplines required and research topics suggested indicated a considerable effort in pure biology, including biochemistry, genetics, gerontology, immunology, cell biology, neurobiology and biophysics: half the scientific staff of 400 would be engaged on biomedical research.

Administration was designed to keep the centre free from political pressures, to which international agencies have been notoriously vulnerable, although, in fact, as finance for the centre (had it been accepted) would probably have been raised on a voluntary basis, the possibility of subsequent pressures being brought to bear when the budget came to be renewed, could not, of course, be ruled out. Direction was to be in the hands of a distinguished scientist working in conjunction with an advisory scientific committee and the Director-General of W.H.O.

The operational costs for the centre were estimated at some $140 million after the first ten years.*

International Reaction at the Eighteenth Assembly – Once the full proposal was presented, national positions were explicitly assumed. Of the thirty-eight representatives who spoke, only twelve were clear supporters of the scheme. It is perhaps worth emphasizing at this point the character of delegates to the assembly; for the most part the chief delegates are political – ministers or deputy ministers of health – with experts drawn from their ministries as reinforcing members of the delegation. While this pattern holds reasonably well for most of the low-income countries, and almost all the Communist countries, the rich countries tend to be led by career health administrators like Sir George Godber for the United Kingdom or Dr L. Terry, the United States Surgeon General.

The most noticeable division was, as the press was quick to observe, between the rich and poor. Thus Gerald Leach, then science correspondent of the *New Statesman* commented: 'The big boys, the U.S., the U.S.S.R., and Britain, did not like it.' Of all the

* This figure corresponds approximately with the rule of thumb currently used by grant-giving bodies – which estimate an approximate cost of $20,000 per annum per qualified biological research worker – if a total scientific staff of 550 is assumed for the centre. On the other hand, the estimated capital expenditure, exclusive of land or buildings, which it was assumed the host country would provide, seemed high at $144 million, even granted the substantial computer facilities demanded. Three ways of raising the money were considered. The first was the regular budget of W.H.O. The second would also draw on the regular budget but with credits given to low-income member-countries who would find increased financial commitment to W.H.O. intolerable. The third envisaged a voluntary plan like the Cancer Agency but with scaled payments, whereby volunteer countries would agree to underwrite the centre, while control, and therefore international accessibility, would remain in the hands of W.H.O.

countries paying more than one per cent to W.H.O., in the final analysis only Italy deviated and supported the centre. The other, and highly articulate deviant was Norway, with a high *per capita* income but a small population, and therefore with a small total contribution. (There was no common Scandinavian attitude, for Finland supported Norway, while Denmark and Sweden both voted against the proposal.)

Why these deviations? The case of Italy might be explained by the fact that while the north of Italy is rich, the south has sufficient similarities in income and life pattern to many of the less developed countries to ensure a sharpened understanding of the problems with which the centre was to have dealt. International schemes of the type earlier sponsored by W.H.O. (such as anti-malarial campaigns) are said to have played a large part in the economic revival of Italy since the war, and there is also a tradition of international research centres within the country (such as, for example, the Stazione Zoologica at Naples). No such explanation applies, however, to Norway and Finland.

The views of the Big Five mattered decisively, as together they contributed some sixty-four per cent of the total budget, West Germany, France, and the United Kingdom paying between them eighteen per cent, the Soviet Union some fifteen per cent and the United States over thirty-one per cent. The five unanimously rejected the scheme. Yet where the French-inspired Cancer Agency was concerned, except for the Soviet Union, which withdrew, the roles were reversed. The remaining Big Four, joined by Italy, underwrote the cancer scheme with a flat payment of $150,000 each. Perhaps not surprisingly, hostile critics at W.H.O. described the cancer scheme as a rich countries' club. Thus the research centre was killed by the virtually unanimous vote of the rich nations.

Although it is not certain, most of the press comment at the time attributed the major opposition to the proposal to Britain, since Britain was the first of the Big Five to take a decisive stand and was thus the most involved of any country in the debate. This view was reinforced by the widely-held belief that the proponents of the centre had chosen Edinburgh as the most acceptable site for the new laboratories. For example, *Medical News* reported: 'Speaking privately in the corridors at Geneva some supporters of the W.H.O. centre idea blamed Britain's representative Sir George Godber', and the *New York Herald Tribune* claimed that Britain led the opposition to the proposal. Although the location of the site was never formally discussed at the assembly meetings, it was known that Edinburgh was favoured as an internationally esteemed centre for medical research (Edinburgh had also established links with the medical problems of developing countries through its association with Baroda Medical School in India). Local councils in the Edinburgh vicinity were already vying with one another in the offer of land and facilities for the centre. For a country steadily losing population in search of better employment opportunities, the possibility of attracting a major research institute had clear socio-economic advantages. Four local authorities bordering Edinburgh openly discussed these possibilities and made immediate offers of sites for the centre. At the national level of politics, the Scottish M.P.s – robustly supported by Lord Ritchie Calder – were similarly concerned to press the specific claims of Scotland within the more general scientific and welfare criteria.

For these reasons, and also because the arguments advanced against the centre by the United States, Soviet Union, Germany and France were essentially variants upon the British theme, we have concentrated here upon the case against the centre made by the British representative. This was presented to the assembly in an important speech made by Sir George Godber of the Ministry of Health. In May 1965, Sir George affirmed the position he had already outlined the previous year. Providing the work was conducted on a 'reasonable scale' and at Geneva, developments in communications sciences and epidemiology (without computers) were welcome. This limited scale suggested a new emphasis on these two new and admittedly vital areas, in much the same way as medical education or maternal deprivation had in their turn been the objects of W.H.O. attention, but it did not indicate support for the new research role of W.H.O. which Dr Candau was espousing. An autonomous biomedical research laboratory was, however, unwelcome. As Sir George made clear, the senior scientists consulted by the British government had 'unequivocally' rejected the scheme, mainly on the grounds of its 'sterilizing effect' and because it was considered inappropriate to the work of W.H.O. By 'sterilization', he meant the shift of research workers from a university environment, where their presence ensured their involvement in undergraduate and graduate teaching, to a purely 'research' institute, where teaching was non-existent or at best minimal.

Sterilization implied not so much the sterility of the research which would be carried on by the workers at the institute, but the fact that they would no longer be available to 'fertilize' the minds of new generations of graduates. Thus, in the British case, it was the internal distribution of scientific research between universities and a non-academic research institution which was emphasized.

International Cooperation versus National Scientific Interest – The framework within which British decisions about centralized research institutions were to be made had been clearly indicated by the Advisory Council for Scientific Policy (A.C.S.P.) in its 1961–2 report with reference to the possibility of joining a N.A.T.O. science and technology institute.[4] The A.C.S.P. distinguished between institutions such as C.E.R.N., which were essentially internationally shared machinery (a point Sir George Godber reiterated at the W.H.O. assembly), and a thoroughly centralized research institute. The compromise policy suggested by the A.C.S.P. was rather like that followed by the American National Science Foundation of investing in centres where promising sectors of research work are being cultivated and then expanding the level of the whole to a 'centre of excellence'. The A.C.S.P. suggested following a similar pattern but scanning the whole of Europe for potential growth points. From this standpoint the A.C.S.P. might well have argued in favour of the centre, particularly at Edinburgh with its recently revamped medical courses and its vigorous interest in epidemiology. On the other hand, the A.C.S.P. report stressed, in the light of the experience of C.E.R.N., that 'proper use of . . . advanced apparatus . . . is not possible by member countries without a substantial measure of activity within the countries themselves'.

This argument concerning the need to develop adequate research institutions within each of the member-countries – particularly in low-income countries – in order to regain their research fellows who would be released to the centre, was never adequately met by the proponents of the scheme. The chief criterion was, however, set out unequivocally:

> Any proposal for an expensive scientific scheme – on an international basis – must . . . raise the question whether from our *national standpoint* the enterprise is worth the cost involved for a heavy contributor (our italics).

The committee added:

domestic scientific efforts may have to be limited if costly centralized international scientific projects are maintained. Considerations such as these, rather than political considerations of aid to smaller countries must be decisive.

Despite the emphatic formulation of this policy, the distinction between national interests and political considerations of foreign aid is perhaps more obscure than the scientists who made it might have imagined and leads to a number of paradoxes.

When the views of the A.C.S.P. and the Medical Research Council (M.R.C.) were sought by the British government on the specific issue of the World Health Research Centre, they expressed a common attitude that, in view of the shortage of teaching biologists and the accelerating demands of the 'biological revolution', Britain could ill afford to spare any research workers for the centre. Biology in Britain, as they saw it, was still starved of manpower. International centres, except where the cost of equipment was prohibitive for a single country, were unenthusiastically regarded, because of their sterilizing effect. National effort and improved international coordination, it was contended, would solve the problem more effectively. For the M.R.C., the practice of taking money to research rather than attracting research workers to equipment was also important, since it had paid off handsomely in the case of such men as the Nobel prize-winners Perutz, Sanger, Crick, Watson and Wilkins, who have worked at the Medical Research Council's molecular biology units.

How valid were the arguments advanced by the M.R.C. and the A.C.S.P. through Sir George Godber? There are three aspects of the case against the centre which merit particular examination, though it should be noted that no aspect was adequately considered, let alone met, by the centre's proponents. Each of these aspects is well illustrated by what we have termed 'the British paradoxes'. The case against the centre was made in arguments presented primarily in terms of the British national interest. Thus one must comment on the paradox that, despite the rejection of the centre by the Advisory Council, at least seven of the thirty-two eminent scientists consulted about the centre by W.H.O. itself were British. These scientists were presumably included in Sir George's dismissal of advocates of the centre, along with other scientific dissenters, as 'not representative', without stating whether they were not representative of biological research or of the national interest. The presence of so many British scientists on the World Health specialist committees suggests that the British criterion of 'national interest' was sufficiently ambiguous in its failure to disentangle and specify the political, economic, military and prestige components, to confuse the scientists themselves as to their role, thus generating divergent views as to the best course of action. To some extent the explanation lies in the different patterns of recruitment to service on governmental and non-governmental committees; there does not seem to be a different kind of scientist on each. Instead, the institutional setting affects the views of the scientist. Thus while Sir George Godber claimed quite properly that both the A.C.S.P. and M.R.C. were 'independent bodies ... and in no way subject in their views to government policy', this formal statement tended to minimize the institutional pressures on the establishment scientists. Consequently, although other important arguments existed both for and against the centre, the overriding and ambiguous criterion of national interest was central to the final negative decision. As the late Dr Robert Grant concluded in a general discussion of international biological research:

> The world's biomedical scientists appear to be much more internationalist in attitude than are the governmental agencies which support them.[5]

The second paradoxical argument employed against the centre stressed the danger of research isolated from the teaching function of the university, as well as the concomitant 'sterilizing effect' of bringing together large numbers of research workers. These organizational arguments are scarcely convincing: for example, the first argument concerning the creative unity of research and teaching is of interest in the light of the physical separation of the M.R.C.'s own main institutes from universities, and the formal limitations on teaching time for members of those research units attached to universities. To date, the separation of research from teaching seems to have been very successful scientifically – at least if the number of Nobel prizes won by such research workers is evidence of scientific success.

This anxiety over sterility never seems to have been shared by the international scientific community. Since the war there has been, as we have seen in the previous chapters, a continuous history of international schemes put forward by the scientists themselves, from the French proposal in 1946 for an international laboratory to the attempt of the European Molecular Biology Organization to establish an institute in 1964. Only the increase in national wealth, and therefore the national acquisition of the facilities urged by scientists, curbs their internationalism, which, to a substantial extent, represents the seeking of facilities otherwise prohibitively expensive. In many ways, the logic of the biological revolution, with its increasing similarity to the physical sciences (which the A.C.S.P. incidentally noted), suggests a matching need for the social organization appropriate to 'big science'.

In any event, the prospect of Edinburgh as the probable site of the centre would have made cooperation feasible at both undergraduate and post-graduate levels. This possibility, combined with the educational role of the short-term fellowships, should have reduced the force of the argument that education and research should be combined – at least so far as Britain was concerned. For the developing countries the case might well hold, for the long distance which would exist between the educational processes of developing countries and the centre would probably ensure that only a few scientists from any one country would be accepted, and the fact that they could expect poorer equipment and resources on their return home might well result in the centre becoming a stimulant to emigration. The location of an international research centre in a rich country may well exacerbate the problem of the brain drain by acting as a magnet to scientists from low-income countries.

The two economic arguments employed against the centre concerned facilities and manpower. It was asserted that the facilities required currently for biological research were not yet beyond the economic resources of those countries with sufficient research capability. Yet this position disregarded the welfare aims of the project, which would have involved a redistribution of research skill between a number of potential biomedical research fields; thus, while research expenditure on health is substantial in industrialized societies, it is primarily concerned with the degenerative diseases characteristic of advanced societies such as cancer and heart diseases. Relatively little money is allocated to the study of communicable diseases either by the advanced or by the developing countries themselves. The possibility that research on these subjects undertaken in the rich countries will benefit underdeveloped countries is thus slight, while the likelihood of the poor countries developing health services from which research would 'spring' (as argued by Sir George Godber) seems remote when the short supply of qualified personnel in these countries is considered. Sir George's view that the building of the health services requires first priority implicitly recognizes the patient acceptance of a long wait for the growth of indigenous research. In contrast with this attitude, scientists who were more committed to a belief in the dynamic power of knowledge and new technology were apparently prepared to attempt the redistribution of research. Yet it must be pointed out that if welfare aims were preponderant among the scientists who supported the proposal for the centre, the intention to locate it in Edinburgh, far from the places where the knowledge was to be applied, seems rather inconsistent.

The other argument focused on the implications of an internal brain drain from other British institutions to the centre. Certainly in the short run, scientists and technicians would leave their jobs, not only because of the facilities, but also because the centre as a United Nations agency would follow the current standard of international organizations in its salary scales, thus creating a little America in Britain. At present, there is already a great demand for biomedical research workers and any new point of demand would increase the strain on existing institutions. This problem was inadequately considered by the centre's advocates and even the proposed scheme of revolving fellowships passed over the difficulty of actually getting the research worker back to his own country. Biological research, unlike high-energy physics, cannot yet compress experimental work into a few weeks in a year, thus allowing the scientist to return to his home institution for the remainder of the year to analyse his results and to teach.

Conclusions – This case study underscores the extraordinary complexity of scientific choice. Even the data which we have adduced here from published records only shows how much more intricate the real issues were in contrast with the original arguments of those who proposed and rejected the centre. The arguments of its advocates, largely made in terms of welfare, turn out to have done much less than justice to the variables which would have had to be considered in a rational choice; they failed to follow up the ramifications of the distinction between basic and mission-oriented research; they failed, too, to grasp some of the very real political nettles involved in the establishment of a centre aimed at aiding developing countries, when it is conceived, planned and argued for by scientists from advanced ones. It may well be that advocates of the centre took for granted a natural harmony of intrinsic and extrinsic criteria. Similarly, the case against the centre involved a very complicated set of considerations. Rejection of the scheme as it stood simply cannot be dismissed, as it was by some sections of the press, as an expression of the attitude of rich countries towards poor ones. Still, the language of the British government's advisers does suggest that they questioned the value of the welfare aims of the centre, and not merely that they did not accept particular arguments for the centre in the proposed form, but rather that their general evaluation accorded a low priority to the welfare criterion. Thus while there remain substantial doubts as to whether the centre was in fact the best way of achieving these welfare ends, the lack of discussion of alternative means indicates that the ends themselves were less than wholly acceptable.

But it is the postscript to the main history which makes the point abundantly clear. Thus the compromise solution which ultimately was accepted, namely to set up a small research organization (forty scientists), within W.H.O. itself at Geneva, to work on problems of epidemiology and communications, could in fact, be exposed to most of the criticism levelled against the original autonomous teaching centre; the split between teaching and research, the base in a rich country, the shortage of researchers etc., plus the major additional criticism that the new scheme seriously risks becoming a service department for the large bureaucracy in which it has been located. It is possible to argue that the research division reflects a foot in the door for the extension of W.H.O.'s researching role, and, while this may be true, a healthy scepticism suggests rather that this small research division is a token rather than an effective response towards the redistribution of biomedical knowledge between the rich countries and the third world. Tokenism is, after all, a central characteristic of most attempts to aid the third world; thus until recently a substantial proportion of current aid has been consumed by interest payments on past loans.

Progress in the Formulation of Basic Science Policy – the C.E.R.N. Decision

Having criticized the concealed or even absent rationale which lay behind the British decision against the autonomous W.H.O. research centre, it is illuminating to turn to a case of another international research centre, that of the C.E.R.N. 300 GEV accelerator. The proposal was that, to follow the successful C.E.R.N. 28 GEV high-energy accelerator, the time was now ripe for building a much larger machine on a similar internationally shared basis. For our purpose, what is relevant is not so much the intrinsic interests of the physicists in furthering the fundamental knowledge of sub-nuclear particles, nor of the extremely expensive machine which they were arguing for, but the way in which the arguments were put for and against the machine. Insofar as these were explicit and not implicit, and the arithmetic of money was publicly displayed, then the joint reports published in January 1968 from the two committees, one set up by the Council for Scientific Policy and one by the Science Research Council, form a substantial improvement on the machinery for decision-making operating in the case of the W.H.O. centre.[6]

The committees themselves were both predominantly manned by physicists, and it is notable that the two dissenters from the majority report were chemists. But it was also true that, for the first time, economists were also on the committees invited to comment on the economic implications of the C.E.R.N. project for Britain. Thus socio-economic implications were not disguised under the scientists' all-purpose criterion of 'national interest' displayed so extensively in killing the biomedical research centre. This time the committees set themselves to establish the intrinsic argument for a new machine, noting the extent to which high-energy accelerators were already distributed within Europe, in some twelve locations with a total of some 35 GEV between them plus C.E.R.N.'s own 28 GEV. They were frank in maintaining that the foreseeable pay-off from such work was predominantly scientific and offered no straightforward applications such as could be derived from a nuclear reactor programme. But it is the discussion of resource allocation which is of greatest interest. Thus the total cost of the machine over the ten years was estimated in December 1967 as £150 million, a figure incidentally almost identical with that of the cost of the biomedical research centre. Almost a quarter of the total cost would be borne by the U.K. which, with devaluation, would be of the order of £40 million. As £40 million is, by anyone's money, substantial, the physicists were concerned to argue why it should be spent. This was mainly in terms of maintaining the research area. Thus if the accelerator was not built, it would mean effectively opting out of high-energy physics and concentrating on the cheaper solid state physics. The argument made against this contracting out of high-energy physics alone was that it was less easy to achieve in practice than might appear in theory, for nuclear science was all of a piece and did not neatly sub-divide. Contraction would certainly mean, as in the pre-C.E.R.N. period, that European physicists would have to emigrate in search of the facilities that Europe could no longer provide.

But the physicists were also uncomfortably aware that Big Science tends, even while it is being built, to get bigger. Thus the original C.E.R.N. was initially planned with a 10 GEV machine and had an annual running commitment of £200,000 for the U.K. In fact, it became a 28 GEV machine with an annual U.K. commitment of £1 million. The Daresbury machine was estimated to cost £3·1 million and, in fact, looks like costing £4·4 million. Nimrod at the Rutherford laboratory was estimated at costing £6·9 million and will probably cost £10·5 million. The Committee were careful to point out that these increases were not only caused by inflations in cost, but were also for better facilities, such as bubble chambers at C.E.R.N. Equally, it did not matter if in fact the machine fell short of a 300 GEV capacity since the building to rigorous performance specifications such as was essential to, say, hydro-electric schemes or reactor plants, was not involved. The conclusions were that the project should be supported and that, so long as costs could be held within the estimate, Britain could and should go ahead. The physicists thought that expenditure could be constrained within the nuclear physics budget, currently rising at seven per cent per year, assuming that this increase continued for the next decade, and that therefore the project would not deprive the rest of science of funds as long as they rose during the same period at about nine per cent per annum.

It is easy to cast doubt on the physicists' hopes that the cost of the 300 GEV machine could be contained within the original budget. In the report itself, Sir Ronald Nyholm and Sir Ewart Jones – both chemists – drew attention to the point that support for the machine would imply that forty per cent of the S.R.C. funds would be allocated to a branch of science which would involve two or three hundred scientists only, while the rest of science was slowed down. Lord Willis Jackson (an engineer) was also cautious as to whether the original costing estimates could, in fact, be kept. It is also easy to see that the physicists' arguments are cyclical; that we do high-energy physics in order to train high-energy physicists to do high-energy physics, and that we must have, and go on having, the machines. There is, on the basis of similar projects, a serious likelihood that the U.K. financial commitment could, if it were initiated, be willy-nilly doubled during the ten years of building, as the 300 GEV became a 400, or even a 500, machine and scientific Parkinsonism sets in. It is also clear that the general law of diminishing returns begins to operate in physics, and that one could get more knowledge in biology for less money and with an almost certain faster pay-off in medicine. And it is difficult, as accelerator sites are technically rather than politically defined, to see how, even within Britain, any useful side-effect of the relocation of industry in priority areas might be attained, since only one British site for the accelerator, Mundford in Norfolk, was considered eligible, and now that too has been ruled out.

But while it is easy to be sceptical of the proposal, it is more important that the bases of scepticism are to be found within the reports themselves. While it is patently unreasonable to expect physicists themselves to argue that the pursuit of physics is other than beneficial, even if they rest their case chiefly on the claims of knowledge for its own sake, the very real improvement over and above the previous published working reports of committees faced with similar problems is that the facts and argument chiefly concerned with the proposal are within the report, and it is therefore possible for the final decision, which is ultimately a political one, to be made responsibly.

Although the British decision finally went against the physicists when Professor Brian Flowers, Chairman of the S.R.C., announced at the C.E.R.N. meeting in April 1968 that the U.K. was not prepared to support the accelerator, the scientific community, and chiefly the physicists themselves in their report, have created the base of this more responsible policy.[7] Yet it is not entirely clear that *because* the base has been formulated the decisions are necessarily derived from the base. The government's readiness *not* to support W.H.O., which had relatively good extrinsic criteria, or the 300 GEV machine which had virtually none, suggests that there may be a merely generalized governmental desire to cut back science spending which will use any justification offered to it. An echo of the Bowden science argument which we quoted in Chapter 5 is heard, that just because the growth rate of science is very rapid it *must* therefore be coming to the saturation point and, precisely because of this, *now* is the time to cut back.

Yet even in its rejection, the government was sensitive to the fact that it could not now proceed on the closed, ingrown and implicit negativism which had ultimately characterized its rejection of the W.H.O. centre. The physicists had made openly known their disapproval of the final 'no'; publicly described, for instance, by *Nature*, as 'shabby'. Even Brian Flowers, in announcing the British rejection at C.E.R.N., had made it clear that he personally dis-associated himself from it. It became known that the physicists had offered to sacrifice virtually all the growth of the indigenous British high-energy physics laboratories, whose costs were scheduled to rise to about £12 million a year in the mid 1970s, if it would help save the big machine. Flowers told the C.E.R.N. council that:

> we were prepared . . . actually to reduce the size of the British nuclear physics community . . . this would have led automatically to a position in which one or other of our accelerators would have to be closed down before the end of its scientifically useful life . . . this project [the 300 machine] was our top priority . . . it will remain the policy of British nuclear physicists to continue to press our government to enter the project if, as I hope, it proceeds. . . . Finally, may I say that although this has been entirely a personal statement, it was shown to the members of the S.R.C., of which I am chairman, at their meeting yesterday. Between them they represent a broad section of science and technology. They wished to place on record, and they wished me to say so here, that my statement has their unanimous support, in every detail.[7]

Similar statements of disapproval were made by several leading physicists and published in *Nature*.[8] Admittedly, many of the statements sounded like special pleading; the possibility that the chosen site might have been at Mundford was restated by Professor Butler, for example, although it had been known for some time that the expert site committee had itself ruled out Mundford. Similarly, Professor Bishop was of the opinion that

> it could well be that future historians will single out such decisions as the markers of a new era of mental stagnation, the Dark Ages of the 20th and 21st centuries. What is threatened with extinction when the needs of pure science are lost sight of is the continuance of a human adventure in thought . . . the substance on which technology draws its inspiration for development is the body of knowledge constituted and enlarged by activity in pure science. Stop that enlargement, and technology will ultimately stagnate . . .

Sir Bernard Lovell uttered his, now customary, dark warnings that even with the big machine the projected growth rate in the science budget was 'at the lower limit of what must be regarded as an absolute minimum for the successful continuation of scientific research in the U.K.'.

So intense was this feeling that the government responded by sending the Secretary of State for Education and Science, Mr Edward Short, to a special meeting of the C.S.P. in July 1968, to explain the negative decision. The text of his statement was published. Mr Short argued that the main ground for the government's withdrawal was expense and the probability of escalation. There was no short- or medium-term hope of economic pay-off, nor a recruitment of researchers from high-energy physics into industry. Closing the Rutherford and Daresbury laboratories, as suggested by the S.R.C., would still not provide adequate facilities for British physicists, as the big machine would not be sited in Britain. This decision

> in no way altered the understanding that the government did not interfere in the exercise of the Research Council's own judgement on the allocation of resources allocated to them. This was their responsibility, and he had no intention of questioning their scientific judgement.[9]

Thus it would seem that, even in the rejection itself, a significant step forward had been achieved in openness of policy-making, with both the politicians' reasons for rejection and the scientists' arguments in favour being made public. This remains the case whether or not in the long run the decision proves to have been the correct one, and whatever the validity of the arguments marshalled on either side. The possibility that these arguments may have warranted more careful examination is indicated by an ironic postscript to the rejection which appeared within a few weeks of the final decision in the form of a detailed report by the U.S. High Energy Physics Advisory Panel of the Atomic Energy Commission.[10]

Entitled 'The Status and Problems of High Energy Physics Today', it was the result of a year's study by the panel of the current problems. In many respects it makes an interesting parallel to the British report on the 300 machine, setting out the case for the continuance of investment in high-energy physics at a time of contracting research budgets, due in part to the exigencies of the Vietnam war.

> It is no coincidence [the report says], that the greatest advances in man's knowledge of the basic nature of matter have always been made in the countries which were also the leaders economically and industrially . . . (i.e.) the United States in the last forty years. There is a causal relationship in either direction . . .

Yet, the panel felt that the U.S. lead in high-energy physics had now been placed sharply in jeopardy. C.E.R.N. and Serpukhov were way ahead, whilst U.S. funds for the continuation of research were in danger. In real terms, West European spending on research had surpassed that of the U.S.A. in 1968 and in the years ahead was expected to pull sharply ahead, whilst U.S. expenditure would level off or even fall. Contractors' dates on the 200 GEV machine at Weston had begun to slip behind as financial restrictions delayed critical ordering decisions and the panel drew up a gloomy balance sheet of the missed opportunities the delays had already cost – only three out of eighteen outstanding research proposals accepted, a three-year backlog of research demands at Brookhaven, etc. If West Europe went ahead with the C.E.R.N. machine while Weston was delayed, the result would be:

> an ominous step towards the situation in which the U.S. found itself before the 1930s, when most of the major discoveries in fundamental science were made in Europe. It would have adverse effects on our scientific life, and consequently on our society as a whole.

And the panel went on to argue a series of public justifications which ran neatly counter to those used in Mr Short's statement of rejection to the British C.S.P., that high-energy physics was a source, not a sink, of qualified manpower going into industry, and that there was an imperative need to designate and support centres of excellence. Finally, they conclude, such is the speed of advance in the U.S.S.R. and West Europe, that 'It is imperative that U.S. physicists collaborate . . . in exploiting the new machine'.

Thus the U.S. justification is set formally in the language of 'national interest'. Science is a tool in raising national prestige, and even national survival, even more than it is worthwhile in its own right. In this report at least the physicists are speaking the language of the national politicians, rather than of scientists urging the intrinsic criteria for the support of their research. And in so far as they argue in these terms, one can be sure that they will be answered – as Mr Short did answer the British physicists – in the same language. Mr Short was careful to make the distinction between the physicists' competence in allotting money within their own field – which he agreed was theirs and theirs alone – and that ultimate government responsibility for the total financial assessment of the situation.

Thus, the assumption by the scientists that they can speak in 'the national interest' and the conflict with the politicians that this entails, which characterized both the W.H.O. and the accelerator decisions, leads one to feel that the phrase may be no more than a stick which anyone can pick up and use to beat his opponent over the head with. But this conflict leads us back to the core of this book: in the long run, who is to be master? And it is to this, in our final chapter, that we can at length turn.

CHAPTER THIRTEEN

Science and Society

Science's Inner Logic

Much of our modern world has been shaped by science. Yet equally, as the preceding chapters have shown, much of our modern science has been shaped by the requirements and constraints placed upon it by the society in which it is performed. It is this integration which makes fallacious any attempt to describe science as some sort of external agent acting upon a society and thus transforming it, an agency suggested, for instance, by the title of a recently published series of essays by Bertrand Russell, *The Impact of Science on Society*[1] – equally inappropriately the title of the journal published by U.N.E.S.C.O. on aspects of science policy. Such a title implies a science which falls upon society like a stone, moulding, bending, or crushing it. Even Karl Mannheim's classic essay on the sociology of knowledge in *Ideology and Utopia* fails to consider science as an aspect of knowledge which could be socially determined.

Many people undoubtedly feel this sense of inevitability – both non-scientists and scientists. Nuclear fission and hence the bomb were inevitable, molecular biology and hence genetic engineering, information science and hence computers and artificial intelligence are inevitable, battery chickens are inevitable, going to the moon and the motor-car are inevitable; in the immortal words of Robert Oppenheimer, one of the leading physicists in the U.S. controversy over whether or not to go ahead on the building of the H-bomb, whatever can be seen by the scientist as technically 'sweet' becomes inevitable to him; it becomes for the rest of society to decide whether to use it or not; all the scientist does is to put the choice in the way, like Eve's snake; society, in some sense, will decide without vitiating the virginal neutrality of science. But whatever the perceptions of the scientists, or the doubts of those within the rest of society who must live with the results of incessant technological innovation and the mixed blessings that they bring with them, science is not an unpredictable act of gods in white coats, nor is it the product of forces of an unspecified 'progress' which are outside our powers to control. The sort of science that is done today, in Britain, the U.S.A. and the U.S.S.R., is neither inevitable nor necessarily in any abstract sense 'the best', as we have seen in tracing the origins of modern scientific society and in comparing national science policies. It is the product of certain philosophies, ideologies, economic and political structures. It is thus to a considerable extent modifiable and plannable.

This is not to imply that science does not have its own inner logic, that certain types of experiments and their results do not lead on systematically to others by the steady and persistent application of that body of procedure which is discussed by philosophers of science under the name of scientific method. This procedure may move by way of the inductive, hypothesis-making structures described originally by Bacon, or, at certain critical points in the history of any science, by a type of 'scientific revolution' – a qualitative change in the nature of our perception of the natural world, of the sort which has been so illuminatingly discussed by the historian Thomas Kuhn.[2] With hindsight, science appears to advance in a more or less ordered manner irrespective of the prevailing social environment in which it is performed. This is the way which, until relatively recently the history of science has been taught.

It is difficult to see how the current phase of the biological revolution, with the cracking of the genetic code and the emergence of bio-chemistry as a unifying science with explanatory power over many areas of biology which had traditionally appeared diverse, could have arisen except on the basis of the prior concepts of nineteenth-century organic chemistry and the gene models introduced following Mendel-Müller genetics in the early twentieth century. Similarly, the experimental techniques, based on X-ray diffraction, which enables molecular shape to be examined, electron microscopy, which makes possible magnifications of half a million and more, and the production and handling of bacterial mutations, superseding the old studies of sweet peas or fruit flies, were all required. Both the conceptual and physical apparatus were needed before the advance could be made.

The evolution of a scientific breakthrough can be related to its experimental and intellectual framework within the corpus of science. It is the existence of this framework which suggests certain types of experiment or interpretation as opposed to others, often to several researchers at about the same time, as is clear from the many instances of simultaneous discovery that have been catalogued over many periods of scientific history by, for instance, the sociologist Robert Merton.[3] Intuitively, the scientist knows he is working in an atmosphere which makes certain experiments appropriate in this way. It is because of this that many workers in fields which are 'fashionable', or 'band-wagon', often work in constant fear that the next issue of their learned journal, be it *Nature*, *The Proceedings of the National Academy of Science of the U.S.*, or *Physical Review Letters*, will contain a description of their research and results – done by someone else. The competitive atmosphere that this engenders is enthusiastically described in Jim Watson's account of how Francis Crick, Maurice Wilkins and he solved the problem of the structure of the genetic material DNA – *The Double Helix*.[4] Watson's account makes clear that he, at least, worked in constant fear that the great chemist and Nobel prize-winner, Linus Pauling, who had already solved the problem of the structure of proteins, would get there first. Pauling seems not to have shown this competitiveness, maybe because he is intrinsically a less anxiety-ridden person, maybe because he had anyhow already 'arrived' scientifically. His immortality was already enshrined; that of Watson, Crick, and Wilkins was yet to come. But had they not 'got there' first, few would doubt, such was the scientific *zeitgeist*, that one of the other workers in the field would have done so before too long.

Other names would be attached to that particular Nobel and *The Double Helix* would not have been written perhaps, but the 'inner logic' of science would have driven molecular biology forward in more or less the same direction.*

* Thus on a micro-scale, for instance, the antecedents of a particular scientific paper can be traced, due to the practice of scientific authors of citing with a reference the authors of work which they feel to be relevant to their own. By following back such citations and looking for the papers cited by

What Watson's story does bring out is the importance of the social relationships between the scientists who worked on the code, the mutual exchange system of skills, and the urgent sense of priority in discovery. No one after reading Watson, whether his accounts of his colleagues are reasonably accurate or wildly biased, could believe that the genetic code was cracked by detached, unemotional men working solely for truth's sake and caring little for the world. The cheerily brash autobiography echoes the careful findings of the sociologist of science, Warren Hagstrom.[5] Hagstrom's sensitive study of *The Scientific Community* is focused systematically on the same area, delineating the autonomous community of scientists, their special training, which binds them both to one another and also to certain values, and the social control system, which maintains the values, through rewarding the gift of new information with recognition and status within the scientific community.

While the inner order of science is a necessary condition of a particular advance being made, so that molecular biology must be preceded by classical genetics and organic chemistry, this does not mean that this condition is sufficient as well as necessary. Resources must also be available. But equally the mere willing of resources will not necessarily promote scientific advance, as the early and unsuccessful attempts at the Royal Society to transfer blood between animals and man showed in 1670. What society can ensure is that the funds, equipment, and trained manpower exist to make a particular discovery possible. At the same time society can prevent a potential advance entirely by diverting the resources and manpower elsewhere or by establishing an intellectual climate in which particular classes of question will not be asked. It is in this sense that even the most basic of science that we do is a product of our society.

---

these authors in their turn, a sort of 'family tree' running through several generations of scientific papers can be built up (except that it is a tree upside-down, for all the cited papers eventually converge on that nearest to us in time, with which the search started). This tree-building exercise, now widely practicable with the establishment of a citation index, which lists references from each paper, has become a research weapon in the hands of de Solla Price, demonstrating clearly the 'inner logic' of scientific advance, where previously the single, illuminating instance had to serve.[6]

Society Shapes Science

Certain types of society therefore do certain types of science; they ask particular questions of nature. Ancient Babylonian religion demanded the accurate prediction of heavenly events and Babylonian science was largely devoted to the intensive study of astronomy. The emergent capitalism of the industrial revolution in Britain required technological advances in power generation and physicists studied the laws of thermodynamics and conservation and transformation of energy. It is no accident that many of these fundamental advances in physics were made in Britain in the half-century 1810–60, whilst in chemistry and physiology the major centres were in France and Germany. This thesis, that science springs from the economic base of society, has been central to the Marxist analysis of the history and philosophy of science. In Britain this type of analysis began to be made in the 1930s by such scientists as Desmond Bernal, J. B. S. Haldane and Joseph Needham, in order to use Marxism as a means of providing a socio-economic account of the development of science. The synthetic tasks they set themselves were ambitious; the successes, such as Needham's studies of Chinese science, and Bernal's *Science in History*, were correspondingly great.[7]

But the negative corollary of this relationship between science and society holds true too; that is, that in certain societies certain types of science are *not* done. They become either unperformable or unthinkable. We have already noted the withering of physics in Nazi Germany and of genetics during the Lysenko period in Russia. Science does not stop, for there are always an infinity of questions that can be asked by a scientist and of papers that can be published, even if the questions are turned to the collection of essentially trivial or repetitive answers and the papers end in the aridity of much of, for example, current inorganic chemistry research in Britain, where particular chemicals are purified and their properties examined for little observable reason than because they exist. (Perhaps also the researcher's supervisor has an interest in a related substance.) This is a sort of Everest complex. Such research, like stamp-collecting, or calculating the number of times the letter 's' appears in *Hamlet* (crawling along the frontiers of knowledge with a hand-lens, as Sir Eric Ashby has called it) can always go on irrespective, in any subject, albeit the resulting paper is read by none but the author, the referee, the editor of the journal in which it appears, and one other. It just happens though, that in this type of society the research relevant to particular types of problem is not done; technological expertise in other fields may remain – witness Nazi Germany's undoubted prowess in rocketry – but intellectual leadership passes elsewhere, as happened in post-Galileo Italy, which lost its leadership of European science to Britain.

In this sense society gets the science it neither demands, nor deserves, nor needs, but some uneasy compromise between the three. This is relatively easy to see in the extreme cases where particular societies in recent history have closed the doors to particular types of science, but even in the pluralist liberal democracy of Britain today the physical and financial restraints are obvious. The rejection of the W.H.O. research centre was at root the expression of a reluctance on the part of science policy-makers to invest more resources in preventive medicine as applied to communicable diseases; the existence of the Cancer Agency or the innumerable Cancer Research Funds and Heart Foundations, or the frantic activities of the transplanting heart surgeons, are an indication of where in biology we would rather put our resources today. Certain fields of biological research lag for want of money; they become virtually unperformable. Similarly, the ultimate rejection by Britain of the 300 machine was a statement by the British government that it was concerned to invest money in physics on a large scale only where it saw the measurable possibility, in the mid-term future, of some sort of economic pay-off.

It is neither avoidable nor wrong that such constraints should exist. The questions we have to ask, in the long run, must take cognisance of them. They are: what sort of science do we want? how much of it do we want? who should do it? how should they and their activities be controlled? But the fundamental question underlying all these is: what sort of society do we want?

Forecasting Science?

It is easy at a simple-minded level to draw up a list of prescriptive *goods* and contrast it with a set of potential pejorative *bads*; we need to increase food production, reduce birth rate, avoid war and environmental pollution; we need to ensure that science grows at such and such a rate, spend more money here and less there; or embark on exercises of 'ministry-building' – setting up an ideal government of science. But it is the failure to recognize this underlying question which has recently led a number of distinguished scientists to play the type of game known as 'technological forecasting'. In this game one takes a particular science and 'guesstimates' how it will develop in the next few (i.e. five, ten, twenty-five, 100) years, what technological innovations will accrue from it, and, therefore, what effect it will have on society over the foreseeable future. Much money is currently being spent, in particular in the United States, on such activities, both short-term, by individual industrial companies anxious to continue to make the correct research choices so as to assist in maximizing short-term profits, and by government hoping to allay its fears for the mid-term future. The techniques of technological forecasting were pioneered by Erich Jantsch,[8] but a particularly striking example of their use is the list of future innovations compiled by Herman Kahn and Anthony Wiener in their book *The Year 2000 – a framework for speculation on the next thirty-three years*.[9]

The trouble with this type of approach is that either it assumes that the technologies studied are in some sense neutral – although by now the McLuhanite *obiter dictum* that 'anyone who thinks that technology is neutral is a numbskull idiot' should have penetrated the forecasters' awareness – or the method involves a set of values, however soft-pedalled they are, which need examining before, rather than after, we choose our future technologies. The question should be whether the sort of society we want should shape our choice of technologies, or whether we should allow our society to be shaped by the 'inevitability' of technological advance. Nor does the 'normative approach', as used by Professor Dennis Gabor[10] in his amended list of 105 inventions set in what he refers to as a 'social frame' help. When such lists include – even ranked at number ninety-three in possible order of solution – the abolition of class war, apparently by abolishing the trade unions, along with the prevention of revolution in under-developed countries by a policy of 'extreme generosity', and 'hope for the *rentier*' in the 'mature society', as well as the more usual forms of speculation about rapid transit systems, organ transplants and the like, then the particular values of this normative framework become manifest. They are, of course, conservative in a way that perhaps only a scientist can be, that is, projecting visions of new technologies ranging from the sure-to-be-achieved to the enchanting fantasy, but couched within a normative framework which is frozen within his own time and social class position. The power structures and values of society are to remain undisturbed, so that, although we know that the factory system transformed men's social relations and evolved industrial society with its present class systems, the new technologies are projected in a futuristic vacuum.*

The social naïveté – and arrogance – of such speculations as these has given credence to the attack on the scientists and their technological society by the French social philosopher, Jacques Ellul,[11] as men who, outside their laboratories, are capable only of trivia. (Ellul argues that, if the choice of what type of human to regard as desirable be left to those now working on ways of making such a choice physically possible, the geneticists, the doom of humanity must result, for the geneticists will make the new human in their own image, which Ellul not unreasonably finds an unattractive one.)

It is not that one cannot or should not plan for the future; there is no advantage gained by throwing out the technological forecasting baby along with his conservative bathwater. Rather, the normative and social implications of new technologies have to be envisaged at the same time as the technologies themselves are reached after in the minds of the forecasters. It is not only the straightforward issues of whether unemployment will result from innovation, but whether social relationships are themselves modified, and whether this modification is desirable. A clear-cut positive example is the role of drug treatments in mental illness, in transforming the human relationships between patients, nurses, and doctors within the psychiatric hospital. The tranquillizing agents,

* About the only omission of note from Gabor's list, in fact, appears to be the abolition of racial tensions – perhaps by the invention of a pill that will colour the entire population of the world to a uniform coffee.

and even electrical shock treatment have made the straitjacket technologically obsolete, offering the patient the possibility of relief, and humanizing mass psychiatric medicine in a way that the humanist Freudians could not.

Few examples can be so unequivocal in their effects on social relations; typically evaluation is easiest in a fairly well-defined setting. Forecasting – or for that matter the application of scientific method to problem-solving, that is, operations research – within a military or even a business context is relatively straightforward, though even here the limitations have been well described by Robert Boguslaw in his book *The New Utopians*.[12] Armies are supposed to win and businesses to make profits, and, while it is clear that military and business institutions have other, more complex functions, these two remain dominant. Yet the failure of the computer-controlled conduct of the Vietnam war, and the failure of the Concorde builders to stay within their financial estimates suggest that the techniques are only partially adequate. For a complex society, societal goal definition is a continuing and difficult task, apart from that of the continuance of the society – and given the Bomb and the Bug even this goal may not necessarily be taken for granted. So far as science is concerned, however, the goal at least as conceived by most science planners is increasingly becoming one of a rather narrowly defined economism.

Planning and the Growth of Science

There can be little doubt that, in terms of short-run management, the management of science policy in most industrial countries is becoming more sophisticated. The similarity of the planning apparatus that exists in Europe, Britain, Russia and America, and the resemblance of the goals perceived for this policy bear witness to this. When Academician Vadim Trapeznikov[13] announces to a Moscow economics conference that every rouble spent on science and its application to production yields a return of 145 kopeks profit in a year, his words ring chords in the U.S.A. as well. And in a period which has seen the slowing down of the growth rate in the totality of scientific spending, not merely in Britain due to the chronic economic crises and the U.S A. due to the Vietnam war, but as part of a general trend in other nations as well, a concentration on 'economic' science may seem a sensible, short-term, pragmatic goal in response to straitened circumstances.

There is a sense in which this economic goal is not only sensible, but desirable in itself, as certainly any policy which results in the syphoning-off of the vast proportion of the science budget which is now spent on defence research in Britain, the U.S.A. or the U.S.S.R. into economic or welfare directions is to be welcomed. The extent to which this could be feasible is shown by comparing the figures of Table 5, on expenditure on defence versus economic goals in science by, say, Britain and Japan – though Japan's special relationship to America is indisputably an important factor. Whereas in Britain, as opposed to France and West Germany, there has been a stagnation and even a diminution in the proportion of effort and reserves allocated to defence research in the past few years, and instead a turning of science towards economic goals, it begins to look as if science is becoming harnessed to the peaceful needs of society. However, the harnessing of science is not a painless procedure.

For the scientists themselves, the response to such attempts has been given in the unequivocal voice of the pained, vested interest; the imminent arrival of a scientific dark age was gloomily presaged by the British physicists whose 300 machine was abandoned by the British government and by the American physicists who saw delays mount up in their own plans for the 200 machine at Weston as Federal spending was slashed. A growth rate of 5–6 per cent to allow for the so-called 'sophistication factor' of inevitably rising expense in science is regarded as an irreducible minimum, below which some sort of national tragedy will befall. But in fact, more money for science, or for anything else, is the cry of an interest group, just as less money for science, or for anything else, is an equally continuous demand of Treasury officialdom dourly pointing to the lack of growth in the economy. The merits of the claim of such an interest group may be legitimate, but they demand assessment by criteria other than the volume or status of the group. The real point is that, in so far as we treat the 'science budget' as a one and indivisible whole, such a slowing of growth is inevitable, if within the next fifteen years (or fifty, if we are concerned only with basic and not with applied science) scientific and technological activities are not to absorb an insupportable proportion of the national budget – any nation's budget, not just Britain's.

In fact, it is likely that those amongst the academic scientists who are most loudly crying woe are doing so, like the White Queen in *Alice*, before they have actually been hurt. Unlike the Queen though, their pain may be more in the mind than the body, and its cause may never materialize, for both those who have been defending the growth rate as inviolate and those who have attempted most valiantly to battle on the side of History's Laws to reduce it may have been fighting a largely sham war. This is because, as both Bernal and the philosopher of science, Stephen Toulmin[14] have pointed out, everything in the debate depends on what one means by science and scientist.

What has been done, in order to draw up science budgets and calculate their growth rates, is normally to clump all of a plurality of scientific activities together. Yet in fact, when one looks at such a grouping in more detail, it is seen to consist of many separate items, which are not always the same at different times, so that the definition of science is itself time-based. What is done as science today perhaps was not twenty or fifty years ago, or may not be twenty or fifty years hence. A nice example of this is provided by the U.S. defence research budget, which, as was pointed out earlier, has been stagnant and even declining over recent years. Yet this does not necessarily mean that all of defence research is being reduced. Within the budget, for example, that for one research field, chemical and biological weaponry, has increased by eight times in the last decade, whilst other areas of research, particularly into atomic weaponry, have declined. This whole picture might change should the Nixon administration opt for a full-scale anti-ballistic missile system, but for the present the Bug is cheaper than the Bomb.

The birth, growth, maturity, and senility of individual sciences follow time-courses which are not identical, so that, for instance, at the most rapid period of growth of inorganic chemistry, let us say the period 1800–1900, sciences which are themselves growing most rapidly today – biochemistry for instance – were virtually non-existent. The sciences which will be the rapid growth points of to-morrow, perhaps aspects of socio-biology, are themselves today in their infancy, whilst others, like inorganic chemistry, are, at the most charitable, now long past middle age. The exponential curve for the growth of science is the sum of a very much larger number of subject curves, whilst which subjects are included in the definition of science is essentially a time-based decision, which has been continuously enlarged over the last 150 years. The possibility that all sciences will arrive at some defined saturation point at the same time in history seems remote in the extreme. As our definition of what constitutes scientific activity broadens, so the limit which we are prepared to set as a desirable proportion of our G.N.P. or human resources to be spent upon it does as well.

Nevertheless, certain areas of both science and technology may be slowing down and even effectively coming to a halt. This is easier to see in the case of technology, perhaps. Thus in many areas of our contemporary technologies we may indeed be approaching some sort of saturation level. Transport is one. As John Platt[15] has pointed out in his book, *The Step to Man*, the last hundred years has been a period in which speeds of transportation have increased dramatically, through trains, the motor-car, the aeroplane. Where the first aeroplanes to go into passenger service cruised at a hundred or so miles an hour, plans for the new supersonic planes, Concorde and the Boeing SST–2707, talk in terms of approaching 2,000 m.p.h., a twenty-fold increase within the past half century. It is unlikely that the next half century will produce a similar rate of increase so that by, say, the year 2010 men are journeying between different parts of the planet at 40,000 miles an hour. (In fact it is impossible, for the speed is greater than escape velocity, and they would find themselves on the moon.) The rate of increase, if indeed there is any at all, will be reduced, simply because this particular technological problem – that of reducing journey times for individuals by increasing the speed at which they travel from point A to point B – is close to the limit; to increase communication speeds further in future, the need will be for a different technology not only in degree but in kind. This is not to argue for the spending of significant research funds on problems of telekinesis and teleportation – far from it. It may instead be that we do not need to seek for more rapid means of communication in this sense at all, that the journey time across the Atlantic will never be so much less than an hour or two; instead the dramatic increases in rates of technological innovation and change will occur in other areas, such as, say, computer communication and information links, which will obviate the need for people to travel long distances merely to talk with one another.

Whilst such an analysis may be acceptable immediately for

specific technologies, it may be less apparent how it can be applied to the basic sciences. For there are, manifestly, an infinity of questions that can be asked of nature, granted the time, patience, technique, and money, for defined knowledge (in the sense of recorded data placed in the 'archives' of the scientific literature) cannot be finite. Even seemingly finite areas, like the number of chemical elements, have gone on expanding since the discovery by radiation chemists that under certain conditions of bombardment of atomic nuclei, new, totally artificial transmutations can occur, producing further 'unnatural' elements. These elements can only exist for a few minutes, or seconds, or tenths of seconds; nonetheless, their chemistry can be studied – if anyone wants to.

What is finite is not the total of scientific knowledge, but the total of *meaningful* scientific knowledge – that is, knowledge which significantly extends man's understanding of himself and his world. The first synthesis of an unnatural element was an intellectual and technical achievement. Elements 100, 101, 102 may be worth working for. Elements 120, 130, 140, 150? The first protein molecule ever to have its entire chemical structure determined was the substance insulin. The man who did it, in 1956, Frederick Sanger of Cambridge, was given the Nobel prize for it. But there are many hundreds of millions of different protein molecules. Are we ever going to or need to analyse them all? And a precisely similar argument may well apply to the investigations by the particle physicists, which demand the 300 machine – a vastly more expensive enterprise. Analysing a few hundred or thousand protein molecules could easily be done for the same cost.

The argument really is that a law of diminishing returns, intellectual as well as social and economic, applies, which provides its own limit to the development of any scientific speciality. Lost in their arcane mysteries, the province of a select few, some areas of science may already have reached this point; and at the same time quite new domains of human activity are being drawn within the boundaries of science.

What we mean by this is not merely that the number of research scientists has increased enormously in the last century, from those few 'cultivators of science' of Whewell's time to the armies of researchers at work in Britain today, but that our definition of what is amenable to a scientific approach has broadened beyond all recognition and goes on doing so. Thus, as well as the creation of new scientific disciplines, there has been a steady expansion of those areas into which it is considered possible to intrude scientific method. To take but three examples unthinkable in Whewell's time, business, sex and religion. The development of techniques of operations research, work study, business management, and management science are attempts – perhaps not wholly successful – to replace the intuitive approach of the 'good businessman' with the rationality of the natural sciences in the task of maximizing profit, whilst, on another side of the fence, the brutal dictum of '*caveat emptor*' – let the buyer beware – has been replaced, for its middle-class readership at least, by the careful assessment of rival products and best buys by the magazine *Which?* Such intrusions would have been regarded as little short of impertinent by the entrepreneurs of a previous century, and still more would the *mores* of the time have been offended by the development of sciences such as 'sexology' – growing fast in the climate of our contemporary culture and reaching a crescendo (one dare not say 'climax') in Master's and Johnson's massive study of *The Human Sexual Response*, made possible by the detailed physiological observation of human subjects during copulation and masturbation.[16] As for religion, one may merely note the flurry of interest that surrounded recent attempts to prove the authorship of particular scriptures by computer analysis of the texts.

Of course, those who argue for a 'levelling-off' of science are right if they mean that it is impossible for 'every man, woman, child and dog to become a scientist by the middle of the next century', if we mean by that term what we understand by research scientist today. What is more likely to happen – and indeed is already happening – is a steady infusion of science and scientific method into the general culture, a diminution of that gap in understanding which Snow has categorized as the two cultures.[17] Such a re-integration would not necessarily mean a centrifuge and a computer in every household, but in some sense the whole community would become, not cultivators, but practitioners of science.

The Retreat from Rationality

But such a rose-coloured portrait of 'Everyman as scientist' can be at best only a partial extrapolation of aspects of our current situation. For our society today, the gulf between the research activities of the scientists and popular understanding and aspirations is still deep. What is more, despite the evidence that we have cited of the extent to which the rational methods of science have already become part of the general culture, there are equally present within the contemporary scene signs of a deep revulsion against science, and something like a movement away from rationality itself, spread through much current philosophical and political writing.

The reasons for this lie in part in the extent to which, with the creation of an increasingly elaborate and extensive body of scientific knowledge, science has become esoteric, accessible only to the high priests, and beyond the comprehension of the laity. Where in art this exclusiveness is optional – the artist can choose, like an Eliot, deliberately to write for the chosen few, or, like Raymond Williams, can write within what he describes as the common culture – for the contemporary scientists there is little choice. Scientific knowledge itself is far less diffuse than literary knowledge within contemporary culture. Those who understand the body of knowledge depend for their understanding on a formalized educational process; there is little of the relatively informal, even casual, picking up of information which characterizes the acquisition of, say, political literacy or an understanding of the modern novel.

This process by which most of science has become obscure to most people and all of science to some is part, albeit a dangerous part, of the specialization of modern society. The earliest cultivators of science neither called themselves nor liked the term *scientist*, because they were not, in fact, *just* scientists. Wren is remembered as an architect; that he was also a competent scientist is less commonly known. Benjamin Franklin was as much a politician and businessman as a pioneer in electrical research and engineering. The point is that it was then possible for almost any man of intelligence to follow recent developments and, if creative, to make a personal contribution to knowledge alongside his main activity. Today this is no longer practicable; to get to even the position that Snow would wish us to acquire, where the intelligent man does know about relativity and the second law of thermodynamics, would require some fairly dramatic changes in the educational system. If anything it seems, with the decline in the number of pupils specializing in science in the schools and despite the growing but modest number of them reading a joint arts and science degree, that this stage is as far off as ever.

Because of this intense polarization between the specialist and the non-specialist, science is increasingly seen through distorting lenses. Science becomes at one and the same time an object of crude veneration and of crude suspicion. The battle over fluoridation highlights this ambivalence. Most research and practical experience make it probable that the adding of fluoride in the correct proportion to drinking water appears to do no harm, but instead has the positive benefit of preserving children's teeth from caries. Yet fluoridation is regarded with intense suspicion; letters in local and, to a lesser extent, national newspapers articulate a generalized if imprecise fear amongst many people that in some way fluoride is 'getting at their life forces', or is disturbing their body fluids, reflecting a conceptual understanding of physiology which owes more to the medieval humours than to contemporary biology. The men in the white coats are felt to be trying to do something unseeable but sinister; anti-science as a twentieth-century version of Luddism prevails. Somehow our chlorinated, sieved and strained water has become 'natural' whilst the addition of fluoride is a grave disturbance of the proper order of events. Simultaneously with this abhorrence goes a servility on the part of the mass media at least at the wonders of science, so that cancer-curing drugs, heart transplant, and space shot are publicly lauded.

This contradiction seems to require more explanation than a comment on the inconsistencies of contemporary man; the scientific researches which speak to our everyday experience are more acceptable than those which rely on an understanding and a cogent grasp of the procedure of science. But this anti-science goes deeper than the mere machine hatred of Luddism-simple; instead the attack on science and technology is transformed into an attack on the dynamic rationality of scientific method itself. Hatred of machines rises where men see that a new technology is replacing their labour. The response of the eighteenth- and nineteenth-century Luddite faced with the mechanization of weaving was to smash the stocking frames. Today's equivalent is that of the print unions in Britain, who opposed or at least delayed the introduction of new technologies like web offset printing. This is not in any sense to dispute the legitimacy of the attempt by the worker through his union to protect his economic existence by way of continual 'holding' battles to preserve his job. This is the necessary activity of groups of workers faced with an innovating capitalist – or Russian-type state socialist – whose economic rationality becomes an end in itself.

But the mere preservation of jobs is often justified by the claim that the obsolete technology is itself in some way more desirable than the new. Lord Robens's vigorous defence of the coal industry tends to underplay the humanitarian conviction that no decent society ought to condemn men to earn their living – and lose their lives – by working underground. Associated with this is the romantic nostalgia for steam as opposed to diesel trains, or veteran cars, or antique typewriters. Others, like the romantic socialist William Morris, have seen the machine as degrading to man, in that the machine dominates the pace of work; men stop and start when the whistle blows. Machines thus depersonalized the worker and were implicated in alienating him from himself and from any joy in the thing which he was making. Both Gandhi and Morris, romantics and reactionaries, invoking some past, golden age where hand-craft, hand-weaving, hand-printing were the dominant forms, rejected the factory with its impersonality and its inhumanity.

But for most of the socialists, although there has always been a harking back to this lost, golden age of craftsmanship and community, there has always been a more optimistic view of the role of science and technology in overcoming the deficiencies of the old, alienated order. The same boundless rationality, which is so much in accord with the revolutionary quality of the scientific method and the new philosophy, certainly as Bacon and the founders of the Royal Society saw it, belonged, more than to any other thinker, to Karl Marx. His conviction was that scientific socialism would extend the logic and universality of science into man's social relations, not only learning the laws of social development, but also deliberately aiding them. He makes this point most clearly in the theses on Feuerbach, written in 1845, uniting science, technology, and society:

> The question whether objective truth belongs to human thinking is not a question of theory, but a practical question. The truth, i.e. the reality and power of thought, must be demonstrated in practice. The contest as to the reality or non-reality of a thought which is isolated from practice is a purely scholastic question. . . . Philosophers have only interpreted the world in various ways, but the real task is to change it.[18]

Those who could not share this sense of the possibility, let alone the inevitability of progress, were troubled, not only by the specific tools of science, but by the dangers they saw in the new philosophy. Towering above those who found themselves disturbed by the increasing rationalization of the world stood Max Weber, who perceived in modern capitalism and in modern science that rationalization led at one and the same time, not only to immense material success and knowledge, but also to an inexorable 'disenchantment of the world'.[19] He apotheosized bureaucracy as the institutional embodiment of rationality in action, yet he also saw it as, not only threatened by its own rules, but becoming so deformed that it ceased to serve its original goals; instead it served only the means by which the goals were to be secured. The bureaucracy too, although just, is not only impersonal, but also inhuman. Rationality as Weber conceived it is itself inhuman. The only alternative Weber could see was the emergence of a charismatic leader who could command authority and loyalty for personal, instead of rational, reasons, but who even so was eventually himself subject to rationalization. Perhaps the intensity of Weber's insight has only become apparent in these days when the extension of rationality in the modern world has made possible the painful experience of the horrors of the rationalization of charisma itself, in the application of scientific procedure and method to the contemporary violence of Hitler's Final Solution for the Jews. (It is the neat book-keeping of the concentration camps which is the key to our revulsion, where obscene rationality has driven humanity out of bounds.) Similarly the tragedy of Stalin's Russia was that the rationalization of political technique in maintaining the position of those with power virtually annihilated the socialist dream which had been part of its inception. And this is above all true today, with the latent violence of the Bomb or the Bug and the actual violence of Vietnam, where the measure of escalation is studiously simulated in war games on a Pentagon computer and the technology of satellite and television enables hundreds of millions to watch the murder of a guerrilla 'live' over their evening meal. Weber's concern, even obsession, with the driving force of rationality only thus becomes meaningful.

We realize that we are saying that scientific method is little more than the application of rational rules of procedure to the pursuit of intellectual and societal problems. For a rigorous definition of what constitutes scientific method this is not really adequate, for there are important differences between the methods of experimental scientists and historians, and also between those of biologists and physicists, and between both groups and their colleagues, the mathematicians. But for our purpose it is enough; rationality of procedure lies at the heart of science and its success in changing the face of the world.

It is the ambivalence of this change which is the key to the dilemma. On the one hand the rigour of science and the integrity of scientific knowledge attracts, on the other, the process by which the factory worker is alienated from his work, the soldier is alienated from his arms and even the scientist from his laboratory, repels. With the increase of big science, alienation in the laboratory becomes more apparent, as scientists work less and less individually and more and more in great teams, and science itself becomes bureaucratized. Not only are the scientists increasingly groups of workers tied to big machines, small parts of large projects, so that for example only 200 researchers would have been able to use the British share of the 300 GEV machine, but the autonomy of the individual researcher is increasingly circumscribed.

This bureaucratic approach to problem-solving is partly obscured by the personalization of discovery, an activity in which the scientists are happy to join; their powerful belief in the 'heroic' quality of science (with, implicitly, the suggestion that every graduate student carries a Nobel prize in his lab. coat pocket) is typified by the manner in which scientific advances carry the name of the man who establishes his priority of discovery. It explains the driving force which Watson revealingly portrays in *The Double Helix*.[4] Yet Bernal, reviewing *The Double Helix*, noted how these men, Watson, Crick, Wilkins, worked together; it was team research, not an individual research exercise. Increasingly too, as in this case, scientific prizes like the Nobel are awarded to groups of workers, not individuals. Research itself has become an exercise where different skills are rationally wielded in combination to crack a particular problem. Despite the conventional academic disparagement, Bacon's dream in which he saw that science, once the rules of method were made apparent, could be carried out with each scientist playing an *equally* valuable role in the creation of knowledge, approaches the contemporary situation. The emphasis on scientific priority in discovery, and to no little extent the habit of recording the history of science as the history of ideas born of great men, has fostered this *élitism* and the myth of the 'great men of scientific history'. But the myth increasingly runs into difficulties when the costs of research rise; five names are common on a research paper, fifteen not unknown, and in particle physics it has happened that the entire staff of a laboratory has been named.

A powerful attack on the rationality of scientific method, 'of technique', as he calls it is that of the social philosopher Jacques Ellul.[11] He argues that this increasing application of scientific method moves to the point when each new technological solution to a problem creates another problem in its wake. The motor-car destroys the city and pollutes the air; indestructible plastic containers mount up till we are threatened with submersion below an overflowing mass of rubbish; psychology begins by understanding man and ends by manipulating him. In bizarre combination, the religious conservative Ellul shares with the socialist revolutionary Herbert Marcuse a passionate contempt for the pseudo-toleration of what he feels is really an increasingly repressive society. For both, the natural social framework for a society totally committed to the application of scientific method is eventually a totalitarian society. Personality control, genetic engineering and space travel as part of the 'Year-2,000' programme are most easily developed in such a framework. For Marcuse,

> The traditional distinction between science and technology becomes questionable. When the most abstract achievements of mathematics and theoretical physics satisfy so adequately the needs of I.B.M. and the Atomic Energy Commission it is time to ask whether such applicability is not inherent in the concepts of science itself. The question cannot be pushed aside by separating pure science from its applications and putting the blame on the latter only: the specific purity of science facilitated the union of construction and destruction, humanity and inhumanity in the progressive mastering of nature.[20]

It is the non-scientific culture which 'preserves the images of the ends which science itself cannot and does not define, namely the ends of humanity'.

Such condemnations mark the highwater of discontent with science and technology. Edmund Leach, the anthropologist, in his Reith Lectures, for example, notes the growing tendency for schoolchildren to opt out of science at school and at university, preferring to read social sciences and the humanities instead.[21] The reports of the British Council for Scientific Policy's Dainton and Swann

Committees attribute this decline essentially to short-term and parochially British factors; an inadequacy amongst science teachers, an inflexibility in the university syllabus, an erroneous 'image' of scientists or engineers amongst the young.[22] Yet this insular concentration on the Britishness of the problem is insufficient. In fact, the phenomenon is widespread; a decline in science student numbers has been noted in the United States and West Europe as well.*

Less coherently the whole hippy/flower-power sub-culture represents a total rejection of science and rationality, conscientiously irrational, deliberately making language opaque; comprehension is sought instead through mystical experience supported by hallucinogenic drugs; a meta-language system is sought to describe the one-ness and unity of man with nature, which by-passes the scientific job of analysing it rationally; non-rational states of mind, typically schizophrenia, are glorified. To the hippies, as to the Russian romantic, Tolstoy, science is meaningless 'because it gives us no answer to our question: What shall we do and how shall we live?' (Though it is not clear that the contemporary equivalent, 'Don't bug me man, I'm doing my own thing' is a constructive alternative.) It is scarcely an accident that, in the lecture lists of the recently established 'Anti-University' of London, science and

* Nor does the painstaking literature review of the psychological and sociological factors influencing occupational choice, carried out by J.R. Butler as the second Science Policy Study for the C.S.P. and the Manpower Committee, sufficiently consider macrosocietal influences. In this paper Butler discusses various theoretical approaches to occupational choice varying from Ginzberg's view that career choice is the culmination of a series of stages whereby the child becomes adjusted to the realities of his own social position and the opportunities afforded him by the occupational structure, to Liam Hudson's explanations involving 'convergent' and 'divergent' personalities.[23] However, Butler to some extent eschews the real problem of why schoolchildren specifically reject science – and within science, why they reject physics and chemistry more than biology? Drawing on insight rather than documentation, but at least as relevantly, Edmund Leach and C.F. Powell, the physicist and Nobel prize-winner, have suggested that this antipathy stems from a youthful distaste at the present-day abuse of science, particularly in the service of war; where 1914–18 was a chemists' war, 1939–45 was a physicists' war, and to some small extent at least, Vietnam today is a biologists' war. When the potential university students learn about Project Camelot, the multi-million American social science study of 'counter insurgency' techniques in Latin America too, they may be less enthusiastic about the man-centred social sciences.

scientists do not figure at all, the nearest approach is that of the existentialist psychologists of schizophrenia like R. D. Laing. Even the language of politics, at least the language of student politics, has elements of conscientious irrationality which argue against the intellectual process itself. 'Don't listen, speak; don't speak, act', becomes a slogan on a university wall (L.S.E. 1969). One strand in student unrest is directed against the dehumanized quality of academic thought in general, and scientific thought in particular.

The Future of Science

The effect, though, has been to modify some of the more optimistic beliefs about the inevitability of scientific virtue; science today is intellectually on the defensive. No one today could say with such certainty as Richard Gregory, the editor of *Nature* in the 1930s, 'My grandfather preached the gospel of Christ, my father preached the gospel of socialism, I preach the gospel of science'. Instead, as the sociologist, Sol Encel, has put it, 'Science has lost its critical function; no longer are natural scientists burned at the stake for their views about the nature of the world'.[24] But even were Ellul right, that the benefits of 'technique' are far outweighed by its disadvantages, the possibility of crying halt to science – at least for long enough to allow society to catch its breath and assimilate the technological developments of the last decades – does not lie realistically to hand. But the crying of halt is little more than a blanket negative reaction to the development of a science and technology which has resulted in the expenditure of immense effort, ingenuity, money and manpower in the pursuit of goals that are alien to man's needs. Nowhere, indeed, is this seen more clearly than in the monstrous and extravagant farce of the Apollo moon mission and its Soviet counterpart, in which billions of dollars and roubles have been invested in order to bring back to earth some of the most expensive holiday snaps ever made, at a time when the investment in a small proportion of this money into more man-centred research could well be expected to yield positive results. For example, the elimination of world hunger by developing alternative sources of dietary protein on the lines, say, of the leaf protein experiments by N. W. Pirie, or the massive investment of desert and ocean farming so as to reclaim the Sahara and the high seas for man's needs. It is not the procedures of natural science which are at fault, but its goals.

This is far from falling into the easy liberal trap of claiming that science is neutral, that for its beneficent or maleficent uses society and not science is to some extent to blame. Science is never neutral, for its goals are never neutral. Science is not done in the abstract, in a vacuum, but in a context which places value judgements upon its goals, just as the scientists themselves are not abstract embodiments of a value-free search after truth.

The real complexity is of a situation where, as we have argued, science, or rather the application of scientific method, is becoming increasingly knitted into the fabric of society. This is not only true for the applied sciences, which are latched into immediate governmental or business need, or the more general seepage of science into the culture, but also for the universities and the basic research institutes.

The universities have traditionally been the organizations which have sheltered the autonomous scientific community, which has generated the myths and value, which serve to protect, among many other things, the necessary degree of freedom to enable the intellectually important questions to be asked. Many, such as Alvin Weinberg, or the American sociologist of science Norman Storer,[25] share an anxiety over the increasing dependence of the university for external sources of money for research and the scale of the teamwork involved in the new 'Big Science'. The danger is that the new organizational structures of science threaten to engulf its traditional values of autonomy, public knowledge, disciplinary communism and personal commitment, making it impossible for the myth of science to be recreated. Science in this archetypal sense would stop.

Others, such as Hagstrom,[5] have offered a more soothing view – soothing, that is, if, unlike Ellul and the antirationalists, one wants science to continue – that the functional tensions which accompany the role of the scientist in industry, delicately balancing his loyalties to 'open' science against his loyalties to his firm, will be retained in other changed institutional settings. Hagstrom regards such tensions as both functional and desirable, and suggests that the problem Storer is discussing for science and scientists is the same for that of any other profession; that is, the problem of reconciling the need to provide them enough freedom to keep the scientists professionally effective as intellectual innovators with the need to keep them socially responsible.

But once again, both Hagstrom and Storer are talking of science as a homogeneous activity. It is when we examine the different portions of science, the separate disciplines, on the new fields within and between disciplines, that the extent of the professionalism of the scientist, at least as measured by his tendency to publish in the open scientific literature, is found to vary widely between disciplines.*

This distinction between different parts even of basic science, which has to some extent been obscured at a time when there was rapidly increasing funding of science as a whole, and is not aided by debates about growth rate, or whether science is to absorb 2·2, 2·5, 2·8 or 3·5 per cent of G.N.P. But now that money is tight, indications of interdisciplinary conflict sometimes emerge, as when the two chemists on the 300 GEV committee dissented from the majority, physicist, viewpoint as to its urgency, or when infighting on budgetary apportionment between disciplines marks attempts by the Science Research Council to allocate funds.

Yet commonsense demands that if science spending is to be limited, it should be done explicitly rather than implicitly, that if priority is to be given to biology, it should be possible to envisage, and accept, the fact of running down high-energy physics. And if high-energy physics is to be run down, there is little point in training high-energy physicists within the university, since they cannot be offered the opportunity of continuing in their research subsequently. This in turn has its own industrial and educational impli-

* Howard Vollmer's extensive survey of nearly 5,000 research scientists reports that biologists published the most, then physicists, mathematicians and chemists in that order. It would be a not unreasonable guess that in the 1930s and 1940s the physicists would have led the publication stakes, and at the turn of the century the chemists. Where the most vigorous growth in scientific thought occurs, the strongest commitment to public knowledge appears. The much weaker commitment of chemists to public knowledge is borne out by Steven Box and Stephen Cotgrove's survey of chemistry undergraduates. They reported that as well as the expected polarization between those who showed 'local' loyalty to the firm and 'cosmopolitan' loyalty to the scientific community, a third group, the largest, were interested in science as a technique but not as public knowledge. This last group was felt to be much better able to accommodate themselves to research within industry; their view of science as private knowledge much more nearly coincided with the view of industry itself.[26]

cations. And whilst this may be the limited implication of science policy for Britain at the moment, when in the next round of accelerator building the need comes for a single world machine of 1,000 GEV, or in space exploration of a 'world' manned voyage to the planets, because such enterprises are beyond the budgetary means of any single state, the same issue will emerge, but on a larger platform.

Still more is this true where the science or technology being paid for latches directly, and not merely distantly, into the structure of contemporary society. Here any decision – as the Labour government found when it scrapped TSR-2 and tried to abandon Concorde – runs head on into a complex of social and economic prejudices and vested interests, the more powerful for representing genuine contradictions, whose resolution is scarcely possible without conflict, a conflict which any consensus-oriented government (as the Wilson government has been *par excellence*), will attempt to resolve either by making no decision at all, or, one which will damage the interests only of the least vocal of the conflicting interests.

It is when we have to face the problem of constructing the mechanism of resolution of these conflicts that the potentially revolutionary role of science in society presents itself. Government is faced with an increasingly complex series of technological choices, opaque to the mass of a population which has received a narrowing, vocationally oriented education designed to enable them to fill a designated place in society – be it unskilled labourer or plant manager. In resolving these choices it increasingly finds decisions being made for it by the growing bureaucracy of experts and specialists. These committees are mainly closed groupings; only rumbles of internal dissent are occasionally allowed to escape, as in the open conflict between Lord Robens of the National Coal Board and the Central Electricity Board over whether future power stations, such as that at Seaton Carew in Northumberland, a traditional mining district, should be coal- or nuclear-powered. On the whole the workings of these committees remain closed; decision emerges from a magic box. No better example of this could be found than in the activities of the gargantuan offspring of Mintech, the Industrial Reorganization Commission. Here gigantic industrial mergers have been fostered throughout British industry, to cries of wonder from the City press and adulation from the shareholders, in the name of technological efficiency, rationalism and international competitiveness: A.E.I. with G.E.C. and then English Electric, Cambridge Instrument with George Kent, one computer firm after another with I.C.T. to create I.C.L. In the process, factories have been closed and workers – not only the unskilled, but technologists and scientists as well – left unemployed without the arguments in favour of such rationalization – as an alternative, say, to public ownership – ever being made open or accessible. Seldom is the decision ever questioned openly (an exception is the rearguard action still being fought over Concorde's sonic booms), rarely are they reversed, the one major rule-breaker here being the success of the public campaign to rethink the Stansted airport decision.

It is this inaccessibility which lies at the root of the problem of contemporary science and its social relations. At a time of rapid technological change, in which the world is being continuously reshaped around us – and not always for the better – the key processes of this reshaping are inaccessible not only to the non-scientist but to the scientist as well. The proportion of those practising science who participate in the decision-making process is small, over the range of science and technology stretching from the 300 machine and the World Health Research Centre through industrial mergers to defence.

Only in rare occasions of emergency, as to some extent during the Second World War, or over specific issues, as in the recent crisis of the *Torrey Canyon*, do the committees briefly open. At the height of the *Torrey Canyon* affair, as oil floated towards the beaches of Cornwall and Brittany, the public were informed of the existence of a special cabinet sub-committee under Sir Solly Zuckerman charged with responsibility for finding the best means of defending the beaches and sinking the oil. Comment and advice to the committee poured in, from laymen and scientists alike: bombs and plastic booms, detergent and sawdust. The committee was in danger of sinking under the weight of suggested solutions. In the event, the choice it made, of spraying the oil with detergent to emulsify and sink it, rather than either bombing the stricken tanker to fire the oil (which was eventually tried, after a large proportion had already leaked away) or using sawdust or chalk, as the French did, was probably the wrong one. The detergent used killed more of the marine life than did the oil, though doubtless the firm which manufactured the detergent (ironically the oil company B.P., for whom the *Torrey Canyon*'s cargo had been destined) – profited. Nevertheless, such was the nature of the emergency that temporarily the crisis generated something approximating to an open, accessible decision-making process.

But in the main, these processes are closed. Research which is likely to be anathema or seem pointless to a large body of the scientific community, or the lay public (chemical and biological warfare research, or space research, for example), is done behind closed doors. And a decision-making community within a community of scientists has grown up around it. Revealingly, a phrase used by the retired President Eisenhower a decade ago, of the domination in the U.S. of an 'industrial-military-complex' before which the apparently democratically elected U.S. government was relatively powerless, was recently amended by American Admiral Rickover to read 'industrial–military–scientific complex'.

In the face of the emergence of such an *élite*, the disenfranchisement of the non-establishment scientist, and still more of the non-scientific public, over whole areas of their existence, becomes apparent, and with it immense dangers. But how can control over scientific affairs be asserted?

It is not as if the existence of such an *élite* assured, or was more likely to ensure, the adequacy of the advice given. Where, as in Britain, the group of scientific advisers and committee men are elderly, or at best middle-aged, so that the magnitude of scientific knowledge may have tripled or quadrupled since they began their professional careers, it would not be surprising to find that the advice eventually rendered may be less than realistic. Indeed, the mere *process* of being a scientific administrator is such as to make it impossible for them to keep in reasonably close touch with the developments at the research front that they must attempt to evaluate. Can it really be, for example, whoever the individual concerned, in the best interests of medical research that its strategy be left largely in the hands of the same man for up to twenty years? Yet long service in the British scientific bureaucracy is the rule rather than the exception. One has only to contrast the two decades and more of science policy-making by Sir Solly Zuckerman with the rapid turnover of scientific advisers to the American President, all coming into government science administration from outside and returning to the outside when their term of office is over.

It may be argued that this makes the science adviser an openly political appointment, but this is essentially a correct evaluation. The British continue to pretend that it is not, so that for all the Labour Party's talk of bringing its own experts into power with it in 1964, the shake-up of Ministries that resulted largely served merely to place the same men in different seats. Membership of science policy-making committees, or Research Councils, remains a continuous process of cooption, 'after consultation with the President of the Royal Society' so that such bodies remain virtually self-electing and oligarchic.

There is a two-fold justification for this attempt to insulate science administration from politics, a belief that scientific advice is not value-laden and that there is therefore possible some approximation to an abstract 'best' advice independent of a politically defined goal; and that for basic science at least, effective continuance demands the appearance of separation from day-to-day governmental control. The first of these arguments, as the preceding chapters have shown, can no longer be maintained. Scientists asked to speak as advisers do so according to values and in pursuit of goals which are frequently neither set clearly for them by their political masters nor adequately perceived by the scientists themselves. The net result is to continue the divorce between the expert and his political control. The second argument for autonomy is perhaps more valid; it is at least time-hallowed in British political thought even before it was so clearly enunciated by Haldane. The problem, though, is that the shape of the structures that have evolved is one which is separated not only from day-to-day governmental control but also from control by the disenfranchised scientist as well – until such time as inexorable gerontocratic advance or the fortunate choice of an effective patron should rocket him into the administrative and decision-making stratosphere.

Meanwhile, the absence of effective political control means that many scientific developments are allowed to proceed from the point where they are nothing but a gleam in a research director's eye to that at which they are so technically sweet that they are virtually impossible to rescind without their *ever* being subject to public scrutiny. The technological imperative will have driven them forward with the public only becoming aware of what has been done in its name *post hoc*. The success stories and the scandals are launched upon a society, its politicians and most of its scientists without any of them having the possibility of passing judgement upon them in time. When did the community decide that it wanted to invest money and skills into the development of heart transplants? Or supersonic airliners? Or chemical and biological warfare? Close examination would show that all of these technological goals had been formulated and major steps towards achieving them taken without at any point an informed and public decision having been made. (However, in the first case at least the British Medical Association, by speaking out against the uncontrolled activities of the transplanters, has tried to make some sort of retrospective amends.) Particularly with research in government establishments, and most of all in defence, even the relevant immediate political master, the Minister himself – let alone Parliament or people – may not be aware of its existence and significance until late in the day. If the recent chemical and biological warfare controversy in Britain did little else, it served to demonstrate that research had been going on for many years at the two Defence Establishments at Porton, without the ostensible political controller of Porton, the Minister of Defence, having any but the vaguest idea of its implications and certainly without any intention, unless forced, of permitting the issues to be discussed in public at all.

The moral of all this is that the continuance of the present structure of, even apparently non-political, scientific administration in Britain, is irreconcilable with the goals of creating an open, accessible and man-centred science, nor yet of one which is effectively planned according to technocratic criteria. In order to achieve these goals, the decision-making processes need to be opened at all levels. Provided the structures are open, accessible and well articulated, it is of little interest to advance arguments of the Ministry-building type rife amongst pre-1964 reformists who all too frequently failed to define the ends of science towards which these structures were means. The questions of one Ministry of Science or two, or of technology versus the universities, are of importance but only as means to these larger goals.

These man-centred goals cannot be achieved in a society whose educational system is as narrowly vocational as our own, so that the 'everyman his own scientist' ideal is so far from realization and our culture is brutally fragmented. At least they should be recognized as our objectives. Not, it should be added, that we are attempting to draw up some finite vision of society, but certain obvious first steps can be taken. Thus those concerned to allocate resources between disciplines and fields in the basic sciences must do so in the context of politically directed goals set by the community, whilst they themselves must be openly elected by the scientific community from amongst its own number; such elections, replacing the present oligarchies, will ensure that the individuals chosen have both the respect and trust of their colleagues and also that the growing points of science are represented, so that policy-making does not atrophy in the hands of the elderly representatives of middle-aged disciplines. Insistence on limited periods of office would equally prevent the development of a generation of professional science policy-makers and make sure instead of the steady appearance of new men and new ideas. That all committees and their decisions should be public and freely challengeable would also be a prerequisite of ensuring internal scientific democracy, so that the government of science in some measure corresponded to its own myths.

Although such proposals would be readily applicable to the basic sciences, even here one must beware of allowing absolutely unchecked reign to even the most free of professional syndicalism, for this would still carry with it the danger of the continuance of a scientific *élite*, and, as Lancelot Hogben has put it, 'no society is safe in the hands of so few clever people'.[27] It is for this reason that one must emphasize the political framework, not merely in overall budgetary allocations but in goal choice as well. The special responsibility that falls upon the scientist, as on the individual, within our divided culture must be that of both interpreting current science to society, and in helping to assess its consequences. This is a role that only he can fill.*

No structure can continue which relies upon the unsupported ethical integrity of the individual professional; even the Hippocratic oath for doctors, which has occasionally been cited as a possible example for scientists to follow, by philosophers of science from Francis Bacon to Aldous Huxley,[28] is almost more honoured

* It would be unwise however to assume that even when a scientist is prepared to speak out on a scientific or technological issue, that he will necessarily be permitted by the mass media to do so. The case of the letter to *The Times* written by a distinguished physicist, drawing attention to the political and social implications of the seemingly neutral agreement between Britain, Germany and Holland to share in the building of a gas-centrifuge for the separation of uranium isotopes – useful for power or bombs – is relevant here. The letter was not published.

in the breach than the observance. Nonetheless, it is interesting that scientific associations which demand a similarly 'ethical' statement of principle from their members, such as the American Society for Social Responsibility in Science and its recently formed British equivalent, do exist. Their function must be dual, to spell out the professional ethics of the scientist (to prevent individual scientists entering such work as creating napalm without recognizing its social and moral implications) and to heighten public awareness of the potential significance of developments in both basic and mission oriented research.[29] As Francis Bacon wrote of the scientists in the *New Atlantis*:

> And this we do also: we have consultations, which of the inventions and experiences which we have discovered shall be published and which not; and take all an oath of secrecy, for the concealing of those which we think fit to keep secret: though some of those we do reveal sometimes to the State, and some not.

That such a sense of ethical responsibility can be felt by scientists is shown, perhaps by those twenty-two from Cambridge, led by Sir Frederick Gowland Hopkins and John Orr (Lord Boyd Orr), who wrote to *Nature* in 1936 protesting against the 'prostitution of science for war purposes'. Yet the same case shows the limits also, for several of these men subsequently put their not inconsiderable talents to the service of war between 1939 and 1945, and felt justified in so doing. As indeed did many of the physicists who worked on the bomb. As Professor Eric Burhop has put it:

> we felt justified then, and I still think it was right. In the same way, it is right for scientists in North Vietnam to work for their country, and right for scientists in the U.S. to refuse to participate in their country's war effort.[30]

What this means is that, important as the fostering of professional ethics amongst the scientists is, ultimately the political choice (i.e., to support particular research) lies with society.

The problem of technological development, of mission-oriented research, remains much the most complex, and one in which the most sharply professional syndicalism ceases to be an adequate response to the control of science in the interests of society. Within a competitive economic framework, a transformation of the structure of technological innovation can at best be only partial. But within the publicly owned or financed sector at least – and this comprises the major portion of research – it should begin to be possible. Mechanisms have to be found for identifying potential technological developments and for public assessment of their desirability and priority. Partly, this is achieved by the manifest statement of goals to be achieved by the technology, of the type of 'a man on the moon by 1970' only applied to a human end. One might be to 'raise the average Indian food intake to 2,500 calories per day by 1980' or, perhaps politically more likely, 'Develop effective means for sub-ocean farming and living'.

Even here, though, means must be found of continuous revision of the programme, to ensure that it does not in itself become a goal divorced from its original significance, as happens, for example, to so much medical research, which rapidly transforms itself into basic biology with only a tenuous link with its original motivation. The continuous tendency for this to happen is evidenced in all the casebook studies on the management of research. It is hard enough to prevent by relatively non-democratic means and on a small scale. To achieve it democratically would imply, on the local level, lay participation in management at every research institute and university. The ineffectiveness and irrelevance of many of the existing managing committees and boards of governors, such as those for schools, hospitals and universities, where it could be argued that there had been some attempt at lay representation, indicates that the actual structures will have to be very carefully thought through. It will not be good enough to continue with the present style of predominantly upper-middle-class, self-recruiting 'representatives', together with a handful of time-serving party and trade-union functionaries and with the contemporary tokenism of two elected scientists/workers/students/teachers. At the centre, the greatly increased development of such bodies as that poor, malnourished infant, the House of Commons Select Committee on Science and Technology, could begin to re-assert control over a burgeoning technology.

But this is not intended as an Ordnance Survey map, with all the footpaths carefully marked in, rather a sketched guide. It is easier to see the quagmire and the precipice than to map out in detail the routes by which society can skirt them. And the evils of the past half-century have been sufficient to warn us all of the danger of vision becoming nightmare, revolution bureaucracy, and the rational logic of science an instrument for man's destruction. That man and his planet survive is a continuing tribute to luck, human ingenuity and society's adaptive capacity. We cannot rely on the permanent success of this combination.

Bibliography and References

These are given by chapter. For some chapters a number of general source books are quoted first, followed by specific references from individual points in the text.

Introduction

1. Price, D. J. de Solla, *Discovery*, vol. 17, 1956.
2. Ziman, J., *Public Knowledge* (Cambridge University Press, 1968).
3. Medawar, P., *The Art of the Soluble* (Methuen, 1967).
4. Orth, C. D., Bailey, J. C. and Wolek, F. W., *Administering Research and Development* (Tavistock, 1965); Walters, J. E., *The Management of Research and Development* (Spartan, Washington, 1962); Cockcroft, J., *The Organisation of Research Establishments* (Cambridge University Press, 1965); Burns, T. and Stalker, G. M., *The Management of Innovation* (Tavistock, 1961); Berners-Lee, C. M., *Models for Decision* (English Universities Press, 1965); Kornhauser, W., *Scientists in Industry* (California University Press, 1963); Vickers, G., *The Art of Judgement, A study of policy making* (Chapman & Hall, 1965); Goode, W., 'A Community within a Community', *American Sociological Review*, vol 22, 1957, p. 2.
5. Bernal, J. D., *The Social Function of Science* (Routledge & Kegan Paul, 1939).

Chapter 1 The Birth of Science

General

Bernal, J. D., *Science in History* (Penguin, 1969), 4th edn.

Dobb, M., *Studies in the Development of Capitalism* (Routledge & Kegan Paul, 1946).

Purver, M., *The Royal Society; Concept and Creation* (Routledge & Kegan Paul, 1967).
Singer, C., *A Short History of Scientific Ideas to Nineteen Hundred* (Oxford University Press, 1959).
Stimson, D., *Scientists and Amateurs* (Schuman, New York, 1948).

References

1. Price D. J. de Solla, *Little Science, Big Science* (Columbia University Press, 1963).
2. Rose, S., 'The S-Curve Considered', *Technology and Society*, Vol. 4, 1967.
3. Joravsky, D., *Soviet Marxism and Natural Science* (Routledge & Kegan Paul, 1961).
4. Ziman, op. cit.
5. Weber, M., *The Protestant Ethic: Religion and the Spirit of Capitalism* (Allen & Unwin, 1948).
6. Merton, R. K., *Social Theory and Social Structure* (Free Press, New York, 1957).
7. Feuer, L. S., *The Scientific Intellectuals* (Basic Books, New York, 1965).
8. Bacon, F., *The New Atlantis*, ed. Gough, A. B. (Oxford University Press, 1924).
9. Singer, C., *A Short History of Science to the Nineteenth Century* (Oxford University Press, 1941).

Chapter 2 Amateurs and Gentlemen: Britain in the Nineteenth Century

General

Armytage, W. H. G., *The Rise of the Technocrats* (Routledge & Kegan Paul, 1965).
Cardwell, D. S. L., *The Organisation of Science in England* (Heinemann, 1957).
Court, W. H. B., *A Concise Economic History of England since 1750*, (Cambridge University Press, 1954).
Hobsbawm, E. J., *Industry and Empire* (Weidenfeld & Nicolson, 1968).

References

1. Cardwell, op. cit.
2. King-Hele, D. G., 'The Lunar Society of Birmingham', *Nature*, vol. 212, 1966, p. 229.

3. Gillispie, C. C., in Barber, B. and Hirsch, W., *The Sociology of Science* (Free Press, New York, 1962).
4. Crowther, J. G., *Statesmen of Science* (Cresset Press, 1965).
5. Cardwell, op. cit.
6. Hammond, J. L., and Hammond, B., *The Town Labourer* (London, 1917).
7. Babbage, C., *Reflections on the Decline of Science in England* (London 1830).
8. Ben-David, J., 'Scientific Growth: A Sociological View', *Minerva* vol. II, 1964, p. 455.
9. Beer, J. J., *The Emergence of the German Dye Industry* (University of Illinois Press, 1959).
10. Pike, M., *The Growth of Scientific Institutions and Employment of Natural Science Graduates in Britain, 1900–1960* (M.Sc. thesis, London University, 1961).
11. Armytage, op. cit.

Chapter 3 The Chemists' War

General

Marwick, A., *The Deluge* (Penguin, 1967).
Clark, R. W., *The Rise of the Boffins* (Phoenix House, 1962).
—, *J. B. S.—The Life and Work of J. B. S. Haldane* (Hodder & Stoughton, 1968).
Pollard, S., *The Development of the British Economy*, 1914–50 (Arnold, 1963).
Mowat, C. L., *Britain between the Wars* (Methuen, 1955).

References

1. Tizard, H., The Haldane Memorial Lecture (Birkbeck College, 1955).
2. Cmd 8005 (H.M.S.O., 1915).
3. Annual Report Privy Council Committee (H.M.S.O., 1916).
4. The Machinery of Government Committee Report, Cmd 9230 (H.M.S.O., 1918).
5. Melville, H., *The D.S.I.R.* (New Whitehall Series, 1962); also, Annual Reports of the D.S.I.R. (1919 onwards).
6. Marwick, op. cit.
7. Hill, D. W., *Co-operative Research in Industry* (London, 1967).
8. Clark, R. W., *Tizard* (Methuen, 1965); Jones, R. V., 'Scientists and Statesmen: the Example of Henry Tizard', *Minerva*, vol. IV, 1966, p. 202.

9. Lambert, R., *Sir John Simon* (MacGibbon & Kee, 1963).
10. National Insurance Act, 1911, Section 16(2), 6.
11. Thompson, L., 'Origins and Development of the M.R.C.', *British Medical Journal*, No. 2, 1963, p. 1290.
12. Dale, H. H., 'Fifty Years of Medical Research', *British Medical Journal*, No. 2, 1963, p. 1287).
13. Wooster, W., Presidential Address, A.S.T.M.S., Section a, 1968. See also *The Scientific Worker*, May and June 1920, April 1927, August 1928, December 1935.
14. Baker, J. R., 'Counterblast to Bernalism', *New Statesman*, no. 440, 1939, p. 174; 'Professor Bernal Replies', ibid., no. 441, 1939, p. 210.
15. Relevant books in this debate include, on the one hand, Hogben, L., *Science for the Citizen* (London, 1938); Levy, H., *Modern Science* (Hamilton, 1939); Waddington, C. H., *The Scientific Attitude* (Penguin, 1948); Russell, B., *The Scientific Outlook* (London, 1931); Crowther, J. G., *The Social Relations of Science* (Cresset, 1941), *Science and World Order* (London, 1942); and on the other, Polanyi, M., *The Logic of Liberty* (Chicago University Press, 1951); Baker, J. R., *The Scientific Life* (Allen & Unwin, 1942), *Science and the Planned State* (Allen & Unwin, 1945).

Chapter 4 The Physicists' War

General

Birkenhead, Earl of, *The Prof. in Two Worlds* (Collins, 1961).
Butler, J. R. M., *Grand Strategy*, Official History of the Second World War, vol. II (H.M.S.O., 1957).
Clark, R. W., *The Rise of the Boffins* (Phoenix House, 1962).
—, *Tizard* (Methuen, 1965).
—, *The Birth of the Bomb* (Pheonix House, 1961).
Grodzins, M. and Rabinowitch, E., *The Atomic Age* (Simon & Schuster, New York, 1963).
Gilpin, R., *American Scientists and Nuclear Weapons Policy* (Princeton University Press, 1962).
Jungk, R., *Brighter than a Thousand Suns* (Penguin, 1964).
Kimball Smith, A., *A Peril and a Hope* (Chicago University Press, 1965).
Snow, C. P., *Strangers and Brothers* sequence (Macmillan, 1940).
Zuckerman, S., *Scientists and War* (Hamilton, 1966).

References

1. See General list.
2. Marwick, op. cit.
3. Lindemann, F. A., letter, *The Times*, 8 August 1934.

4. Snow, C. P., *Science and Government* (Oxford University Press, 1961).
5. Zuckerman, op. cit.
6. Irving, D., *The Virus House* (Kimber, 1967).
7. Statements relating to the atomic bomb, the Prime Minister and Mr Churchill, 6 and 12 August (H.M.S.O., 1945).
8. See *The Bulletin of the Atomic Scientists*, and for selected readings Grodzins and Rabinowitch, op. cit., and essays by Born, M. in *Science and Society*, eds Vavoulis, A. and Colver, A. W. (Holden Day, San Francisco, 1966).
9. *Hansard*, 7 November 1945.
10. ibid., 26 February 1952.
11. Crossman, R.H.S., *Encounter*, March and April 1963.
12. D.S.I.R. Annual Report, 1948–9, Cmnd 7761, with review of unpublished reports 1939–45 (H.M.S.O., 1949).
13. Butler, op. cit.
14. House of Lords Debates, vol. 124, 1941–2, p. 75.

Chapter 5 The Aftermath: Science and the End of Empire

General

Books cited in notes to Chapter 4 are also relevant to Chapter 5.
In addition:
Gowing, M., *Britain and Atomic Energy* (Macmillan, 1964).
Vig, N. J., *Science and Technology in British Politics* (Pergamon, 1968).

References

1. H.M.S.O., Scientific Manpower: Report of the committee appointed by the Lord President of the Council (the Barlow Report), Cmnd 6824 (H.M.S.O., 1946).
2. H.M.S.O., The Civil Service Report of the Committee 1966–8, Cmnd 3628 (H.M.S.O., 1968).
3. A.C.S.P. First Annual Report, Cmnd 7665 (H.M.S.O., 1948); see also subsequent reports.
4. *The Times*, 28 April 1967.
5. Central Organisation for Defence, Cmnd 2097 (London, 1963), also The Management and Control of Research and Development (The Zuckerman Report) (H.M.S.O., 1961).
6. Gowing, op. cit.
7. Annual Reports of the D.S.I.R., see also Melville, op. cit.
8. A.C.S.P. Committee on Scientific Manpower and Engineering Manpower in Great Britain, Cmnd 902 (H.M.S.O., 1959); see also other reports in this series, especially Cmnd 1490, 3102, 3103.

9. Payne, G. L., *Britain's Scientific and Technological Manpower* (Oxford University Press, 1960).
10. Report of the committee to consider the future numbers of medical practitioners and the appropriate intake of medical students (The Willinck Report) (H.M.S.O., 1957).
11. Linstead, H., in *Science and Society* (Conservative Political Centre, 1962).
12. Hailsham, Lord, ibid.
13. Report of the Committee on Higher Education (The Robbins Report), Cmnd 2145 (H.M.S.O., 1963).
14. Committee of Enquiry into the Organisation of Civil Science (The Trend Report), Cmnd 2171 (H.M.S.O., 1963).
15. One aspect of this group's thinking was reflected in Russell, P. 'The Social Control of Science', *New Left Review*, July–August 1962.
16. Rose, H. and Rose, S., 'Science and the Politicians', *Guardian*, 25 August 1964; 'Science in the New Britain', ibid., 12 January 1965.
17. Crossman, R. H. S., 'Scientists in Whitehall', *Encounter*, July 1964.

Chapter 6 The New Britain

References

1. Carter, C. F. and Williams, B. R., *Industry and Technical Progress* (Oxford University Press, 1957).
2. Freeman, C., 'Research and Development: a Comparison between British and American Industry', *National Institute Economic Review*, no. 20, May 1962.
3. Rose, S. and Rose, H., 'Science in the New Britain', *The Guardian*, 12 January 1965; 'Where is the Scientific Revolution?', ibid., 15 April 1966; 'Science's Dodo Race', ibid., 27 May 1966.
4. Boyle, Sir E., 'Parliament and University Policy', *Minerva*, vol. V, 1967, p. 3; and Gunn, L. A., 'Organising for Science in Britain: some relevant questions', *Minerva*, vol. V, 1967, p. 167.
5. See for instance Cousins, F., 'Technology and the New Britain', speech to the London Labour Party, 27 February 1966 (Ministry of Technology, 1967); Wedgwood Benn, A., 'The Government's Policy for Technology' (Ministry of Technology, 1967), 'Developments in Technology' (Ministry of Technology, 1968); Clarke, R., 'Industry and the Ministry of Technology', lecture at Royal Institute of Public Administration, 21 November 1967.
6. Hastings, S., *The Murder of T S R-2* (Macdonald, 1966).
7. The Proposed 300 G E V Accelerator, Cmnd 3505 (H.M.S.O., 1968).
8. Rose, S., 'The S-Curve Considered', *Technology and Society*, vol. 4, 1967, p. 1.

9. Council for Scientific Policy, Report on Science Policy Cmnd 3007 (H.M.S.O., 1966).
10. Annual Report of the Advisory Council on Scientific Policy 1963–4, Cmnd 2538 (H.M.S.O., 1964).
11. Council for Scientific Policy, Report on Science Policy Cmnd 3420 (H.M.S.O., 1967).
12. *Nature*, vol. 215, 1967, p. 1013.
13. Science Research Council, Annual Report 1965–6 (H.M.S.O., 1960).
14. Cohen, A. V. and Ivins, L. N., 'The Sophistication Factor in Science Expenditure', Science Policy Studies no. 1 (Department of Education and Science, 1967).
15. *Nature*, vol. 215, 1967, p. 567.
16. ibid., vol. 207, 1965, p. 1113.
17. Report of a Joint Working Group on Computers for Research (The Flowers Report), Cmnd 2883 (H.M.S.O., 1966).
18. See *The Times Business News* over the period October-November 1967, and in particular, 30 October 1967, 4 November 1967, 21 June 1968, 6 July 1968, 23 May 1968 and 13 September 1968.
19. Wedgwood Benn, A., speech at the annual dinner of the Society of British Aerospace Companies, 28 June 1967.
20. Blackett, P. M. S., reported in *Nature*, vol. 213, 1967, p. 747.
21. Report from the Select Committee on Science and Technology, 1966–7, United Kingdom Nuclear Reactor Programme (H.M.S.O., 1967).
22. ibid., 1967–8, Defence Research Establishments (H.M.S.O., 1968).
23. See *Nature*, vol. 220, 1968, p. 216; ibid., vol. 221, 1969, pp. 790 and 891.
24. Zuckerman, S., 'The Limitations of Advisers', *Nature*, vol. 214, 1967, p. 341.
25. Annual Report of the Civil Service Commissioners, 1965 (H.M.S.O., 1967).

Chapter 7 Science in Western Europe

General

For this chapter and Chapter 8 see especially the several O.E.C.D. Country Reviews on Science Policy (O.E.C.D., Paris) and Problems of Science Policy (O.E.C.D., Paris, 1968); the U.N.E.S.C.O. series of science policy studies (U.N.E.S.C.O., Paris) and especially nos. 5, *Principles and Problems of National Science Policies*, and 6, *Structural and Operational Schemes of National Science Policy*; and the *World Directory of National Science Policy-making Bodies* (U.N.E.S.C.O., Paris, 1966).

References

1. Lenin, V. I., *Works* (4th Russian edn), vol. 27, pp. 288–9, quoted in Zvorykin, A., 'The Organisation of Scientific Work in the U.S.S.R.', *Impact of Science on Society*, vol. 15, 1965, p. 67.
2. The Frascati Manual, 1964, see *O.E.C.D. International Statistical Year* (O.E.C.D., Paris, 1967).
3. Freeman, C., and Young, A., *The Research and Development Effort, an experimental international comparison of research expenditures and manpower in 1962* (O.E.C.D., Paris, 1965).
4. Davies, R. in *Review of National Science Policy*: *Soviet Union* (O.E.C.D., Paris, 1965)
5. Freeman, op. cit.
6. *Review of National Science Policy: France* (O.E.C.D., Paris, 1966).
7. McElheny, V., 'Pasteur Institute Rebels Lose a Round', *Science*, vol. 153, 1966, p. 1276.
8. *Country Reports on the Organisation of Scientific Research*: *Germany* (O.E.C.D., Paris, 1962).
9. Stoltenberg, G., *Forschungsplanung – Möglichkeiten und Grenzen Institut für Weltwirtschaft* (Kiel University, 1966).
10. *Review of National Science Policy*: *United Kingdom/Germany* (O.E.C.D., Paris, 1967).

Chapter 8 America, Russia and the Third World

References

1. A by no means comprehensive list includes: Barber, R. J., *The Politics of Research* (Public Affairs Press, Washington, 1966); Dupre, J. S and Lakoff, S. A., *Science and the Nation* (Prentice Hall, New Jersey, 1962); Gilpin, op. cit.; Gilpin, R. and Wright, C., *Scientists and National Policy-making* (Columbia University Press, 1964); Greenberg, D., *The Politics of Pure Research* (Penguin, 1969); Penick, J. L., Pursell, C. W., Sherwood, M. B. and Swain, D. C., *The Politics of American Science, 1939 to the Present*, (Rand McNally, Chicago, Price, D. K., *The Scientific Estate* (Harvard University Press), 1965); Government and Science (New York University Press, 1954); Skolnikoff, E. B., *Science, Technology and American Foreign Policy* (M.I.T. Press, 1967).
2. Kimball Smith, op. cit.; Jungk, op. cit.
3. Greenberg, D. S., *Science*, vol. 154, 1966, p. 491; Nelson, B., ibid., p. 618.
4. For example, Daddario, E., 2nd Progress Report on Science,

Research and Development, 89th Congress, 2nd Session, 69–209 (1966).
5. Klare, M., *Viet Report*, January 1968.
6. Rose, S., *C.B.W., Chemical and Biological Warfare* (Harrap, 1968).
7. Horowitz, I. L., *The Rise and Fall of Project Camelot* (M.I.T. Press, 1967).
8. *Review of National Science Policy: United States* (O.E.C.D., Paris, 1968).
9. Greenberg, D. S., *Science*, vol. 152, 1966, p. 1485; ibid., vol. 158, 1967, p. 230; Boffey, P., ibid., vol. 159, 1968, p. 509.
10. Greenberg, D. S., *Science*, vol. 154, 1966, p. 1628.
11. Weinberg, A., *Reflections on Big Science* (Pergamon, 1967).
12. Aber, J., Benjamin, J. and Martin, R., *Germ Warfare Research for Vietnam: Project Spicerack on the Pennsylvania Campus* (Philadelphia Area Committee to end the War in Vietnam, 1966).
13. *Review of National Science Policy: Soviet Union* (O.E.C.D., Paris, (1969).
14. Joravsky, op. cit.
15. Zvorykin, op. cit.
16. Joravsky in Barber and Hirsch, op. cit.
17. Bernal, *Social Function of Science*.
18. Trapeznikov, V., 'The Efficiency of Science in the U.S.S.R.' *Minerva*, vol. V, 1967, p. 546.
19. Science Policy and the Organization of Research in the U.S.S.R., Science Policy Studies, No. 7 (O.E.C.D., Paris, 1967).
20. Gill, R. R., 'Problems of Decision-making in Soviet Science Policy', *Minerva*, vol. V, 1967, p. 198.
21. Kaplan, N. in Barber and Hirsch, op. cit.
22. Šorm, F., *Science in a Socialist Society* (Academia, Prague, 1967).
23. Vladimir, L., 'Soviet Science – A Native's Opinion', *New Scientist* 28 November 1968.
24. Polanyi, M. in Woolf, H. ed., *Science as a Cultural Force* (Baltimore, 1964).
25. Mukerjee, D., 'Indian Science: Policy, Organisation and Application', *Minerva*, vol. III, 1964, p. 361; see also 'Indian Science Policy', ibid., vol. II, 1964, p. 519; Karve, D., 'The Universities and the Public in India', *Minerva*, vol. I, 1963, p. 263.
26. Mao Tse-tung, *Selected Readings* (Foreign Languages Press, Peking, 1967).
27. Uchida, G., 'Technology in China', *Scientific American*, no. 5, 1966, p. 215.
28. Oldham, G., Cantor Lecture, Royal Society of Arts (1968).
29. McFarlane, B., *Scientific American*, no. 8, 1967, p. 216.
30. *Review of National Science Policy: Japan* (O.E.C.D., Paris, 1967);

New Scientist supplement, 16 November 1967; MacKay, A., 'An Outsider's View of Science in Japan', *Impact of Science on Society*, vol. 12, 1962, p. 177.

31. Aron, R., in *Decision Making in National Science Policy* (Ciba Foundation Symposium, Churchill, 1968).
32. Kapitsa, P. L., *Minerva*, vol. IV, 1966, p. 391, and Frankland, G., evidence to the Devonshire Committee on Scientific Instruction and the Advancement of Science, 1872–5.

Chapter 9 International Science

General

International Scientific Organisations (O.E.C.D., Paris, 1965).

References

1. Bernal, *Social Function of Science*.
2. Quoted by Hill, A. V., *The Ethical Dilemma of Science* (Science Book Guild, 1962).
3. Salomon, J. J., 'International Science Policy', *Minerva*, vol. II, 1964, and 'Some Aspects of International Science Policy', *International Scientific Organisations* (O.E.C.D., Paris, 1965).
4. Ryle, J. A. in *The Doctor's View of War*, ed. Joules, H. (Allen & Unwin, 1939).
5. Lerner, D. and Teich, A. M., *International Scientists Face World Politics* (Center for International Studies, M.I.T. Press, 1968).
6. World Federation of Scientific Workers, founding document (London, 1948).
7. Science Policy Studies Series (U.N.E.S.C.O., Paris).
8. *Ministers Talk About Science* (O.E.C.D., Paris, 1965); *Science and the Policies of Governments* (O.E.C.D., Paris, 1963): *Problems of Science Policy* (O.E.C.D., Paris, 1968); *Fundamental Research and the Policies of Governments* (O.E.C.D., Paris, 1966).
9. For example, *The Frascati Manual, Government and the Allocation of Resources to Science*, 1964; International Statistical Year (O.E.C.D., Paris, 1967).
10. McElheny, V., *Science*, vol. 148, 1965, p. 205.
11. *Nature*, vol. 219, 1968, p. 1.
12. ibid., p. 15.
13. *Science*, vol. 152, 1966, p. 326; ibid., vol. 156, 1967, p. 1713.
14. Gatland, K. W., 'E.L.D.O.: Case History of an International Venture', *Science Journal*, January 1966, p. 75; Walsh, J., 'E.S.R.O.: Space Science Research in Europe Suffers Growing Pains', *Science*, vol. 158, 1967, p. 242.

15. Brown, N., 'What Follows E.L.D.O.?', *New Scientist*, 2 May 1968, p. 225; *Nature*, vol. 218, 1968, p. 407.
16. Thirteenth Report from the Estimates Committee: Space Research and Development (H.M.S.O., London, 1967).

Chapter 10 International Gaps and Drains

References

1. Servan-Schreiber, J.-J., *Le défi americain* (Denoël, Paris, 1967); Layton, C., *European Advanced Technology – A Programme for Integration* (Allen & Unwin, 1969).
2. de Tocqueville, A., *Democracy in America* (Oxford World Classics, 1946).
3. Ben-David, J., *Fundamental Research and the Universities* (O.E.C.D., Paris, 1968).
4. Gray, G. W., 'Which Scientists Win Nobel Prizes?' in Barber and Hirsch, op. cit.
5. For example, Goodeve, C., 'A Route 128 for Britain?', *New Scientist*, 9 February 1967, p. 346.
6. For example, *Nature*, vol. 217, 1968, p. 891; *New Scientist*, 12 December 1968, p. 620; ibid., 8 February 1968, p. 296.
7. *Nature*, vol. 212, 1966, p. 896; ibid., vol. 214, 1967, p. 643.
8. For example, Wedgwood Benn, A., speeches to Council of Europe, January 1968, and O.E.C.D. Science Ministers, March 1968; also *Science*, vol. 151, 1966, p. 976; *Nature*, vol. 216, 1967, p. 837; Copisarow, A. C., *New Scientist*, 1 June 1967, p. 522.
9. Royal Society, *The Emigration of Scientists from the U.K.* (London, 1963).
10. Report on the 1965 Triennial Manpower Survey of Engineers, Technologists, and Technical Supporting Staff, Cmnd 3103 (H.M.S.O., 1966).
11. The Brain Drain, Report of the Working Group on Migration, Cmnd 3417 (H.M.S.O., 1967).
12. Abel-Smith, B. and Gales, K., *British Doctors at Home and Abroad* (Bell, 1966).
13. West, K. M., 'Foreign Interns and Residents in the U.S.', *Journal of Medical Education*, vol. 40, 1965, p. 1110.
14. Thomas, B., 'The International Circulation of Human Capital', *Minerva*, vol. V, 1967, p. 479.
15. The Proposed 300 G E V Accelerator, Cmnd 3503 (H.M.S.O., 1968).
16. Johnson, H. G., 'The Economics of the Brain Drain: The Canadian

Case', *Minerva*, vol. III, 1965, p. 299; Sutherland, G., 'The Brain Drain', *Political Quarterly*, vol. 38, 1967, no. 1; Mishan, E. J., 'The Brain Drain: Why Worry So Much?', *New Society*, 2 November 1967, p. 619; Rose, H. and Rose, S., 'Why Britain is Losing Scientists', *Aspect*, no. 1, 1964.

17. Bernal, J. D., 'Introduction to the Sciences of Science', address to the Science of Science Foundation, London 1965.

Chapter 11 Criteria for Choice

References

1. For example, for a more sophisticated presentation of this viewpoint Polanyi, M., 'The Republic of Science: its Political and Economic Theory', *Minerva*, vol. I, 1962, p. 54, and 'Science and Man's Place in the Universe', in *Science as a Cultural Force*, ed. Woolf, H. (Johns Hopkins Press,Baltimore, 1964).
2. Much of the recent debate on criteria for choice has been conducted in the pages of *Minerva*, under the editorship of Professor Shils. See especially, Weinberg, A. M., 'Criteria for Scientific Choice', vol. I, 1963, p. 159 and vol. III, 1964, p. 3; Toulmin, S., 'The Complexity of Scientific Choice', vol. II, 1964, p. 343; Maddox, J., 'Choice and the Scientific Community', vol. II, 1964, p. 141; Rottenberg, S., vol. V, 1966, p. 30.
3. Rose, S., *Chemical and Biological Warfare*.
4. Swann, M., speech at the opening of Science Policy Seminar, Edinburgh, 1966.

Chapter 12 Decisions: Megamouse and C.E.R.N.

1. Rose, H., 'The Rejection of the W.H.O. Research Centre: a Case Study of Decision-making in International Collaboration', *Minerva*, vol. V, 1967, p. 340.
2. Kuraşov, A., *World Health Organisation Official Records*, vol. 128, 1963, p. 25.
3. Candau, M., ibid., vol. 143, 1965, p. 53.
4. H.M.S.O., Annual Report of the A.C.S.P. 1961–2, Cmnd 1920 (London, 1963).
5. Grant, R. P., 'National Biomedical Research Agencies: a Co-operative Study of Fifteen Countries', *Minerva*, vol. IV, 1966, p. 488.
6. The Proposed 300 G E V Accelerator, Cmnd 3505 (H.M.S.O., 1968).
7. *Nature*, vol. 219, 1968, p. 1.

8. Quoted in ibid., p. 15.
9. Short, E. at the C.S.P. Meeting, July 1968; D.E.S. Press Release.
10. 'The Status and Problems of High Energy Physics Today: Report of the High Energy Physics Advisory Panel of the A.E.C.', *Science*, vol. 161, 1968, p. 11.

Chapter 13 Science and Society

References

1. Russell, B., *The Impact of Science on Society* (Allen & Unwin, 1968).
2. Kuhn, T. S., *The Structure of Scientific Revolutions* (Chicago University Press, 1962).
3. Merton, R. K., 'Priorities in Scientific Discovery: a Chapter in the Sociology of Science', *American Sociological Review*, December 1957.
4. Watson, J. D., *The Double Helix* (Weidenfeld & Nicolson, 1968).
5. Hagstrom, W. O., *The Scientific Community* (Basic Books, New York, 1965).
6. Price, D. J. de Solla, 'Networks of Scientific Papers', *Science*, vol. 149, 1965, p. 510; Garfield, E. *et al.*, *The Use of Citation Data in Writing the History of Science* (Philadelphia, 1964).
7. Needham, J., *Science and Civilisation in Ancient China* (Cambridge University Press, 1954–65); Bernal, *Science in History* (Penguin, 1969); Haldane, J. B. S., *Science and Life* (Pemberton, 1968).
8. Jantsch, E., *Technological Forecasting in Perspective* (O.E.C.D., Paris, 1967); also special issue of *Science Journal*, October 1967.
9. Kahn, H. and Wiener, A., *The Year 2000 – a framework for speculation on the next thirty-three years* (Daedalus, 1967).
10. Gabor, D., 'Technological Forecasting in a Social Frame', *S.S.F. Newsletter*, vol. III, 1968, no. 5.
11. Ellul, J., *The Technological Society* (Cape, 1965).
12. Boguslaw, R., *The New Utopians* (Prentice—Hall, New York, 1965).
13. Trapeznikov, op. cit.
14. Toulmin, S., 'Is There a Limit to Scientific Growth?', *Science Journal*, August 1966.
15. Platt, J., *The Step to Man* (Wiley, New York, 1966).
16. Masters, W. H. and Johnson, V. E., *The Human Sexual Response* (Churchill, 1966).
17. Snow, C. P., *The Two Cultures and a Second Look* (Cambridge University Press, 1963).
18. Marx, K., *Theses on Feuerbach*, Collected Works (Moscow, 1845).
19. Gerth, H. H. and Mills, C. Wright, *From Max Weber* (New York University Press, 1958).

20. Marcuse, H., *One-Dimensional Man* (Routledge & Kegan Paul, 1962).
21. Leach, E., The Reith Lectures, B.B.C., 1968.
22. Enquiry into the Flow of Candidates in Science and Technology into Higher Education (The Dainton Report), Cmnd 3541 (H.M.S.O., 1968), and The Flow into Employment of Scientists, Engineers and Technologists (The Swann Report), Cmnd 3760 (H.M.S.O., 1968).
23. Hudson, L., *Contrary Imaginations* (Penguin, 1968); Butler, J. R., Science Policy Study No. 2, 1968.
24. Encel, S., at conference on 'A Policy for the Social Sciences', Loughborough University, December 1968.
25. Storer, N. W., *The Social System of Science* (Holt, Rinehart & Wilson, New York, 1966).
26. Vollmer, H. M., *Work Activities and Attitudes of Scientists and Research Managers* (Stanford Research Institute, 1965); Box, S. and Ford, J., 'Commitment to Science', *Sociology*, vol. 1, 1967, p. 225; Box, S. and Cotgrove, S., 'Scientific Identity, Occupational Selection and Role Strain', *British Journal of Sociology*, March 1966.
27. Hogben, L., *Science in Authority* (Allen & Unwin, 1963).
28. Huxley, A., *Science, Liberty and Peace* (Chatto & Windus, 1947).
29. Rose, H. and Rose, S., 'Knowledge and Power', *New Scientist*, 21 April 1969.
30. Burhop, E. H. S., at a teach-in on chemical and biological warfare, King's College, March 1969.

Index

Index